REMOTE
SENSING
IN CIVIL ENGINEERING

p. 172 missing

REMOTE SENSING

IN CIVIL ENGINEERING

Edited by

T. J. M. KENNIE
Lecturer in Engineering Surveying
University of Surrey

and

M. C. MATTHEWS
Lecturer in Geotechnical Engineering
University of Surrey

Surrey University Press

Glasgow and London

Halsted Press, a Division of
John Wiley and Sons

New York

Published by Surrey University Press
A member of the Blackie Group
Bishopbriggs, Glasgow G64 2NZ and
Furnival House, 14–18 High Holborn, London WCIV 6BX

Distributed in the USA by
Halsted Press, a Division of
John Wiley and Sons Inc., New York

British Library Cataloguing in Publication Data

Kennie, T. J. M.
  Remote sensing in civil engineering.
  1. Civil engineering—Remote sensing
  I. Title II. Matthews, M. C.
  624'.028   TA153

ISBN 0-903384-48-5

Library of Congress Cataloging in Publication Data
Main entry under title:
Remote sensing in civil engineering.
  Includes bibliographies and index.
  1. Civil engineering—Remote sensing.
  I. Kennie, T. J. M.   II. Matthews, M. C.
  TA153.R36 1985   624'.028   84–25184
  ISBN 0-470-20135-5

Photosetting by Thomson Press (India) Limited, New Delhi
Printed in Great Britain

Contributors

Elaine M. Amos   Image Interpretation Specialist, Clyde Surveys Ltd, Maidenhead, Berkshire.

K. H. Bagot   Space Scientist, National Remote Sensing Centre, Royal Aircraft Establishment, Farnborough, Hampshire.

T. Beaumont   Consultant, Scott Wilson Kirkpatrick, Consulting Engineers, Basingstoke, Hampshire.

P. J. Beaven   Engineering Geologist, Overseas Unit, Transport and Road Research Laboratory, Crowthorne, Berkshire.

K. Blyth   Project Leader in Remote Sensing, NERC Institute of Hydrology, Wallingford, Oxfordshire.

T. J. M. Kennie   Lecturer in Engineering Surveying, University of Surrey, Guildford, Surrey.

C. J. Lawrance   Engineering Geologist, Overseas Unit, Transport and Road Research Laboratory, Crowthorne, Berkshire.

P. A. Mason   Energy Consultant, Granlund (UK) Ltd, West Drayton, Middlesex.

M. C. Matthews   Lecturer in Geotechnical Engineering, University of Surrey, Guildford, Surrey.

G. Petrie   Professor of Topographic Science, University of Glasgow, Scotland.

Contents

4   Digital processing of remote sensing data   87
K. H. Bagot

5.   Remote sensing in civil engineering practice   106
T. J. M. Kennie, M. C. Matthews and P. J. Beaven

6   Remote sensing and topographic mapping   119
G. Petrie

Preface

The use of remote sensing in civil engineering has until recently been restricted to the measurement and interpretation of aerial photography. The value of remote sensing in this role should not be underestimated since, for many years, aerial photography has proved to be a highly cost effective source of survey data.

During the past 10 to 15 years, however, users have gained access to new sources such as side-looking radar and satellite multispectral imagery. These systems offer the engineer the opportunity to examine regions which are cloud covered and also to view, on a repetitive basis, vast areas of the globe. In parallel with the increase in the number of sources of data has been the development of sophisticated computer-based systems to assist with the measurement and interpretation of the imagery.

Whilst many users are currently making use of these technological developments, many others, including those in the civil engineering community, appear to be unaware of the enormous potential that these developments offer, both at present and for the near future. It is perhaps indicative of the potential importance of remote sensing that the government of the United Kingdom has recently published a House of Lords Select Committee Report on Remote Sensing*. Among the recommendations made by the report is the need to shift the emphasis in remote sensing towards applications. It is the aim of this book to assist in this process by providing a source of information on the application of remote sensing to civil engineering.

The book is based to a large extent on material which was produced for a short course on 'The Use of Remote Sensing in Civil Engineering' held at the University of Surrey in July 1983. The objective of the book is to review the theoretical background to the subject and to consider its use for civil engineering purposes. In particular it is hoped that it will answer the following questions: what is remote sensing? how can it be of assistance to the civil engineer? and what is the most appropriate type of remote sensing system to be used for a specific civil engineering problem?

* Select Committee on Science and Technology (House of Lords) (1983) *Report on Remote Sensing and Digital Mapping.* House of Lords Report 98/L, HMSO, London.

The book is divided into two parts. The first part deals with the principles of the subject, and also reviews data acquisition and processing systems. The second half of the book deals with applications. An introductory chapter acts as an overview, providing a framework to illustrate the role which remote sensing can play in civil engineering. This is followed by chapters which discuss the application of remote sensing in topographic mapping, regional planning, site investigation, highway engineering, environmental engineering and water resources engineering. Each chapter contains an extensive bibliography from which the reader can select further reading material.

The editors wish to acknowledge the assistance of Mrs Veronica Brown in checking the text and proofreading, The National Remote Sensing Centre, Royal Aircraft Establishment, in particular Mr Islywn Thomas and Mr Graham Davidson, and Dr Peter Martin-Kaye, Hunting Geology and Geophysics Ltd, for providing examples of satellite and aircraft imagery.

T. J. M. K.
M.C.M.
University of Surrey

1 An introduction to remote sensing

T. J. M. KENNIE

1.1 Introduction

The use of aerial photography as a means of assessing ground conditions can be traced back to the middle of the last century. These early photographs, obtained by the French army from hot air balloons, were soon realized to offer considerable benefits. The instantaneous record of the terrain not only provided an overall view of the ground surface, but also enabled specific sites to be examined in great detail. It was not however until the invention of the aeroplane had taken place at the beginning of the 20th century that aerial photography could be obtained over large areas on a repetitive basis.

The need for strategic and tactical reconnaissance during World War I gave rise to several major advances in the technology of obtaining aerial photography. In addition, the need for up-to-date maps gave added impetus to the developments which were taking place in aerial photogrammetry. Following World War I the use of aerial photography increased dramatically in many fields, including geology, forestry, agriculture, land surveying and civil engineering and led to the manufacture of much-improved camera systems. Concurrent developments in aircraft technology meant that by the outbreak of World War II the sciences of aerial photo-interpretation and photo-grammetry were well established. Again the war provided the impetus for further developments, both in conventional photographic systems, and also in non-photographic systems such as radar.

Following this period the pace of technological advance increased enormously, particularly during the early 1960s. This led to the coining of the term 'remote sensing' by a group operating in the US Office of Naval Research, to describe this 'new' branch of science which was developing.

In its broadest sense remote sensing could be defined as 'the science of acquiring information about some property of an object through the use of a measuring device which is not in physical contact with the object under investigation'. Clearly, techniques such as magnetometry, gravimetry, sonar and spectroscopy could all thereby be considered to be examples of remote sensing systems. The definition of remote sensing has, however, developed a much more restricted meaning in the world of science. A more precise and more generally accepted definition of remote sensing therefore is that provided by the American Society of Photogrammetry (Anon., 1983).

> Remote Sensing is an application of photogrammetry in which imagery is aquired with a sensor, other than (or in addition to), a conventional camera through which a scene is recorded, such as by electronic scanning, using radiations outside the normal visual range of the film and camera—microwave, thermal infrared, ultraviolet as well as multispectral. Special techniques are applied to process and interpret remote sensing imagery for the purpose of producing conventional maps, thematic maps, resource surveys, and so on, in the fields of agriculture, archaeology, forestry, geography, geology and others.

Whilst this definition is a useful starting point it is rather misleading in that by stating 'remote sensing is an application of photogrammetry' the impression may be given that the subject is entirely quantitative, involving precise measurement of the image. In practice a substantial proportion of remote sensing work is qualitative in nature, involving subjective interpretation of the imagery which is produced.

In general terms however the subject can be seen to consist of two distinct stages: firstly that of data acquisition involving the use of different 'remote sensors' and, secondly, data analysis in order to process and interpret the data. The primary aim of this chapter will be to discuss in more detail the procedures required in order to process and interpret the data. However, before discussing the attributes of specific acquisition systems in detail, it is useful to briefly examine the basic physical principles underlying the subject of remote sensing.

1.2 Basic physical principles of remote sensing

In physical terms, remote sensing is concerned with the measurement and recording of the variations in electromagnetic (EM) energy which occur when energy of this type interacts both with the earth's atmosphere and with the earth's surface.

The term EM energy refers to all energy which travels in a periodic harmonic manner at the velocity of light. Using the well-known relationship

$$\lambda = c/f$$

where λ is the wavelength, f the frequency and c the velocity of EM energy, it is possible to categorize EM energy according to its position along a continuum of wavelengths commonly referred to as the EM spectrum.

1.2.1 The electromagnetic (EM) spectrum

The range of wavelengths, and the names generally assigned to those regions of the EM spectrum which are of interest for remote sensing purposes, are shown

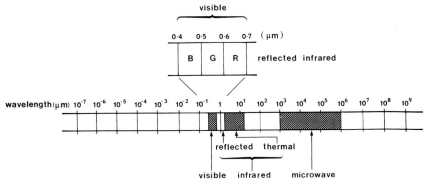

Figure 1.1   The electromagnetic spectrum and its relationship to remote sensing systems.

in Figure 1.1. The wavelength bands indicate broad regions of the EM spectrum and the boundaries between regions should be considered as general areas rather than as highly specific cut-off points.

Several regions of the EM spectrum are of particular interest for remote sensing, those of most importance being the visible, infrared and microwave regions. The visible region of the EM spectrum lies within the spectral range from about 0.36 to 0.75 μm. The significance of this region stems from the fact

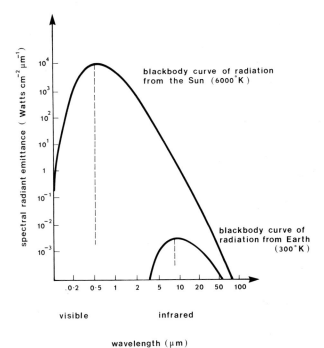

Figure 1.2   Spectral energy distribution of black bodies at temperatures approximating to those at the surface of the Sun and the Earth.

that the radiation emitted from the sun reaches a peak value within this region, at about 0.5 μm. This can be illustrated by Figure 1.2 which shows the spectral energy distribution for a theoretically perfect emitter or 'black body' at a temperature of 6000 K. Figure 1.2 also illustrates the spectral energy distribution associated with the earth's surface, assuming an ambient temperature of 300 K. In this case it can be seen that the peak value of emittance occurs at 9.7 μm, within the infrared region of the EM spectrum.

The infrared portion of the EM spectrum is represented by the spectral band which lies between the visible and microwave regions. Within this broad band there are two regions of significance. The first is termed the reflected infrared and the second the thermal infrared region. The latter is centred around the peak spectral emittance value associated with the surface of the earth.

The third significant region of the EM spectrum, from a remote sensing point of view, is the microwave region. In this case, the range of wavelengths lies between 1 mm (10^3 μm) and 1 m (10^6 μm).

1.2.2 Reflected and emitted EM energy

A secondary feature of EM energy to which reference has already been made is the distinction between reflected and emitted energy. During daylight, the radiant energy from a scene consists of two components. Firstly, at wavelengths up to about 3 μm the energy is predominantly *reflected* sunlight. Since human eyes and photographic film are sensitive to reflected energy within this wavelength range, it is possible to discriminate between features on the basis of the amount of energy reflected by the object. In contrast, at longer wavelengths greater than about 3 μm the dominant type of radiant energy is that which is *emitted* by a body rather than that which is reflected.

The distinction between reflected and emitted radiation can best be illustrated by examining the infrared region of the EM spectrum. Within this region it is apparent that as the wavelength increases, the emitted infrared component becomes progressively more significant. However, unlike the reflected infrared it cannot be sensed by photographic emulsion and has to be detected by the use of some other medium such as, for example, crystal detectors.

It is possible to quantify the amount of energy a body is emitting by means of the Stefan-Boltzmann Law, which states that

$$W = C\varepsilon T^4$$

where W is the radiant emittance in watts m^{-2}

ε is the emissivity of the object

C is the Stefan-Boltzmann constant equal to 5.7×10^{-8} watts m^{-2} K^{-4} and

T is the absolute temperature of the object (K).

Three significant conclusions may be drawn from this law. Firstly, it can be

Table 1.1 Emissivities of a selection of materials (within the 8 to 14 μm wavelength band).

Material	Average emissivity
Clay soil	0.98
Water	0.97
Sandy soil	0.88
Grass	0.88
Buffed stainless steel	0.16

seen that the energy emitted from a body increases very rapidly with an increase in temperature. The second point relates to the emissivity (ε) of an object. Emissivity is a factor which describes how efficiently an object radiates energy in comparison to a 'black body' which has an emissivity value of one. Emissivity is defined as:

$$E(\lambda) = \frac{\text{radiant emittance from an object at a given temperature}}{\text{radiant emittance from a black body at the same temperature}}$$

where $E(\lambda)$ represents the emissivity at a particular wavelength value λ.
Emissivity is quoted as having a value between 0 and 1. Table 1.1 indicates some typical emissivity values which may occur for a selection of materials.

Because of emissivity variations it is clearly possible for features to be at the same temperature and yet have completely different radiant emittance values. Thirdly, given a knowledge of the radiant emittance of a body, together with its emissivity, it should be possible to infer indirectly the temperature of the body. This represents the basis of the technique of thermal infrared remote sensing.

It is also possible, using Wien's displacement law, which states that

$$\lambda_{MAX} = \frac{2897}{T}$$

where λ_{MAX} = wavelength of maximum spectral emittance
and T = temperature (K),
to quantify the wavelength at which maximum spectral radiance will occur. This helps explain the wavelength shift, or displacement, discussed previously which occurs in the values associated with the energy emitted from the sun (0.5 μm) and from the earth's surface (9.7 μm).

1.2.3 *EM radiation and the atmosphere*

The discussion so far has dealt with the general characteristics of EM radiation, without regard to the influence of the medium through which the signal passes: the earth's atmosphere. The principal effects of the atmosphere on remotely sensed EM radiation are illustrated by Figure 1.3. It can be seen that the atmosphere influences EM radiation in two respects, firstly by scattering and secondly by absorbing the EM signal.

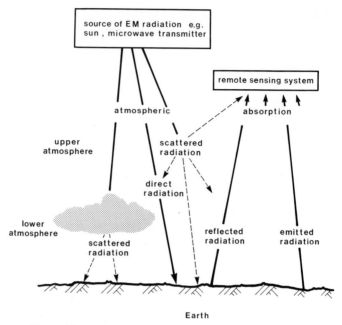

Figure 1.3   The influence of the atmosphere on EM radiation.

1.2.3.1 *Scattering.* Scattering of the incoming EM radiation to the earth, and of the reflected EM radiation from the earth's surface, is caused primarily by the presence of molecules of gas as well as dust and smoke particles in the atmosphere. In the upper atmosphere this scattering is caused predominantly by the interaction of gas molecules which have diameters much less than the radiation wavelength. Scattering of this type is termed 'Rayleigh scatter' and is one of the main reasons for the presence of haze on remotely sensed imagery. In contrast, scattering in the lower atmosphere is mainly a product of the interraction of dust and smoke particles with the EM signal. This type of scattering is termed 'Mie scatter'. A third type of scattering often referred to as 'non-selective scatter' occurs when the particles causing the scattering have diameters several times greater than that of the radiation wavelength. A good example of this type of scattering is that caused by water droplets (diameter $\sim$ 50 μm) as they interact with radiation within the visible spectrum ($\lambda \sim 0.5 \, \mu$m).

1.2.3.2 *Absorption.* Absorption of EM radiation occurs primarily as a consequence of the attenuating nature of molecules of ozone, carbon dioxide and water vapour in the atmosphere. Because these gases absorb EM radiation in specific wavelength bands they govern which regions of the spectrum can be sensed.

Figure 1.4 explains this concept in relation to the visible and infrared parts of the spectrum.

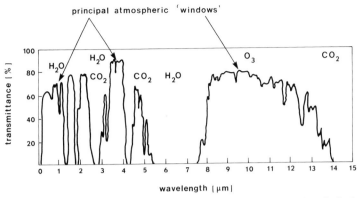

Figure 1.4 Atmospheric transmittance in the 0 to 15 μm wavelength range (the principal regions of absorption by gaseous elements of the atmosphere are also shown).

It can be seen from the graph that in several regions, for example the visible zone, the atmosphere is highly transmittive and consequently is almost totally free from the effects of absorption. Regions with a high atmospheric transmittance are generally referred to as atmospheric 'windows'. Not surprisingly, it is important that remote sensing systems should operate within those portions of the EM spectrum which coincide with these atmospheric 'windows'. A good example of this selective nature of remote sensing systems is the thermal infrared region. Figure 1.4 illustrates that within this wavelength region (3 to 14 μm), two atmospheric windows exist. The first is from 3 to 5.5 μm and the second from 8 to 14 μm. Not unexpectedly, these coincide with the operational bands for most thermal infrared remote sensing systems.

Similar atmospheric windows can be identified in other regions of the spectrum, such as for example, the microwave region. Whilst an understanding of the influence of the atmosphere is of critical importance in remote sensing, it is also essential to appreciate how the EM signal interacts with the terrain.

1.2.4 EM radiation and the earth's surface

When EM radiation is incident upon the earth's surface it will tend to be either reflected, absorbed or transmitted by that surface.

The magnitude and extent to which each of these processes occurs enables features to be differentiated from each other. For example, within the visible region of the spectrum, the concept of colour is simply a manifestation of the extent to which different features reflect different proportions of the visible spectrum.

It is also interesting to note that the same feature may appear very different when it is examined by sensors which are able to record reflectance or

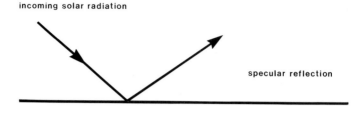

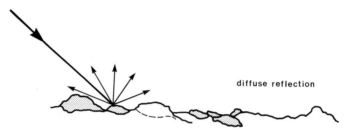

Figure 1.5   Specular and diffuse reflection and its relation to surface roughness.

emittance outside the visible spectrum. For example water surfaces appear black when imaged on to a photographic emulsion sensitive to reflected infrared radiation. This is a consequence of the almost total absorption of infrared radiation by water. In contrast, viewing the same water surface with a photographic emulsion sensitive to the visible region of the spectrum may provide details about submerged features which may not have been sensed previously.

The reflective properties of the terrain can be classified as being either specular or diffuse in nature. This concept is illustrated by Figure 1.5. It can be seen that this factor is essentially a function of the surface roughness. In cases where the surface is relatively smooth, a specular reflection occurs, whereas with rougher surfaces the reflection tends to be more diffuse in nature. Surface roughness in this context refers to the roughness of the terrain relative to the wavelength of the energy incident upon it. Rough surfaces tend to be those where the surface variations are equal to or greater than the wavelength of the source of illumination. An appreciation of this concept is crucial when radar imagery is being interpreted (see Chapter 3 for further details).

Finally, mention should also be made of the use of spectral reflectance patterns.

1.2.4.1 *Spectral reflectance patterns.* The reflectance characteristics of features on the earth's surface can be quantified by measuring the proportion of energy reflected by the feature at different wavelengths. For example, Figure 1.6

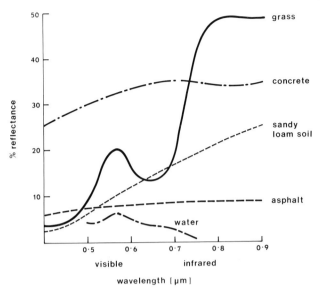

Figure 1.6   Spectral reflectance curves for selected features. (Adapted from Jensen, 1983.)

illustrates the spectral characteristics of several surfaces which may be of interest to the civil engineer.

Three significant points can be deduced from this example. Firstly, it can be seen that certain surfaces, such as grass, have considerably different reflectance characteristics in the visible and infrared regions of the spectrum. In contrast a surface such as asphalt has a relatively stable, low reflectance in both regions. Secondly it can be seen that the most appropriate region of the spectrum for differentiating between the surfaces is the infrared. In this region a clear hierarchy of reflectance exists, from grass with a high reflectance through concrete and sandy loam soil to asphalt and water which have a relatively low reflectance. In contrast, in the blue/green region of the visible spectrum (~ 0.5 μm) the discrimination between asphalt and sandy loam soil surfaces is very poor. This may indicate, for example, that difficulty may arise in the interpretation of these surfaces from conventional aerial photography. Thirdly, the graph again illustrates the very low reflectance of water surfaces in the infrared region of the spectrum.

This ability to spectrally define a feature or surface is often referred to as defining the 'spectral signature' of the feature. This term does, however, imply that features are uniquely and absolutely defined by measuring this parameter. There is, unfortunately, a degree of variability in these 'spectral signatures'. A more appropriate term which should be used is spectral reflectance pattern. This term is intended to suggest that features can be identified by a distinctive spectral response without implying that this response is necessarily unique.

1.3   Classification of remote sensing systems

Remote sensing systems can be classified on the basis of many different criteria. For example, one criterion which could be used as a basis for classification is the wavelength of the remotely sensed radiation. Using this criterion it would be possible to identify three broad categories: systems which sense either visible, infrared or microwave radiation. Classifications based on a single criterion such as this do, however, produce a rather general and also incomplete categorization.

A more complete classification can be obtained by categorizing systems on the basis of several different criteria, so producing a multidimensional classification. One such classification involves examining three different characteristics of remote sensing systems, namely whether the system is active or passive, photographic or scanning, and aircraft- or satellite-based.

1.3.1   *Active and passive systems*

Passive remote sensing systems are concerned with the detection of naturally occurring reflected or emitted radiation. In contrast, a remote sensing system which supplies its own source of energy is known as an active system. This system-generated energy, normally of microwave wavelengths (30 to 250 mm), is directed at the earth's surface and the multiple reflections from the terrain are recorded in order to produce an image.

1.3.2   *Photographic and scanning systems*

Two distinct methods can be used in order to detect and record the variations in reflected or emitted radiation which may occur when passive solar energy or actively generated microwave energy interact with the earth's surface.

The most common detection and recording technique used in remote sensing is the aerial camera. A lens and shutter assembly within the camera ensures that incoming radiation is focused and exposed instantaneously onto a photosensitive emulsion. The latent photographic image is subsequently developed by chemical processing, so producing a conventional aerial photograph. Photographic systems, however, only operate over a narrow wavelength band from 0.3 to 0.9 μm. They nevertheless produce relatively cheaply an image which is of high geometric fidelity and resolution.

An alternative detection and recording system which overcomes the spectral range limitations of the photographic systems is the airborne scanning system. The image produced by the airborne scanner differs fundamentally from the aerial photograph. Firstly, rather than the image being exposed at one instant by means of a shutter, the image is exposed sequentially, line by line, as shown by Figure 1.7. Thus a scanner image can be seen to consist of a series of adjacent scanlines perpendicular to the line of flight of the aerial platform. The second difference relates to the method of recording

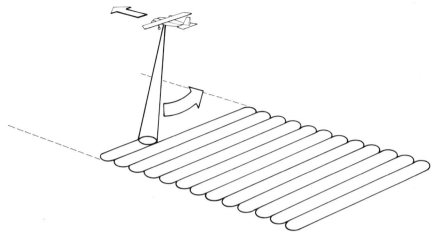

Figure 1.7   Airborne scanning.

the spectral variations over a scene. Conventional aerial photography records the variations in spectral reflectance by means of a film emulsion; in contrast, scanner systems employ crystal detectors. These detectors transform the incident reflected or emitted radiation into electrical signals. Consequently, using the scanner approach, the image is normally recorded directly in digital format on to magnetic tape. In addition, a much broader spectral range can be accommodated using these detectors. One significant disadvantage of the scanner approach is the much poorer spatial (ground) resolution associated with the image when compared with an equivalent-scale aerial photograph.

Finally, mention should be made of the distinction between the terms 'photograph' and 'image'. In remote sensing, the term 'photograph' is normally restricted to images that have been both detected and recorded by means of photographic film. In contrast, the more general term 'image' is normally used to describe any pictorial representation of image data. Thus, although scanner data may be used to create a photographic product, this should be referred to as a scanner image and not a scanner photograph, since the original detection mechanism was not a photographic film emulsion.

1.3.3 Characteristics of sensor platforms

The final characteristic to be used as a basis for classifying remote sensing systems is that of sensor platform.

Very broadly the distinction can be made between those remote sensing systems which are based on aircraft and those which are based on satellites as the sensor platform. The relative merits of each type of platform are summarized in Figure 1.8.

Finally, using these three characteristics of remote sensing systems, it is

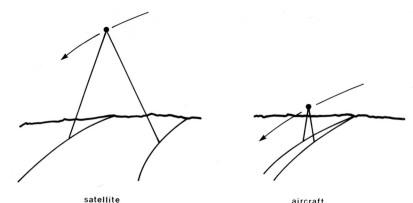

satellite   aircraft

Figure 1.8   Relative merits of satellite and aircraft-based remote sensing systems.

Wide, synoptic view   Narrow, limited view
Very stable platform   Platform less stable
Small scale   Large scales
(> 1:500 000)   (1:1000 to 1:30 000)
Limited repeat   Flexible repeat coverage
coverage (16 to 18 days)
Low spatial resolution   High spatial resolution
(10 m to 500 m)
Highly cost effective   Less cost effective

Table 1.2 Classification of some typical remote sensing systems (see Chapter 3).

Mode of operation	Mode of recording			
	Photographic		Scanning	
Passive	Aircraft	Satellite	Aircraft	Satellite
	Wild RC-10 Mapping Camera	Skylab S-190B etc.	Daedalus 1230 Thermal Scanner	NOAA 1–8 HCMM
		Spacelab		
	Zeiss (Jena) MKF-6M Multispectral Frame Camera	Zeiss (Ober.) RMK 30/23 Metric Camera	Daedalus 1268 MSS Scanner PNC MSS Scanner	Landsat MSS SPOT MOMS
		Landsat RBV		
	TRRL Multi-spectral Camera			
Active			Radar	
			SAR 580	Seasat SIR-A/B ERS-1 Radarsat
			Lidar	
			LARSEN 500	

possible to devise a classification table which can be used in order to categorize any system. One particular classification is illustrated by Table 1.2.

Further details concerning remote sensing photographic systems are discussed in Chapter 2 and details of the scanning systems listed in Table 1.2 are discussed in Chapter 3.

References

Anon. (1983) What photogrammetric engineering and remote sensing is. *Photogrammetric Engineering and Remote Sensing*, 49:2.

Jensen, J. R. (1983) 'Urban/suburban land use analysis', in *Manual of Remote Sensing*, Vol. II, 2nd edn., Colwell, R. N. (ed.), American Society of Photogrammetry, Virginia, 2417 pp.

Bibliography

Barret, E. C. and Curtis, L. F. (1982) *Introduction to Environmental Remote Sensing*. 2nd edn., Chapman and Hall, London, 352 pp.

Bullard, R. K. and Lakin, P. J. (1981) *First Steps in Remote Sensing*. Working Paper No. 3, Dept. of Land Surveying, N. E. London Polytechnic, 61 pp.

Colwell, R. N., (Ed.) (1983) *Manual of Remote Sensing*. Vols. I and II, 2nd edn., American Society of Photogrammetry, Virginia, 2417 pp.

Lillesand, T. M. and Kiefer, R. W. (1979) *Remote Sensing and Image Interpretation*. John Wiley and Sons, New York, 612 pp.

Lintz, J. and Simonett, D. S. (1976) *Remote Sensing of Environment*. Addison-Wesley, Reading, Massachusetts, 694 pp.

Rudd, R. D. (1974) *Remote Sensing: A Better View*. Duxbury Press, N. Scituate, Massachusetts, 135 pp.

Slater, P. N. (1980) *Remote Sensing Optics and Optical Systems*. Addison-Wesley, Reading, Massachusetts, 575 pp.

Swain, P. H. and Davis, S. M. (1978) *Remote Sensing: The Quantitative Approach*. McGraw-Hill, New York, 396 pp.

2 Remote sensing photographic systems

T. J. M. KENNIE

2.1 Introduction

Photographic processes are by far the most common and economical means of sensing the visible and reflected infrared regions of the EM spectrum. Whilst ground-based or terrestrial photographs may be used for this purpose, a much more efficient method is to mount the camera in an aircraft and take aerial photographs.

The aim of this chapter is therefore to review in broad terms firstly the principal characteristics of the camera systems which can be used, secondly the main features of the photography which can be produced by these cameras, and thirdly the various methods of viewing the photography. The contents of this chapter also form the basis for the material discussed in Chapter 7, which deals with the interpretation of aerial photography for site investigation purposes.

2.2 Types of aerial camera

Aerial photography can be obtained using many different types of cameras, ranging from very expensive permanently mounted 'mapping' cameras to inexpensive, hand held 35 mm single lens reflex cameras. In general, however, the majority of photographs which have been obtained for remote sensing purposes have been taken using a single lens frame camera.

2.2.1 Single lens frame camera systems

Cameras of this type are a very common means of obtaining high-quality photographs for mapping or interpretation. The main distinguishing feature of this type of camera is that the internal geometrical characteristics are precisely known. Thus data relating to the lens distortion, focal length and so on are known and monitored periodically by a laboratory-based camera calibration

14

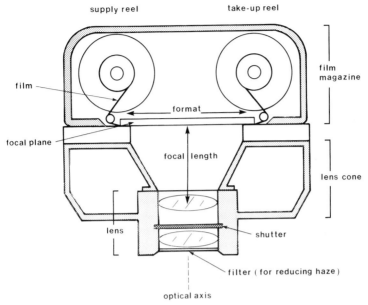

Figure 2.1 Components of a single lens frame camera.

Figure 2.2 Wild RC 10 aerial camera. By kind permission of Wild Heerbrugg, Switzerland.

procedure. The principal components of a typical single lens frame camera are illustrated by Figures 2.1 and 2.2.

Further relevant features of this type of camera are, firstly, that the lens consists of several components and its position is fixed relative to the focal plane; secondly, the focus is set for infinity, the image being brought to focus on the focal plane; thirdly, in view of the speed at which the aircraft or satellite platform is travelling it is important that a very efficient shutter system is used if image blur is to be avoided. In order to achieve this, and in order to ensure all parts of the format are exposed instantaneously, a 'between the lens' shutter arrangement is used with shutter speeds ranging from 1/100 to 1/1000 of a second. In some instances the camera may also incorporate an image motion compensation (IMC) system in order to further reduce the effect of image blur. It is also common with this type of camera to have the facility to be able to rotate the entire camera assembly in order to correct for any crabbing of the aircraft. This aspect is illustrated by Figure 2.3.

Single lens frame cameras are generally classified on the basis of the angular field of view of the lens. This parameter is directly related to both the focal length of the camera and also the format size. For the general case of a 230 mm × 230 mm format the following classification can be made:

	Angular Field of View (°)	Focal length (mm)
Normal Angle (NA)	60	300
Wide Angle (WA)	90	150
Super Wide Angle (SWA)	120	90

It can be seen from Figure 2.4 that the principal advantage of the shorter focal length, SWA lens is the greater ground surface which is covered by the lens when compared with NA and WA photography taken from the same flying height. This has the twin benefits of reducing the number of photographs

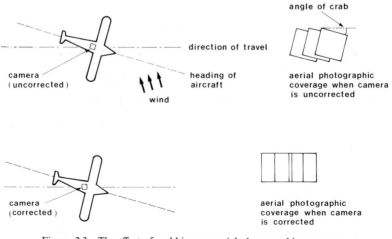

Figure 2.3   The effect of crabbing on aerial photographic coverage.

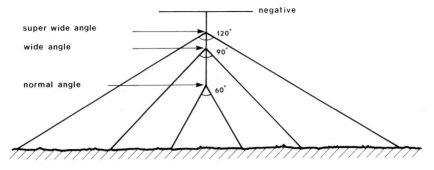

Figure 2.4 Variation in ground coverage of normal, wide and super wide angle camera systems.

which are required for coverage of an area and secondly of reducing the number of control points required if the photograph is to be used for mapping purposes. It can be shown however (see section 2.3.1.1), that whilst the ground covered by a SWA lens may be greater than that obtained from a NA lens, the scale of the photography will be much smaller, again assuming equal flying height. In addition, a SWA lens is much more susceptible to the production of 'dead ground'. Dead ground refers to the loss of detail which occurs because of the screening effect of features, particularly at the extremities of the photography. For these reasons, and others, the most common type of lens system, particularly for aircraft-based camera systems, is the WA lens, which is a good practical compromise between the SWA and NA lens systems.

Finally, the specifications relating to a selection of aircraft and satellite based single lens frame cameras are listed in Table 2.1. Further details relating both to the design features of single lens frame cameras, and also to the flight planning aspects of the aerial survey may be found in Burnside (1979).

Table 2.1 Specifications of a selection of single lens frame cameras.

Camera Platform ⟍ Specification	Aircraft-based		Satellite-based	
	Wild (Heerbrugg) RC-10	Zeiss (Oberkochen) RMK A 8.5/23	Skylab S-190B Earth Terrain Camera	Spacelab Zeiss (Oberkochen) RMK 30/23 Metric Camera
Type	Wide Angle	Super Wide Angle	Normal Angle	Normal Angle
Focal length (mm)	152	85	457.2	300
Angular field of view (°)	94	125	32	42
Format size (mm)	230 × 230	230 × 230	115 × 115	230 × 230
Typical operational altitude (m)	1 525	1 700	38 500	25 000
Area covered by format (km²)	5.4	8.7	12 300	36 200
Ground resolution	< 1 m	< 1 m	30 m	20 m

2.2.2 *Multispectral frame camera systems*

A multispectral camera is a camera system which is designed in order to allow (normally) four photographs of the same ground area to be obtained simultaneously. The photographs produced by such a camera system consist either of black-and-white and colour images of the ground, or, alternatively, black-and-white photographs which have been filtered in order to record radiances within restricted wavelength bands. For example, it is common with this type of system to record the same scene on black-and-white infrared film using filters to restrict each image to the blue, green, red and infrared parts of this spectrum. By subsequently projecting each black-and-white photograph through colour filters in a colour additive viewer (see section 2.2.3.1), it is possible to produce colour composites. This may help to enhance features which are of interest.

Several alternative designs of multispectral camera exist. Two specific designs which are worthy of mention are the multispectral frame cameras and the low-cost multispectral cameras of the type discussed in section 2.2.3.1.

One example of a multispectral frame camera is the Zeiss (Jena) MKF-6M

Figure 2.5 Zeiss (Jena) MKF-6M multispectral frame camera. By kind permission of Carl Zeiss (Jena) Ltd, Borehamwood, Herts.

camera system, illustrated by Figure 2.5. This East German camera has been used aboard the Soviet space station Salyut 6 and also on the Soyuz missions, for the production of space photography. Further details relating to this camera may be found in a publication by the Academy of Sciences, USSR (1982).

It can be seen from Figure 2.5 that the camera consists of four lenses which are integrated into the camera body. All four lenses have a calibrated focal length of 125 mm and very low lens distortion characteristics. Users may choose from a selection of six spectral filters which extend over a range from 0.48 to 0.84 μm.

Details relating to a further example of a multispectral frame camera, the Itek S-190A multispectral camera flown on board the Skylab mission in 1973, are given in Chapter 6.

In conclusion therefore, frame cameras of the types which have been discussed are a very appropriate means of obtaining aerial photographs where both geometric stability and high image quality are important. They do suffer from one major drawback, namely cost, particularly in situations where photography has to be commissioned for a specific project. For many civil engineering projects, however, whilst geometric stability of the photograph may be beneficial, it may not, on all occasions, be of paramount importance. Thus, using an expensive camera system of the types which have been discussed so far may not be a very cost-effective solution to the problem. Consequently several authors have advocated the use of alternative low-cost camera systems.

2.2.3 Low-cost camera systems

The potential benefits of using small-format camera systems for the production of aerial photographs have been the subject of several research reports in recent years. Clegg and Scherz (1975), for example, have carried out extensive tests on the performance of conventional 230 mm (9 inch), 70 mm and 35 mm format camera systems. Apart from the obvious cost benefits of the small-format photography this research has also indicated that for certain types of interpretation, e.g. vegetation mapping or for general pictorial representation, the performance of enlarged small-format photography may be as good as conventional 230 mm photography.

In view of these comments it is worth considering in some further detail the attributes of these low-cost, small-format camera systems.

2.2.3.1 *70 mm camera systems.* The use of a 70 mm camera system for obtaining aerial photographs has been discussed by Heath (1980). Heath lists the following advantages of the small-format system, particularly for site investigations and traffic studies. Firstly, the cameras are made to high standards and are both reliable and robust. Secondly, the small size enables the cameras to be combined in order to form multicamera systems for

Figure 2.6   TRRL multispectral camera system (Heath, 1980). (Crown copyright reserved.)

multispectral photography. Thirdly, the equipment itself is relatively simple and can therefore be operated by persons with very little training or photographic skill. Finally, and very significantly, the compact nature of the camera system allows the camera to be mounted in a wide range of light aircraft. This makes the technique very much more versatile since almost any airfield with light aircraft facilities may be used. Hence not only can the capital cost of the basic equipment be maintained at a low level, but also the operating costs of the system can be kept down.

    Two particular 70 mm camera systems are those which have been developed by the Transport and Road Research Laboratory (TRRL) and that developed by W. Vinten Ltd. The camera system developed by the TRRL consists of four 70 mm Hasselblad EL cameras mounted in a hinged aluminium frame, as shown in Figure 2.6. The system is collimated to produce four images of the same ground area. Each camera may be fitted with either a 60 mm or 100 mm focal length lens. In situations where the camera is being used in an aircraft not fitted with a suitable aerial camera mounting, or alternatively which does not have a suitable hole in the fuselage, the camera may be mounted on a camera pod which is located at the side of the aircraft (Figure 2.7). A second design is

Figure 2.7   Pod to carry up to four 70 mm cameras shown fitted to Cessna 172 aircraft (Heath, 1980). (Crown copyright reserved.)

that produced by W. Vinten Ltd. In this case the individual cameras are Vinten 518 reconnaissance cameras. Several different lenses may be used, a typical focal length being 38 mm ($\sim 1\frac{1}{2}$ inch).

If the maximum benefit is to accrue from the interpretation of multispectral photographs it is essential that a colour additive viewer (CAV) is used. One example of such an instrument is illustrated by Figure 2.8. It can be seen that the CAV consists of three projectors which are aimed on to a common viewing table. Each projector has a variable brightness and colour filter control. Operation of the viewer involves projecting the black-and-white positive transparencies through blue, green or red colour filters. By superimposing these three projected images, a true colour composite image can be produced. Alternatively, if the green, red and reflected infrared transparencies are projected through the blue, green and red filters, a 'false colour' composite image can be produced. Images of this type are similar in appearance to photographs produced using colour infrared film emulsions (see section 2.3.2.4). Further details regarding the use of multispectral photographs and CAV can be found in Ross (1973) and also in Beaumont (1977).

Whilst 70 mm format camera systems of the type discussed may be considered as low-cost systems in comparison with single lens frame cameras, they may, nevertheless, appear in absolute terms to be expensive for certain types of operation. An alternative and cheaper approach therefore is to use a conventional 35 mm camera.

Figure 2.8 TRRL multispectral colour additive viewer (Heath, 1980). (Crown copyright reserved.)

2.2.3.2 *35 mm camera systems.* In common with the larger-format camera systems, 35 mm cameras may be operated either singly or as a bank of up to four cameras to provide multispectral coverage. The former approach is discussed by Mountain and Garner (1980) in relation to traffic surveys, whilst the later approach is discussed by Blyth (1983) in connection with hydrological applications.

In recent years, however, the cost benefits of mounting a 35 mm camera in a model aircraft or remotely piloted aircraft (RPA) have been the subject of considerable interest. Tomlins (1983) argues the case for RPA and suggests four principal benefits of this approach. Firstly RPA do not require prepared landing strips and may be launched from a nearby road or field. Secondly, the aircraft can operate at low altitudes and low speeds in areas which may be too dangerous for piloted aircraft. Thirdly, they are easy to operate and do not require specialized personnel for their operation. Finally, they offer the

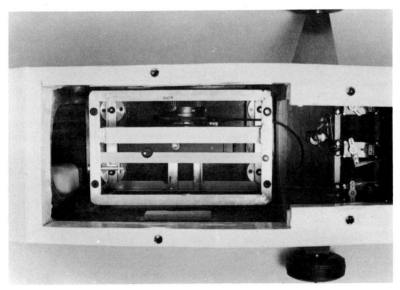

Figure 2.9 Remotely piloted aircraft fitted with a 35 mm camera system and adapted to take oblique aerial photographs. (Reproduced by kind permission of Sigma Visuals.)

opportunity to obtain an aerial view of very small sites extremely cheaply. An example of this approach is illustrated by Figure 2.9.

2.3　Types of aerial photography

Aerial photographs differ considerably both in appearance and in form. They can, however, be broadly classified according to two criteria, firstly the orientation of the camera axis, and secondly, the type of photographic emulsion which is used.

2.3.1　Camera orientation

Aerial cameras can be oriented either with the camera axis in a vertical, or near vertical position, or alternatively with the camera axis intentionally inclined out of the vertical. The resulting photographs are termed respectively vertical and oblique aerial photographs. The distinction is illustrated by Figure 2.10.

2.3.1.1 *Vertical aerial photographs.* Vertical aerial photographs are by far the most common type of aerial photographic product currently in use. When vertical aerial photographic coverage of a particular area of interest is requested, it is normal practice to arrange that exposures are taken to ensure that successive photographs overlap each other. This overlap is usually about 55 to 60%. This process is illustrated in Figure 2.11. A typical example of a vertical aerial photograph is illustrated by Figure 2.12. An adjacent pair of aerial photographs is called a stereopair. This term relates to the fact that by viewing the photographs using a stereoscope it is possible to perceive a three-dimensional image of the ground. Almost all quantitative interpretations of vertical aerial photographs involve stereoviewing. This aspect is dealt with in greater detail in section 2.4.

Although a vertical aerial photograph provides a map-like view of the earth's surface, it differs fundamentally in geometrical terms from a map in two respects. The first geometrical difference is that of image displacement. Image

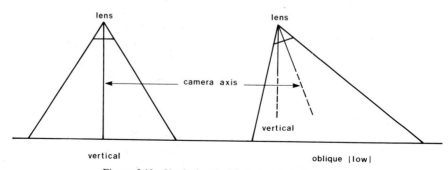

Figure 2.10　Vertical and oblique aerial photographs.

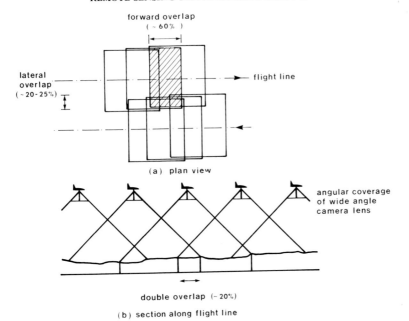

Figure 2.11 Aerial photograph overlap.

Figure 2.12 Vertical aerial photograph of the University of Surrey. (Crown copyright reserved.)

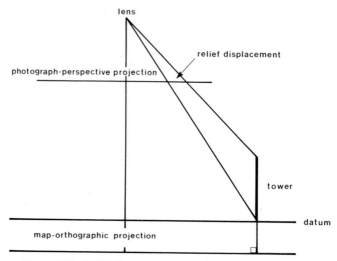

Figure 2.13   Relief displacement on a vertical aerial photograph.

displacement refers to the alteration in the position of points which is caused by the effects of ground relief and photographic tilt. One practical consequence of image displacement is particularly well illustrated by tall towers when they have been imaged on a vertical aerial photograph. Towers, rather than appearing as they would do on a map as, for example, small circular features, appear to be leaning outwards and hence are not imaged as single points. This leaning, which radiates from the principal point, is termed relief displacement. The effect of relief displacement is illustrated by Figures 2.13 and 2.14.

It should be noted that all features on the photograph will be affected by image displacement unless the photograph is truly vertical and the variations in ground elevation are zero.

The second geometrical distinction, which is a consequence of image displacement, is the scale variation which occurs on a near vertical aerial photograph. This scale variation is a function of the same two factors: changes in ground elevation and tilt of the camera axis at the moment of exposure. The effect of the first of these factors is illustrated by Figure 2.15.

Figure 2.15 is a section taken through a vertical aerial photograph with the lens positioned at O. The elevation of the lens above datum, or flying height, is indicated by H. The distance from the lens to the photograph is the focal length of the camera (f). It can be seen that the scale of the photograph is varying according to ground elevation. The scale at point A will therefore be larger than, for example, at the ground principal point. The average photoscale (scale$_{AV}$) or 'contact scale' is often indicated on the negative (Figure 2.14).

It can also be seen from Figure 2.16 that an aerial photograph which has been inadvertently tilted at the moment of exposure (for example because of atmospheric turbulence) will also exhibit scale variations. The combined effect

Figure 2.14 Shoreham, Kent, UK, indicating relief displacement. Reproduced by kind permission of Meridian Airmaps Ltd.

of both factors is to produce a photograph which contains an infinite number of small-scale variations.

2.3.1.2 *Oblique aerial photographs.* Oblique aerial photographs may be classified as either high obliques, in which case the photograph includes the horizon, or low obliques, in which case the horizon is not imaged. This distinction is illustrated by Figures 2.17, 2.18 and 2.19.

Obliques have several advantages in comparison with vertical aerial photographs. Firstly, the view which is produced is much easier to interpret since it affords a more recognizable image of the ground. Secondly, oblique photographs provide far greater ground coverage than vertical aerial

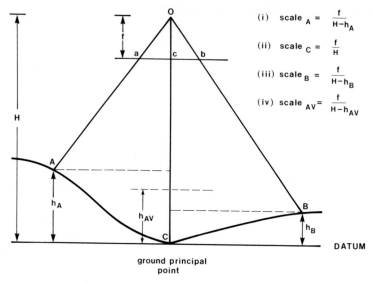

(i) $\text{scale}_A = \dfrac{f}{H - h_A}$

(ii) $\text{scale}_C = \dfrac{f}{H}$

(iii) $\text{scale}_B = \dfrac{f}{H - h_B}$

(iv) $\text{scale}_{AV} = \dfrac{f}{H - h_{AV}}$

Figure 2.15   Scale changes on a vertical aerial photograph caused by variations in the elevation of the ground.

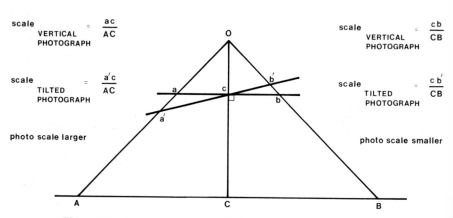

$$\text{scale}_{\substack{\text{VERTICAL}\\\text{PHOTOGRAPH}}} = \frac{ac}{AC}$$

$$\text{scale}_{\substack{\text{TILTED}\\\text{PHOTOGRAPH}}} = \frac{a'c}{AC}$$

photo scale larger

$$\text{scale}_{\substack{\text{VERTICAL}\\\text{PHOTOGRAPH}}} = \frac{cb}{CB}$$

$$\text{scale}_{\substack{\text{TILTED}\\\text{PHOTOGRAPH}}} = \frac{cb'}{CB}$$

photo scale smaller

Figure 2.16   Scale variations on a tilted near-vertical aerial photograph.

photographs taken from the same altitude. Obliques do however suffer from several drawbacks, which limit their value. Firstly, since the scale of the photograph is continually changing, it is much more difficult to take accurate measurements from obliques. It should however be mentioned that many maps have been produced in the past using oblique photography. Secondly, the view which is afforded by an oblique photograph may mean that objects in the foreground of the photograph obscure other detail on the photograph. Finally, the availability of oblique aerial photographic coverage is much more limited than vertical coverage. For these reasons oblique aerial photographs

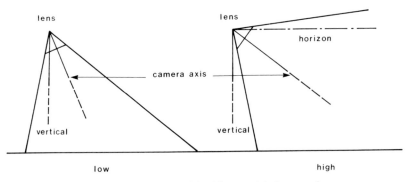

Figure 2.17   Low and high oblique aerial photographs.

Figure 2.18   Low oblique —University of Surrey. (Reproduced by kind permission of AVA unit, University of Surrey.)

are normally considered as complementary to vertical aerial photographs. It is rare for oblique photographs alone to be used for a project. One particularly interesting and unusual application of obliques is reported by Siddans (1980), who discusses a method of superimposing perspective drawings of a proposed highway on to oblique aerial photographs in order to produce photomontages for public exhibitions.

Figure 2.19   High oblique—University of Surrey. (Reproduced by kind permission of AVA unit, University of Surrey.)

2.3.2 *Photographic emulsions*

The second criterion which can be used in order to classify aerial photography is the type of photographic emulsion employed. A large number of photographic emulsions has been developed for use in photography. Each emulsion has been designed to be sensitive to a particular region of the EM spectrum and has associated with it specific advantages and limitations. Four emulsions can be identified which have particular relevance to the production of aerial photography; black-and-white panchromatic, black-and-white, infrared colour and 'false' colour infrared emulsions.

2.3.2.1 *Black-and-white panchromatic.* Panchromatic emulsions are used in order to produce the conventional black-and-white aerial photograph. The emulsion consists of a very thin layer of light-sensitive silver halide crystals. These crystals when exposed to light undergo a photochemical reaction which produces an invisible latent photographic image. In order to release this latent image, a chemical processing or development stage is undertaken. During this processing stage the previously exposed silver crystals are reduced to silver and subsequently to various shades of grey on the photographic image. The spectral sensitivity of this type of emulsion is illustrated by Figure 2.20.

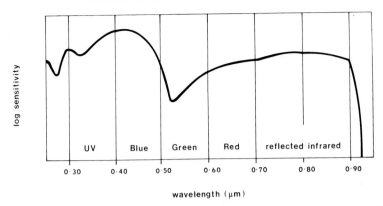

Figure 2.20 Spectral sensitivity—black-and-white panchromatic emulsion. (Adapted from Eastman Kodak, 1972).

It can be seen that the spectral sensitivity of the emulsion extends from the ultraviolet to just over 0.7 μm. The sensitivity of the emulsion in the region below 0.4 μm is not normally of interest and is usually eliminated by means of a minus blue filter. This helps reduce the effect of haze. Thus the spectral sensitivity of the emulsion covers the spectral range from 0.4 to 0.7 μm. By design, this range correlates closely with the sensitivity of the human eye and thus produces a relatively familiar view of the terrain.

Black-and-white aerial photography which has been produced using a panchromatic emulsion is a very common remote sensing product, particularly for large-scale detailed site investigations. (see Chapter 8). This popularity stems largely from its wide availability and relatively low cost in comparison with other remote sensing products.

2.3.2.2 *Black-and-white infrared* An alternative type of black-and-white emulsion which is sensitive not only to the UV and visible portions of the EM spectrum, but also to the reflected infrared part of the spectrum in the black-and-white infrared emulsion. The spectral sensitivity of this type of emulsion is illustrated by Figure 2.21. It can be seen that the range of spectral responses which can now be sensed has been increased to include part of the reflected infrared (0.4 to 0.9 μm). Although much less common than conventional black-and-white photography, this type of emulsion does have several features which can be useful for particular applications. Firstly, since infrared radiation tends to be strongly absorbed by water, the boundaries between water and land are very clearly illustrated. Secondly, maximum reflectance from vegetation occurs in the reflected infrared region of the spectrum. Thus it may be possible to differentiate between different species of vegetation, for example between coniferous and deciduous trees. Finally, black-and-white infrared emulsions have improved haze penetration in comparison with conventional black-and-white emulsion.

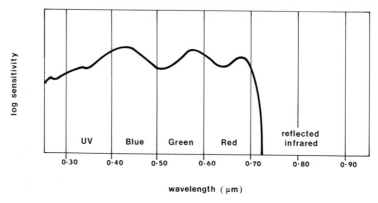

Figure 2.21 Spectral sensitivity—black-and-white infrared. (Adapted from Eastman Kodak, 1972.)

2.3.2.3 *Colour.* The human eye can detect about 20 to 30 shades of grey on a black-and-white aerial photograph. In contrast, over 200 different colours can be discriminated on a colour aerial photograph. Thus a colour photograph contains much more information than the corresponding black-and-white photograph.

Perception of colour depends largely on the relative amounts of the three primary colours, blue, green and red, which are reflected by a particular object. Combining or adding the three primary colours therefore enables all possible colours to be produced.

An alternative approach which can be used in order to produce a particular colour is that of subtractive colour mixing. In this case, rather than adding the

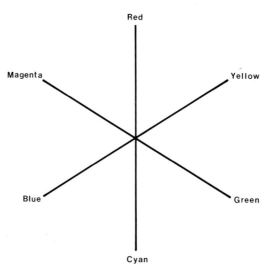

Figure 2.22 Subtractive colour mixing.

three primary colours, the three subtractive primaries, yellow, magenta and cyan, are combined. Subtractive primary colours are so named because each is obtained by subtracting one of the primary colours from white light. This can be illustrated diagrammatically by Figure 2.22.

Thus, for example, yellow is obtained by the subtraction of blue light from white light; combination of the two remaining primaries, red and green, produces yellow. Similarly, cyan is formed by subtracting red light and combining the remaining blue and green primaries.

It is this second approach which colour aerial photography uses in order to recreate the various colours of a scene. In order to accomplish this, colour film is manufactured with three silver halide emulsion layers, each of which is sensitive to blue, green and red light respectively. However, during processing, yellow, magenta and cyan dyes are introduced into each emulsion layer. The amount of dye which is absorbed is inversely proportional to the intensity of the corresponding primary colour which was initially present. When viewed together the dyes reproduce the colours of the original scene. The spectral sensitivity and cross section of a colour film is shown in Figures 2.23 and 2.24.

2.3.2.4 *'False' colour infrared.* Colour infrared or 'false' colour infrared emulsion act in a similar manner to black-and-white infrared emulsions by extending the spectral sensitivity of the image to incorporate the near infrared portion of the spectrum. In contrast, however, this type of emulsion consists of three emulsion layers, and is therefore similar in structure to conventional colour film emulsions. The spectral sensitivity of a typical colour infrared emulsion is illustrated by Figure 2.25. It can be seen that, unlike 'normal'

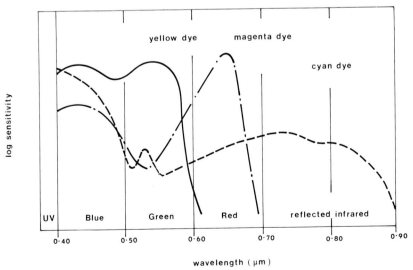

Figure 2.23   Spectral sensitivity—colour emulsion. (Adapted from Eastman Kodak, 1972.)

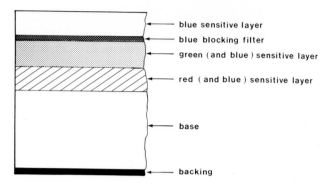

Figure 2.24   Cross section—colour emulsion. (After Lillesand and Kiefer, 1979.)

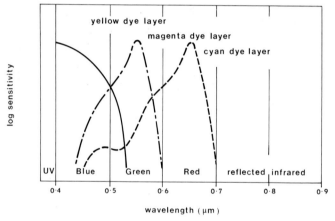

Figure 2.25   Spectral sensitivity—false colour infrared. (Adapted from Eastman Kodak, 1972.)

colour emulsions, colour infrared emulsions are designed in order to record green, red and infrared energy. However, since the emulsion dyes which are used are the same as colour emulsions, that is, yellow, magenta and cyan, the result is that the colours ascribed to particular features do not correspond to their natural colours. The result therefore is a 'false' colour image in which a blue image results from objects reflecting primarily green energy, green images result from objects reflecting primarily red energy and red images result from objects reflecting primarily in the near infrared portion of the spectrum.

Finally, Table 2.2 summarizes the principal characteristics and relative merits of each of the four types of photographic emulsion.

2.4   Methods of viewing aerial photographs

Overlapping vertical aerial photographs can be viewed either monoscopically or stereoscopically.

Table 2.2 Characteristics of photographic emulsions used for the production of aerial photography.

Film type	Structure	Sensitivity	Advantages	Limitations	Cost
Black-and-white panchromatic	Single layer emulsion	0.4–0.7 μm	Good definition and contrast, wide exposure latitude. Boundaries are often clearly portrayed. Subtle textural variations can be identified and geometric patterns are more obvious	Sometimes difficult to interpret ground features due to the inability of the eye to distinguish between subtle differences in grey tones	Low
Black-and-white infrared	Single layer emulsion	0.4–0.9 μm	It provides specific enhancement of different forms of vegetation and clearly defines bodies of water and ground moisture distribution. Helps to penetrate haze giving a sharper more contrasting image	Contrast may be excessive and detail is often lost in areas of shadow	Low
True colour	Multi-layered emulsions Top layer is sensitive to blue light, the 2nd layer to green and blue light and the 3rd to blue and red light. A blue absorbing filter is introduced between the 1st and 2nd layers.	0.4 –0.7 μm	Good contrast and tonal range. Wide exposure latitude for negative film types. Materials are more identifiable and hence moisture conditions are also more identifiable	Less good definition than panchromatic film	Intermediate to high
False colour infrared	Multi-layered emulsion incorporating a reflected infrared sensitive layer. Top layer is sensitive to blue and reflected infrared light, 2nd to green and blue light and 3rd to red and blue light. The film is normally used with a filter to block out blue light.	0.4 –0.9 μm	Helps to penetrate haze, provides accurate identifiable data on vegetation, rocks, soils, water bodies and moisture distribution	Lower resolution than colour film. Slow and exposure difficult to determine	High

One of the simplest and most efficient means of examining a large area for which photography exists is by examining, monoscopically, a print laydown or photomosaic. A print laydown is produced by laying down, untrimmed, each succeeding photograph in order to form a single semi-continuous picture of the area under investigation. A more useful type of product which can also enable the interpreter to view a large region is the photomosaic. In this case the photographs are trimmed and matched along features which are common to adjacent photographs. In cases where the mosaic is fitted to mapped ground detail, the mosaic is termed a controlled mosaic. A less common, orthophoto-mosaic may be produced in situations where high positional accuracy is necessary. In this case each photograph is scanned in order to eliminate the effects of relief and aircraft tilt.

Further details relating to the instrumentation required for this type of operation can be found in section 6.2.4. Whilst mosaics are a very useful means of examining large areas, the most appropriate method of examining in detail a small area is stereoscopic viewing. As discussed in section 2.3.1.1, vertical aerial photographs are normally exposed so that successive photographs in a strip overlap each other by 55–60%. This overlapping of photographic images allows a three-dimensional model of the terrrain to be formed by viewing the area of overlap between adjacent photographs simultaneously. The stereo-scopic effect is possible because the observer's eyes are separated by a small distance (the eye base) which allows objects to be viewed simultaneously from two different positions. The brain is then able to merge the two resulting images to form a single three-dimensional image. This phenomenon is termed depth perception. A pair of photographs which can be viewed in this way is termed a stereopair.

The effect of viewing stereopairs with an eye base far less than the air base of the photographs and a viewing height considerably less than the distance between the camera and the ground (flying height) is an exaggeration of vertical scales. This is referred to as the vertical exaggeration. The amount of vertical exaggeration is dependent upon the ratio of air base to flying height compared with the ratio of eye-base to eye-photo viewing distance. For a 60 per cent overlap, the terrain is normally seen exaggerated in height about three or four times. The vertical exaggeration will also cause slopes to appear steeper than they are in reality.

The stereoviewing of vertical aerial photographs is generally performed by means of a specialist instrument termed a stereoscope. Several different designs of stereoscope exist, of which the most significant are the pocket, mirror, and zoom stereoscopes.

2.4.1 *Pocket stereoscope*

The pocket stereoscope, so named because of its small size, is the least expensive and also the most common type of stereoscope, particularly for field

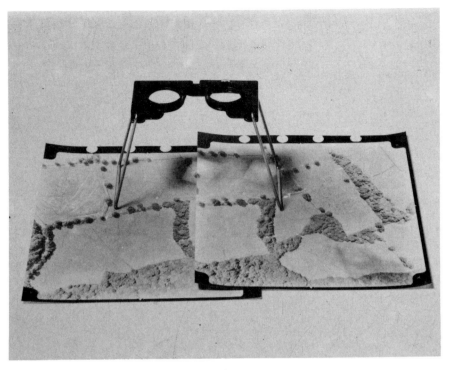

Figure 2.26   Pocket stereoscope.

use. Figure 2.26 illustrates an example of this type of stereoscope. It can be seen that the instrument consists of two glass lenses mounted in a simple frame. The distance between the lenses can be varied in order to accommodate various eye bases. The photographs are placed close together so that corresponding images are slightly less than the eye-base distance apart. The main disadvantage of this type of stereoscope is that it is not possible (with 60% overlap) to view the entire overlap region without bending one of the photographs. An alternative design of stereoscope which overcomes this limitation is the mirror stereoscope.

2.4.2 Mirror stereoscope

Mirror stereoscopes of the types shown in Figures 2.27 and 2.28 enable the entire overlap region to be viewed stereoscopically without bending the photographs. This is achieved by separating the photographs. A further benefit of the mirror stereoscope is the ability to magnify the stereoscopic model of the terrain. The Wild ST4, for example, may be equipped with binocular eyepieces which enable the model to be magnified × 3 or × 8.

A more sophisticated design of stereoscope which incorporates several

Figure 2.27   Wild TSP 1 mirror stereoscope.

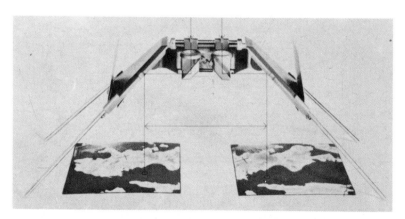

Figure 2.28   Wild ST4 mirror stereoscope.

additional features in addition to those which have been discussed so far, is the zoom stereoscope.

2.4.3 *Zoom stereoscope*

An example of the zoom stereoscope design is the Wild Aviopret APT 1 (Figures 2.29, 2.30). The practical benefits of this design of stereoscope are discussed by Williams (1982). In addition to the zoom facility (1:5 continuous range) and up to × 31 magnification, the instrument can also be equipped with peripheral units such as the photographic unit illustrated by Figure 2.29 for

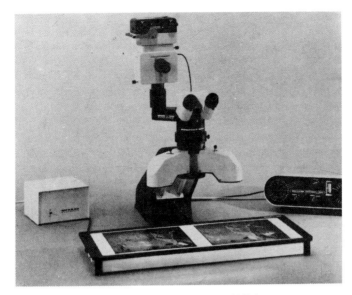

Figure 2.29   Wild Aviopret APT 1.

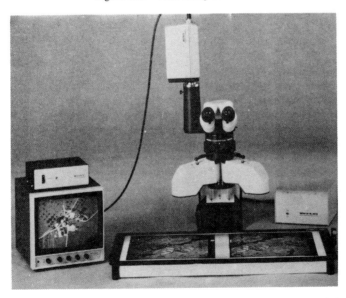

Figure 2.30   Wild Aviopret APT 1 with monitor. Figures 2.27–2.30 by kind permission of Wild Heerbrugg, Switzerland.

the recording of selected excerpts during the interpretation stage. Further facilities include the possibility of incorporating dual optics or of projecting the image onto a television monitor as shown by Figure 2.30. The main disadvantage of this design is its high cost in comparison with the other types of stereoscope.

References

Academy of Sciences, USSR., 1982. *Atlas for Interpretation of Multispectral Aerospace Photographs*. Methods and Results. Akademie Verlag, Berlin.

Beaumont, T. E. (1977) *Techniques for the Interpretation of Remote Sensing Imagery for Highway Engineering Purposes*. Dept. of the Environment, Dept. of Transport, Transport and Road Research Laboratory Report 753, Crowthorne, Berks, 24 pp.

Blyth, K. (1983) *Remote Sensing at the Institute of Hydrology, Wallingford*. Unpublished report, 5 pp.

Burnside, C. D. (1979) *Mapping from Aerial Photographs*. Granada Publishing, London, 304 pp.

Clegg, R. H. and Scherz, J. P. (1975) A comparison of 9 inch, 70 mm and 35 mm cameras. *Photogrammetric Engineering and Remote Sensing* 41, 1487–1500.

Eastman Kodak Co. (1972) *Kodak Aerial Films and Photographic Plates*. Eastman Kodak Company, Rochester, New York.

Heath, W. (1980) *Inexpensive Aerial Photography for Highway Engineering and Traffic Studies*. Dept. of the Environment, Dept. of Transport, Transport and Road Research Laboratory Supplementary Report 632, Crowthorne, Berks, 24 pp.

Lillesand, T. M. and Kiefer, R. W. (1979) *Remote Sensing and Image Interpretation*. John Wiley and Sons, New York, 612 pp.

Mountain, L. J. and Garner, J. B. (1980) Application of photography to traffic surveys. *The Highway Engineer* 27 (11) 12–19.

Ross, O. S. (1973) Simple multispectral photography and additive colour viewing. *Photogrammetric Engineering* 39, 583–591.

Siddans, D. R. (1980) Photomontages from oblique aerial photographs. *The Highway Engineer* 27 (3) 14–19.

Tomlins, G. F. (1983) Some considerations in the design of low cost remotely piloted aircraft for civil remote sensing applications. *The Canadian Surveyor* 37, 157–167.

Williams, V. (1982) *Practical Experience with the New Zoom Stereoscope Wild Aviopret APT 1*. Report published by Wild Heerbrugg, 7 pp.

3 Remote sensing scanning systems

T. J. M. KENNIE

3.1 Introduction

Photographic remote sensing systems are capable of sensing the visible and near infrared regions of the EM spectrum ($\lambda = 0.4$ to $0.9\,\mu m$). There are, however, other longer-wavelength regions of the EM spectrum, which are potentially useful for remote sensing purposes. Unfortunately, however, conventional glass lenses and photographic emulsions are not able to detect and record these regions of the EM spectrum.

An alternative method of detecting and recording both the visible, near infrared and longer-wavelength bands, such as thermal infrared and microwave energy, is the airborne scanner. The airborne scanner differs from an aerial camera in that it collects energy sequentially from the ground below, as a series of scanlines, each of which is perpendicular to the line of flight (see Figure 1.7). Scanning is carried out by a rotating mirror, which directs the incoming radiation on to a detector. The scanner detector is analogous to the emulsion of a conventional film camera. Its purpose is therefore to detect, measure and record EM energy. However, in contrast to film emulsions, scanner detectors are available which are sensitive to wavelengths longer than $1\,\mu m$, such as the thermal infrared and microwave regions of the EM spectrum.

Airborne scanning systems can be very broadly classified as being either passive, that is, sensing naturally occurring EM energy, or alternatively active, that is, sensing system-generated EM energy.

3.2 Passive scanning systems

Two distinct types of passive scanning system are currently in use. The first type of system is one which is only sensitive to a single spectral band, such as, for example, the thermal infrared and microwave regions of the EM spectrum. In contrast, the second, generally more complex, system is sensitive to several spectral bands. These bands may range from the visible to the microwave regions of the spectrum.

3.2.1 *Thermal infrared scanning systems*

The technique of airborne infrared scanning was originally developed after the Second World War for military purposes. Its use in the civilian field has, however, only developed during the past 10 to 15 years.

3.2.1.1 *General principles.* Thermal infrared scanning systems are concerned primarily with the measurement of earth-emitted energy within the spectral wavelength bands from 3 to 5.5 μm and 8 to 14 μm. Because these energy bands coincide with the wavelengths normally associated with heat emitted from the earth's surface, they are normally termed thermal infrared energy bands. Systems of this type therefore differ from the photographic infrared systems, which were discussed in section 2.3.2.2. Those systems were, in contrast, concerned with the detection and measurement of reflected infrared energy. One significant consequence of this independence from reflected energy is that thermal infrared systems can be operated both during the day and at night if required.

Although the technique is based on the detection of heat and the production of 'heat pictures', the system does not record surface temperatures directly. Rather, the system senses temperature differences between the various components of the scene.

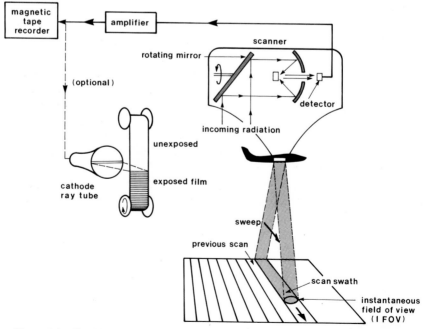

Figure 3.1 Simplified diagram of thermal scanning system (adapted from Rudd, 1974).

The design of a typical thermal infrared scanner is illustrated in Figure 3.1. It can be seen that the thermal scanner is, in very general terms, a telescope which focuses the earth-emitted thermal radiation on to a detector assembly. A selection of typical detectors is listed in Table 3.1. The function of the detectors is to convert the incoming radiation into electronic signals. These electronic signals are then normally recorded directly on to magnetic tape for processing after the flight. Some systems may also incorporate the facility to record a 'quick look' image during flight by means of a cathode ray tube (CRT) and film recorder.

In order to calibrate and quantify the thermal data, two black-body reference temperatures are normally recorded at either end of each scan line. These black-body temperatures are controlled and set by the operator. One is usually set at the ambient ground temperature, whilst the other is set above the highest expected temperature. Thus the data sets for the flight are captured between two known temperatures. Since the detectors are recording thermal variations close to those within the aircraft, it is necessary to cool the detector assembly in order to reduce the effect of background radiation from the aircraft or scanner itself. Hence the temperature variations which are recorded are those which are due solely to temperature changes associated with the earth's surface. Temperature variations as small as $0.2°$ C can be resolved using this type of system. For absolute temperature determinations, information about the emissivity of the objects being sensed becomes a critical factor.

After the thermal data has been stored on magnetic tape it is necessary to play back the data to produce imagery from which interpretation can be undertaken. This involves transforming the stored electronic signal into a light beam by use of an optic fibre beam and exposing on to a continuous strip of 125 mm panchromatic black-and-white film which moves across the face of the beam. The intensity of the light beam is proportional to the electronic signal. This is illustrated by Figure 3.2. The scale along the line of flight is corrected by controlling the speed at which the film moves across the optic fibre. The scale across the flight path is corrected by varying the speed at which the optic fibre crosses the film. In all cases the two speeds are correlated to ensure that x and y axes have approximately the same scale.

On the film negative, ground surfaces having high radiant temperatures give rise to light photographic tones on the image. The remaining areas are

Table 3.1 Characteristics of thermal scanner detectors (adapted from Lillesand and Kiefer, 1979).

Type of detector	Chemical abbreviation	Spectral sensitivity range (μm)
Mercury doped germanium	Ge:Hg	3 to 14
Indium antimonide	InSb	3 to 5
Mercury cadmium telluride	HgCdTe	8 to 14

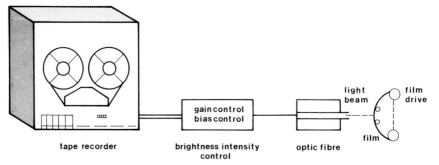

Figure 3.2   Playback of data for reproduction of image.

composed of grey tones which can be interpreted according to the data provided by the black-body reference sources. Figure 3.4 is an example of this type of imagery.

The data recorded in flight, later processed and printed in the form of black-and-white imagery, are essentially a 'qualitative' assessment of the ground temperature. For many applications there is also the requirement for accurate temperature measurement of specified points on the ground—'quantitative' assessment. Quantitative values can be obtained by converting the analogue data recorded on the magnetic tape to a digital format by computer processing. This analogue to digital (A to D) conversion involves transforming the continuous format of the analogue signal to a series of discrete numerical values.

The continuous analogue signal is sampled at a set time interval and the signal level at each sample point is numerically sampled. In computer compatible form the data may be processed, analysed and displayed in a variety of manners. For example, the image may be 'density sliced' (see Chapter 4) and a colour assigned to a range of grey levels. Since each range of

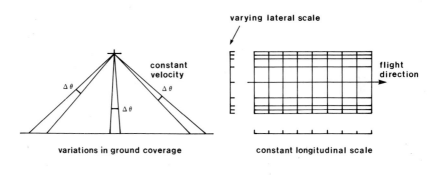

Figure 3.3   Scale variations in thermal scanning imagery. (a) Geometry of rotating scanning mirror. (b) Resulting scale distortion in unrectified scanner imagery. (After Lillesand and Kiefer, 1979.)

grey levels will have associated with it a particular temperature band, it is possible to produce a colour-coded image. Plate 18 illustrates an example of this technique in which each colour corresponds to a small temperature difference.

3.2.1.2 *Geometric characteristics.* Although a thermal infrared image has the appearance of an aerial photograph, it does, however, differ significantly in geometrical terms.

The first and most obvious characteristic difference is that of scale. Unless it is geometrically rectified, thermal scanner imagery manifests severe scale distortions, primarily in the direction perpendicular to the flight direction. In the main, this scale distortion is caused by the geometry of the scanner's mirror. The geometry of the scanning mirror and the consequent scale variation are illustrated by Figures 3.3 and 3.4. It can be seen from Figures 3.3 and 3.4 (*a*) that the scale along the scan direction is compressed at the edges of the image. This is because the scanning system, which has a nearly uniform angular velocity, images a greater length of ground in a given time interval when it is pointing obliquely down from the aircraft than when it is pointing to the nadir position. Fortunately, this source of scale variation is normally eliminated during the subsequent ground processing of the image, so producing a rectified image (illustrated by Figure 3.4 (*b*)). Smaller-scale variations may be induced by variations in the attitude of the aircraft. Again, however, these scale changes can be controlled, both in flight and also during processing.

The second fundamental geometrical difference between thermal scanner imagery and aerial photography is in terms of relief displacement. In the case of a truly vertical aerial photograph, relief displacement is radial from the centre of the image (from the principal point). In contrast, however, relief displacement on thermal scanner imagery is perpendicular to the centre line of the image. Therefore the displacement only occurs in one dimension, that is along the scan line.

3.2.1.3 *Aircraft-based systems.* Several aircraft-based thermal scanners are currently in use. A selection of the specifications relating to these scanners is given in Table 3.2. Further details regarding the practical operation of airborne thermal scanners are discussed in Chapter 10.

3.2.1.4 *Satellite-based systems.* Many thermal infrared images of low resolution have been acquired by meteorological satellites. The very low resolution severely limits the usefulness of these systems for engineering purposes. Nevertheless, two systems which are worthy of further comment are the National Oceanic and Atmospheric Administration (NOAA) satellites, and the Heat Capacity Mapping Mission (HCMM) satellite.

One example from the National Oceanic and Atmospheric Administration

Figure 3.4 Thermal infrared images: (left), unrectified; (right) rectified. (Reproduced by kind permission of Clyde Surveys Ltd.)

Table 3.2 Thermal scanner specifications (after Bullard and Lakin, 1981)

Scanner	Spectral range (μm)	IFOV (mrad)	Resolution (m) at a flying height of 500 m	Temperature sensitivity (°C)	Field of view (°)	Scan rate (oscillations/s)	Detector
EMI							
Airscan	3.5 to 5.5	1.5	0.75	0.3	140	50	InSb
Hawker-Siddeley (British Aerospace)							
201/204/214	8 to 14	1.5	0.75	0.25	120	500	HgCdTe
401	8 to 14				120	500	HgCdTe
Daedalus							
DS–1250	8 to 14	2.5	1.25	0.25	77	80	HgCdTe
DS–1230	8 to 14	1.7	0.85	0.20	77	80	HgCdTe
Bendix							
BTM	3 to 5.5	2.5	1.25	0.50	120	—	InSb
	8 to 14	2.5	1.25	0.50	120	—	Ge:Hg
Texas Instruments							
RS–310	0.3 to 14.0	1.5	0.75	—	90	200	—

series of satellites was NOAA-5. This satellite was operational during the period 1976–1979 and circled in a near polar orbit at an altitude of 1510 km. It carried on board several sensors, including a Very High Resolution Radiometer (VHRR). This instrument was a scanning radiometer capable of producing thermal infrared images within the 10.5 to 12.5 μm wavelength band, with a spatial (ground) resolution of about 900 m.

One interesting application of NOAA-5 imagery is reported by Berg and McGinnis (1980). Berg discusses the use of computer-enhanced VHRR data for river flood mapping in the Kentucky river basin.

The Heat Capacity Mapping Mission satellite (HCMM) was launched in early 1978 and placed in a near circular orbit at an altitude of 620 km. On board it carried a two-channel scanning radiometer, which obtained data both in the visible near IR (0.5 to 1.1 μm) and thermal IR (10.5 to 12.5 μm) portions of the EM spectrum at times of maximum and minimum temperature (1330 and 0230 h). The field of view of the radiometer was rotated through a scan angle of 60° producing images with a swath width of 720 km. Ground resolution in the thermal channel was 600 m. HCMM was essentially built to test the feasibility of measuring thermal variations of the earth's surface features in order to infer their identity and condition. Temperature difference and thermal inertia model data were produced by first geometrically correcting the day and night data and then digitally overlapping the data sets. Thermal inertia data were derived by the application of a mathematical thermal model to the day/night data and visible band data.

These thermal inertia data have been used to discriminate rock types and mineral resource locations (Watson *et al.*, 1982). HCMM data has also been used to evaluate soil moisture and the depth to shallow groundwater (Heilman and Moore, 1982). One further application worthy of mention is that reported by Schowengerdt (1982); in this paper he discusses a digital processing method of combining the higher resolution Landsat band 7 MSS data (see section 3.2.3.3) with HCMM data to produce a thermal map of a lake in Virginia.

The future may possibly bring satellites with improved resolution in the thermal channels. Townsend (1981) rates the proposed Thermal Inertia Mapper, a successor to the HCMM satellite, as 'semi-credible to credible'. If built, the Thermal Inertia Mapper would have 10 m resolution in the 8–13 μm band from a 600 km orbit. It is intended that this satellite would be used to map the thermal inertia of the earth's terrain with sequential passes over the same area at 0400/1000 h and 1600/2200 h local time crossings. A satellite system of this type would have great potential for geological mapping in remote areas of the world where it is prohibitively costly to produce airborne thermal data.

3.2.2 *Microwave scanning radiometers*

A second, and much less common, passive scanning system, is the microwave scanning radiometer.

As with the thermal scanning systems, this type of system senses naturally-occurring radiation. However, in this case it is sensing the emitted EM energy at microwave wavelengths ($\lambda = 1$ mm to 1 m). All features emit energy at these wavelengths, although it is extremely faint in comparison to thermal infrared radiation. Also, much less is known about the characteristics of microwave scanner imagery, when compared with thermal imagery. From the literature it appears that the most promising application of passive microwave sensing is for the determination of soil moisture conditions (see Chapter 11). Further details about this application can be found in Estes *et al.* (1977).

3.2.3 *Multispectral scanners (MSS)*

The discussion so far has been concerned with either the photographic systems which sense reflected radiation, or the thermal and microwave scanning systems which detect and measure emitted radiation. An instrument which allows us to detect and record simultaneously both reflected and emitted radiation, in several spectral bands, is the MSS.

3.2.3.1 *General principles.* The technique of data collection used with this type of instrument is very similar to that previously described for thermal scanners (section 3.2.1.1). The system therefore produces imagery in a sequential fashion by recording the radiation (emitted or reflected), along a scan line, perpendicular to the line of flight. As before, the forward motion of the sensor platform advances the strip being scanned and so produces a linescan image.

The operation of a typical MSS can be illustrated by the flow diagram shown in Figure 3.5. Points on the earth's surface are scanned in a raster fashion, normally by means of a continuously spinning prism, or oscillating mirror in the case of a satellite system. This is usually termed an optical mechanical MSS. An alternative approach, the multilinear array or 'pushbroom' scanner, is discussed in section 3.2.3.3. Radiation then passes through a converging optical system to focus it.

The radiation is next dispersed into its spectral components by means of a prism or diffraction grating system. This splits the incoming radiation into a series of spectral channels or bands. An array of electronic detectors, placed at

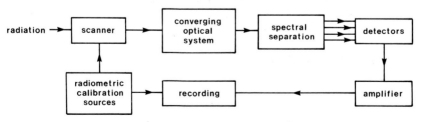

Figure 3.5 Components of a multispectral scanner system (adapted from Swain and Davis, 1978).

the appropriate geometric position behind the grating, detects the radiation within the wavelength region to which it is sensitive. The amplified signal is then recorded on to some suitable medium, commonly a tape recorder, or is telemetered to a ground or satellite receiving station. In addition, most MSS systems also incorporate an internal reference source to radiometrically calibrate the data collected in each channel. This calibration source is therefore scanned by the system and recorded at the beginning and end of each scan line with the radiance data.

3.2.3.2 *Aircraft-based systems.* In recent years a considerable amount of interest has been shown in the use of aircraft-based MSS systems. The early work in this field began in 1965 at the Environmental Institute of Michigan (ERIM). This led to the development of an eleven-channel scanner covering the spectral range from 0.38 to 12.25 μm. Several other organizations also developed scanners, but it was not until relatively recently, particularly in Europe, that airborne MSS data became available on a commercial basis. Two organizations which are currently operating airborne MSS systems in the United Kingdom are Programmed Neuro Cybernetics (PNC) and Hunting Geology and Geophysics Ltd. The specific features of the systems they are presently operating are given in Table 3.3.

The benefits of using an airborne system of the type outlined in Table 3.3 are several. Firstly, the spatial resolution is much higher than that which can be obtained from a satellite system. By flying at low altitude, it is possible to obtain a spatial resolution of the order of 1 to 2 metres. Secondly, in comparison with satellite systems, the user generally has available a greater

Table 3.3   Examples of aircraft-based MSS systems

Detail	Hunting system	PNC systems	
	Daedalus AADS 1268 Airborne Thematic Mapper	Mk II	Mk II(a)
No. of wavebands	11	4	3
Spectral ranges (μm)			
Channel 1	0.42 – 0.45	7.2– 8.9	2.05–2.15
2	0.45 – 0.52	8.8–10.2	2.15–2.25
3	0.52 – 0.60	10.1–10.9	2.28–2.40
4	0.605– 0.625	10.9–13.9	
5	0.63 – 0.69		
6	0.695– 0.75		
7	0.76 – 0.90		
8	0.91 – 1.05		
9	1.55 – 1.75		
10	2.08 – 2.35		
11	8.50 –13.00		
Spatial resolution (mrads)	2.5 (1.25 optional)	1.5	3.3
Swath width (°)	85	120	70

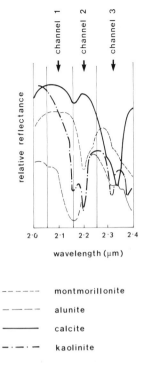

Figure 3.6 Spectral characteristics of clay minerals and carbonates. (After Anon., 1983.)

number of spectral wavebands. More importantly these bands may be chosen in order to aid the discrimination between features of interest. For example, the spectral bands chosen for use in the PNC Mk II(a) scanner enable certain clay minerals and carbonates to be detected by restricting the spectral range of the scanner to the 'clay band' which exists between 2.00 and 2.40 μm. The relationship between the spectral characteristics of certain clay minerals and carbonates and the PNC Mk II(a) wavebands is illustrated by Figure 3.6. Further discussion relating to the use of the PNC scanner system for geological purposes can be found in Barnett et al. (1984).

A third benefit of airborne MSS data accrues from the opportunity to use these data either to 'simulate' the appearance and form of imagery obtained directly from satellites, or to simulate the imagery which can be expected from future satellite systems such as SPOT (see section 3.2.3.3 and Figure 3.21). For example, by using bands 2, 4 and 5 of the Daedalus 1268 scanner it is possible to simulate the appearance of a 'true colour composite' which would be obtained using bands 1, 2 and 3 of the Thematic Mapper on board Landsat 5 (see section 3.2.3.3 for further details). Plate 1 illustrates an example of this type of imagery. There is no doubt that in the future, airborne MSS will become an increasingly important source of terrain information for the civil engineer.

3.2.3.3 *Satellite-based systems.* In contrast to the limited use and availability of aircraft-based MSS imagery, satellite-based MSS imagery is used extensively and is also easily obtainable.

The development of satellite-based MSS systems for commercial rather than military use is a very recent phenomenon. Although a great deal of satellite photography had been taken from space from the early manned space programmes of the 1960s, it was not until the early 1970s that MSS imagery became available. Although some experimental imagery has been obtained from manned satellites, such as Skylab in 1973, the majority of satellite MSS imagery has been obtained from unmanned platforms, in particular from the Landsat series of satellites.

The *Landsat Satellite System*, previously known as the Earth Resources Technology Satellite (ERTS), was initiated in 1967 by NASA in conjunction with the US Department of the Interior. The system was initially designed as an experiment in order to assess the feasibility of collecting earth resource data from unmanned satellites.

To date, five of the six satellites originally planned in 1967 have been launched. Table 3.4 lists a selection of the satellite specifications for Landsats 1 to 5. The table illustrates that Landsats 1 to 3 have many common characteristics which

Table 3.4　Landsat satellite system specifications

	Landsat satellites				
Specification detail	1	2	3	4	5
Orbital details					
Launch date	23/7/72	22/1/75	5/3/78	16/7/82	1/3/84
Ceased to operate	6/1/78	25/2/82	7/9/83	2/83 (T.M. only)	—
Orbital altitude (km)	900	900	900	705	705
Orbital period (mins)	103	103	103	99	99
Equatorial spacing of orbits (km)	2760	2760	2760	2752	2752
No. of orbits/day	14	14	14	14	14
No. of days for repeat coverage	18	18	18	16	16
Equator crossing time	09.42	09.42	09.42	09.45	09.45
Sensor details					
Return Beam Vidicon (RBV)					
No. of spectral bands	3	3	2	—	—
Ground resolution (m)	80	80	30	—	—
Multispectral Scanner (MSS)					
No. of spectral bands	4	4	5	4	4
Ground resolution (m)	79	79	79	79	79
Thematic Mapper (TM)					
No. of spectral bands	—	—	—	7	7
Ground resolution (m) (Bands 1–6/7)	—	—	—	30/120	30/120

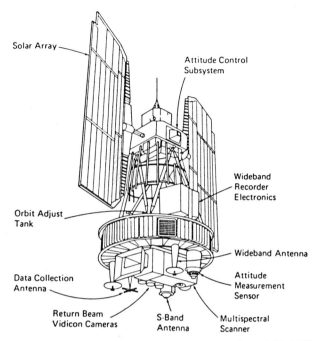

Figure 3.7   Physical characteristics of Landsats 1–3. (After NASA, 1978–83.)

differ significantly from the orbital and sensor characteristics of Landsat 4 and 5. In view of this we will deal specifically with the characteristics of Landsats 3 and 5.

The physical characteristics of Landsat 3 are illustrated by Figure 3.7. The satellite has a weight of about 815 kg and, with the solar panels extended, it has a diameter of about 4m. All Landsat satellites operate in near-polar sun synchronous orbits, which are designed to ensure that the satellite images the same area on the earth's surface at the same local time (about 0940 h). This ensures that the sun illumination conditions are similar for each image and thus repeatable during specific seasons. Repeatable illumination conditions are desirable when producing mosaics from adjacent tracks of imagery and comparing annual changes in land cover. The global orbital pattern for a single day's coverage of Landsat 3 is illustrated by Figure 3.8.

Landsat 3 was launched with two remote sensing systems on board: (a) a five-channel multispectral scanner (MSS) system and (b) a two-channel return beam vidicon (RBV) camera system. The MSS is a line scanning device which uses an oscillating mirror to scan at right angles to the satellite flight direction. This is illustrated in Figure 3.9. This approach contrasts with the spinning scan mirror normally adopted for aircraft MSS systems. The total field of view scanned is approximately 11.56°, with a scanner instantaneous field of view (IFOV) of 0.086 mrad (for the first four channels), or a nominal ground

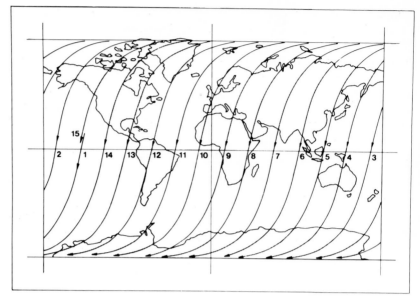

Figure 3.8   Daily orbital pattern of Landsat 3. (After NASA, 1978–83.)

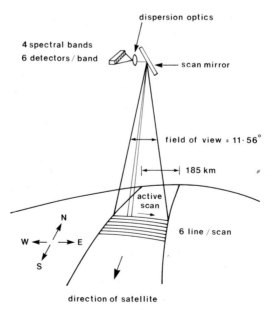

Figure 3.9   Landsat MSS. (After NASA, 1978–83.)

resolution cell of approximately 56 m × 79 m. The fifth channel has an IFOV of 0.258 mrad, or a ground resolution of about 235 m.

The MSS scans each line from west to east with the southward motion of the satellite providing the along track progression of the scan lines. Each Landsat MSS scene covers an area approximately 185 km × 185 km. In view of the extremely high mirror oscillation rate which would be required using this approach, the system is designed to scan six lines simultaneously with each oscillation of the mirror. This results in an area 474 m × 185 km being recorded with each sweep.

The spectral bands used in the Landsat 3 MSS are as follows:

Band number	Spectral range (μm)		Application
4	0.5 to 0.6	Visible (green)	Water penetration –sediment, turbidity studies.
5	0.6 to 0.7	Visible (red)	Vegetation discrimination
6	0.7 to 0.8	Near infrared	Land cover discrimination
7	0.8 to 1.1	Near infrared	Water discrimination
8	10.4 to 12.6	Thermal infrared	Thermal mapping

Unfortunately, band 8, the thermal channel of the MSS, developed operating problems that caused it to fail shortly after launch. The data relating to Landsat 3 MSS are therefore confined to bands 4, 5, 6 and 7. Detection of individual spectral radiances therefore requires four arrays (one for each band) of six detectors (one for each line). The analogue signal from each detector is then converted into digital form by an on-board analogue to digital converter. Each radiance is then associated with a digital number (DN) in the range 0 to 63.

A typical Landsat scene, 185 km × 185 km, consisting of 2340 scan lines with about 3240 picture elements or pixels per line therefore consists of over 7.5 million DN. With four spectral observations per pixel this amounts to over 30 million DN values which have to be recorded for every Landsat scene. Since a new scene is imaged every 25 s, the rate of data generation is enormous (about 15 megabits per second).

A further distinguishing feature of a typical Landsat scene is the parallelogram shape of the final processed image. This is a consequence of the effect of the earth's rotation during the 25 s interval required to image a 185 km × 185 km Landsat scene.

After the scene has been imaged, the data is then either telemetered to one of the twelve ground receiving stations in real time if the receiving station is within range, or recorded on to two on-board tape recorders. The recorded data can then be transmitted to one of the ground receiving stations when the satellite passes within range. Figure 3.10 illustrates the receiving ranges of the Landsat ground stations. European Landsat scenes are recorded at Fucino in Italy and also at Kiruna in Sweden. By means of the Space Informatics

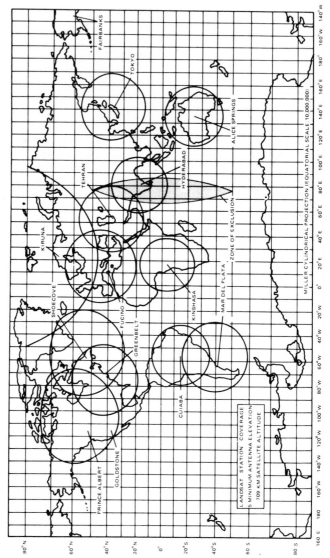

Figure 3.10   Range of Landsat ground stations. (After NASA, 1978–83.)

Network Experiment (SPINE), data can be transferred from Fucino and Kiruna via the European communications satellite OTS to RAE Farnborough within 24 hours of the data being received.

All imagery acquired by Landsat satellites is recorded and archived at the Earth Resources Observation Systems (EROS) Data Center at Sioux Falls, South Dakota. Customers can request imagery direct from EROS in the form of computer compatible magnetic tapes (CCTs) or as photographic products. For United Kingdom, European and a selected number of other areas, RAE Farnborough act as the UK National Point of Contact (NPOC). Further details on the procedure required in order to obtain data may be found in Appendix A.

The digital processing of the CCTs produced by Landsat is beyond the scope of this section and will be discussed in detail in subsequent chapters. Mention should, however, be made of the optical processing of Landsat imagery.

The simplest Landsat MSS photographic product consists of a black-and-white image for each spectral band. Although the resulting image is vaguely familiar, in that it is similar to a conventional panchromatic aerial photograph, much of the information content of the image is lost. An alternative approach is to assign a different colour to each spectral band and superimpose these to produce a colour composite image. Although there are a vast number of combinations which could be used, the one which is the most common is that which produces an image similar in form to the 'false' colour photography discussed in Chapter 2.

In order, therefore, to produce a 'false colour composite' satellite image, the following combination of spectral bands and colours are used:

Band 4	imaged in blue
Band 5	imaged in green
Band 6 or 7	imaged in red

As with false colour photography, this results in healthy vegetation, which reflects strongly in the reflected infrared part of the spectrum, appearing bright red on the image. Figure 3.11 illustrates the appearance of each of the four spectral bands, and its ability to penetrate the water surface for an area of the Red Sea.

This ability to penetrate the water surface may, in conditions where the water is free from suspended sediments and other material, enable the imagery to be used as an aid to bathymetric charting (Benny and Dawson, 1983). For example Plate 2 illustrates the same area as that shown by Figure 3.11, in the form of a false colour composite. By computer processing it is possible to construct lines of equal brightness using the band 4 (green) data of the sea, and colour code these to indicate areas of equal water depth. Using this approach the image shown in Plate 3 can be produced. By interpreting this image it is

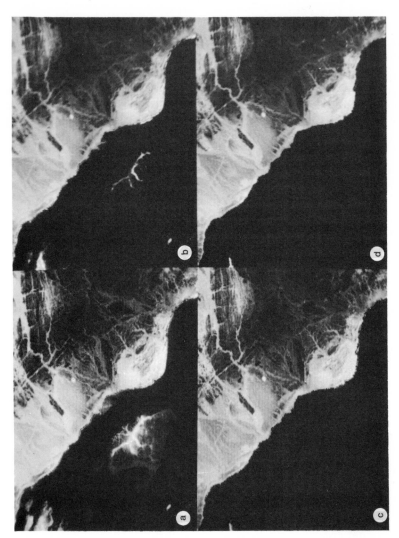

Figure 3.11   Landsat 3 MSS image of the northern region of the Red Sea. Note the transparency of the sea in the green part of the spectrum (a) and the strong absorption in the near infrared (c), (d). (a) band 4 (0.5–0.6 μm), visible (green); (b) band 5 (0.6–0.7 μm), visible (red); (c) band 6 (0.7–0.8 μm), near infrared; (d) band 7 (0.8–1.1 μm), near infrared. (Reproduced by kind permission of National Remote Sensing Centre, Royal Aircraft Establishment).

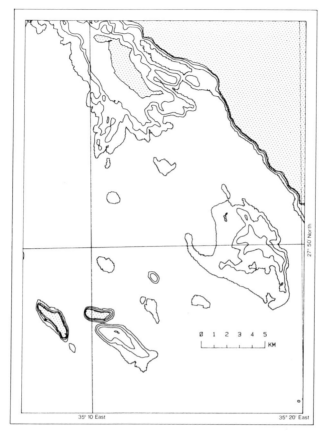

Figure 3.12 Bathymetric chart produced from Landsat 3 MSS image illustrated by Plate 3. (After Benny and Dawson, 1983.)

possible to produce a bathymetric chart of the area. Figure 3.12 illustrates an example of such a chart which extends over part of the area covered by the Landsat scene shown in Plate 3.

The second remote sensing system on board Landsat 3 was the two-channel RBV. The development of the vidicon camera has provided satellites with a method of obtaining high-resolution pictures without the need for conventional photographic film. The principle of operation of the RBV can best be described by first considering the simple direct beam vidicon as illustrated by Figure 3.13.

It can be seen that the direct beam vidicon consists of an evacuated glass envelope containing an electron gun which faces a thin photoconductive insulating layer (the target) which is deposited on the end window of the tube. An electron gun scans across the target surface and removes any positive charge, so stabilizing the target surface at zero voltage. An exposure is made in the conventional manner by means of the shutter and lens assembly. An

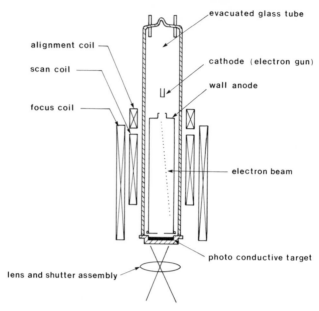

Figure 3.13   Direct beam vidicon tube.

image then forms on the target, the illuminated regions inducing a positive charge in proportion to the brightness of the reflected signal. This charged pattern is retained on the target surface until it is scanned a second time, in this case the magnitude of the pattern being measured and recorded.

The return beam vidicon differs slightly from the description above, in that it relies on the strength of the returning electron beam after it has neutralized the charge on the target as a means of measuring the charge pattern. The advantages of this design are firstly that the camera can operate in poorer illumination conditions, and secondly the resolution is generally higher than that associated with direct beam vidicons.

The RBV cameras on board Landsat 3 covered one spectral band 0.505 to 0.750μm, (green to near infrared) and imaged an area approximately one-quarter that of the MSS. Mounted side by side and operating alternately, the RBVs acquired four subscenes to provide the same ground coverage as the MSS scene, as shown in Figure 3.14. The resolution of the RBV imagery was about double that of the MSS and there was a réseau grid superimposed on the image. For these reasons several investigators have examined the potential of using RBV products for topographic mapping. See Chapter 6 for further details.

Landsat 5, the second of the new generation Landsat satellites, was launched in March, 1984, following the failure early in 1983 of the Thematic Mapper sensor on board Landsat 4. The design of this second-generation series of satellites began in the early 1970s and has led to the development of a

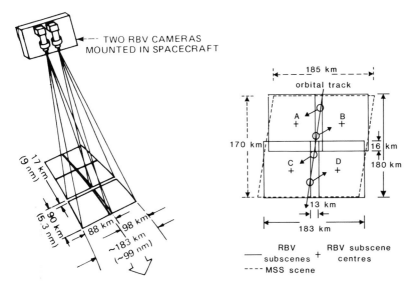

Figure 3.14(a) Landsat 3 RBV; (b) coverage. (After NASA, 1978–83.)

system which differs considerably from the first-generation Landsat satellites (numbers 1 to 3). By far the most significant change has been the introduction of a new sensor with improved spatial resolution, spectral separation, geometric fidelity and radiometric accuracy known as the Thematic Mapper (TM). In addition, and in common with the previous satellites, Landsat 5 also has a four-channel MSS with identical spatial and spectral characteristics to the previous Landsats' MSS.

In terms of basic design, the TM differs fundamentally from the MSS in five ways. Firstly, the TM obtains data on both the west to east and east to west scans, in contrast to the single-scan method employed on Landsats 1 to 3. This bidirectional approach was introduced in order to further reduce the mirror scan rate. Secondly, the TM detector arrays are located within the primary focal plane of the instrument, allowing incoming light to be reflected directly onto the detectors without transmission through the fibre optics employed in the MSS. By the introduction of this scanner design feature, it was hoped to minimize any loss in the intensity of the incoming radiation. An unfortunate consequence, however, is that the detector arrays for different spectral bands are spaced apart in the focal plane by a small amount; hence the same point on the ground is not simultaneously scanned in all spectral bands. Precise band-to-band registration is therefore an extremely important aspect of the subsequent data processing.

A third distinguishing design feature of the TM is the use of seven spectral bands in contrast to four for the MSS. The band designations, spectral ranges and principal applications are as follows:

Band number	Spectral range(μm)	Application
1	0.45 to 0.52	Water penetration
2	0.52 to 0.60	Measurement of visible green reflectance
3	0.63 to 0.69	Vegetation discrimination
4	0.76 to 0.90	Delineation of water bodies
5	1.55 to 1.75	Differentiation of snow and cloud
6	10.40 to 12.50	Thermal mapping
7	2.08 to 2.35	Geological mapping

In addition to the increase in the number of spectral bands, the TM also has an increased radiometric sensitivity. The range of discrete radiometric levels which can be sensed had been increased from 64 to 256.

Finally, the spatial resolution of the TM is much improved over the MSS. A pixel size of 30 m is used in all bands except band 7 which has a pixel of 120 m. This contrasts with the 79 m pixel associated with the MSS. The effect of this improved spatial resolution is apparent from Plate 4 which illustrates the comparative spatial resolution capabilities of both Landsat MSS and TM imagery. Several alterations to the orbital parameters of the satellite had to be introduced in order to obtain this much improved ground resolution capability. The major alterations are listed in Table 3.4 and some of the orbital parameters are shown in Figure 3.15.

One consequence of the lower orbit of Landsat 5 has been a significant change in the earth coverage cycle. Figure 3.16 illustrates that for Landsat 5 the orbital strip adjacent to the initial orbital strip is scanned after a time lapse of seven days. This contrasts with the time lapse of a single day for the Landsat 3 system. A further alteration is the reduction in the repeat coverage period from 18 days to 16 days. Both alterations have necessitated the

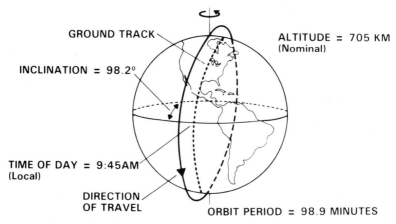

Figure 3.15   Orbital parameters: Landsat 5. (After NASA, 1978–83.)

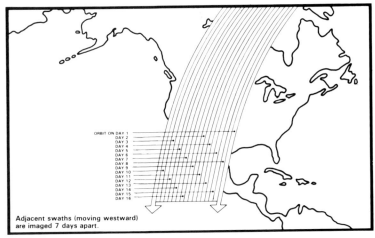

ORBIT ON DAY 1
DAY 2
DAY 3
DAY 4
DAY 5
DAY 6
DAY 7
DAY 8
DAY 9
DAY 10
DAY 11
DAY 12
DAY 13
DAY 14
DAY 15
DAY 16

Adjacent swaths (moving westward)
are imaged 7 days apart.

Figure 3.16   Landsat 5 orbital pattern. (After NASA, 1978–83.)

introduction of a new worldwide reference system for defining the path and row parameters of each Landsat TM image.

A further major advantage of the Landsat 5 system will be the satellite's capability to communicate with other complementary satellites. The various components of Landsat 5 and its relationship with the other communications satellites in the system are illustrated by Figures 3.17 and 3.18.

One of the most significant drawbacks from which Landsats 1 to 3 suffered was their requirement to store MSS data upon onboard tape recorders when not within range of a ground station. The recorders not only had a limited lifetime, but they also proved to be rather erratic in operation. In order to circumvent this problem, Landsat 5 will in the near future relay data to earth by communicating with one of the two Tracking and Data Relay Satellites (TDRS), which will then telemeter the data to a single ground receiving station. Most of the existing Landsat receiving stations should be able to receive TM data by mid-1985.

A domestic communications satellite (DOMSAT) system will then be used to transmit sensor data from this ground receiving station to the Goddard Space Flight Center (GSFC) and subsequently to the EROS Data Center. In addition, it is hoped that the Global Positioning System (GPS) navigation satellites will provide Landsat with highly accurate position and velocity data.

Landsat imagery is by far the most common source of satellite-based remote sensing data available to the civil engineer. The previous few pages have discussed some of the technical features of the system and subsequent chapters will discuss several examples of the application of Landsat imagery to civil engineering. It is therefore appropriate at this stage to summarize the principal advantages and limitations of the system.

The main advantages of Landsat imagery can be stated as follows:

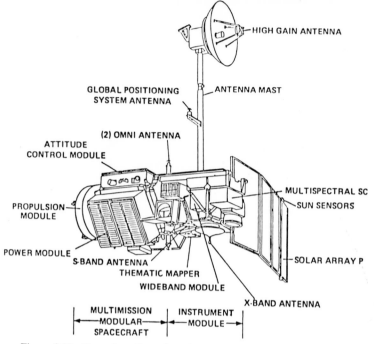

Figure 3.17   General configuration of Landsat 5. (After NASA, 1978–83.)

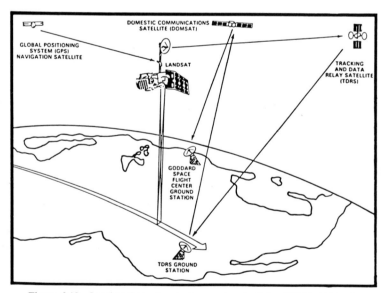

Figure 3.18   Landsat 5 communications network. (After NASA, 1978–83.)

(a) Coverage of large areas. Each Landsat scene, for example, covers an area of some 33000 km². Since the first launching in 1972, the Landsat satellites have recorded all the land surface of the globe except those areas persistently covered by cloud.

(b) Repetitive cover. Most Landsat scenes have been recorded more than once, enabling the interpreter to compare views of the terrain taken in different years, or at different seasons. Such comparisons are valuable in regional hydrological studies involving changing river courses, coastal modification or deforestation.

(c) Data are computer compatible. Landsat data can be digitally processed by computer in order to produce images that are easier to interpret, thereby improving the quality of the interpretation.

(d) Availability. Landsat data is easily obtainable either directly from the EROS Data Center in the USA or from any of the growing number of regional remote sensing centres which now exist in various parts of the world (for further details refer to Appendix A).

(e) Low cost. The cost of utilizing Landsat data depends largely on whether the image is examined on photographic film or paper, or on an image processing system. In the latter case the costs are obviously higher since access is required to both the computer-compatible tapes and an image processing system. In both cases however, the costs are relatively small when compared with the benefits which can be obtained from interpretation of the imagery.

In spite of the significant benefits which Landsat offers to the engineer its use in nevertheless restricted. The following are some of the main limitations of the imagery.

(a) Spatial resolution. The present generation of Landsat satellites offer a spatial resolution of ~ 30 m. Whilst this is a significant improvement over the MSS imagery it is nevertheless only suitable for basic planimetric mapping at scales of less than 1:100 000. Map revision at scales of up to 1:50 000 may be possible under limited circumstances. An associated disadvantage is the lack of height information from the imagery, which restricts its usefulness for the civil engineer.

(b) Cloud cover. In spite of the repetitive nature of Landsat there are still several areas of the world, including the UK, for which there is only restricted coverage because of the problems of cloud coverage.

(c) Ground verification. In order to be able to make maximum use of the Landsat system it is important that ground data are available both to improve the interpretation and also to verify the results which are obtained. In some instances problems can arise at this stage because, firstly, few or no data have been obtained, or secondly, the data which have been obtained are out of date.

Landsat 5 is one of many remote sensing satellites which will be operating in the 1980s. Several other systems are planned for launch in the next five years. One of these, which should prove to be of great interest, is the French *SPOT system.*

The SPOT ('Le Système Probatoire d'Observation de la Terre') satellite is due to be launched in January 1985 by the French developed Ariane launch vehicle. The payload will consist of two high resolution visible (HRV) imaging instruments employing the multilinear array or 'pushbroom' design of MSS. This design of MSS differs from the optical-mechanical design, discussed

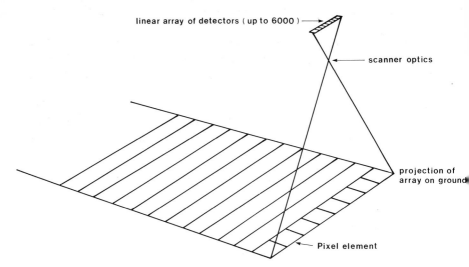

Figure 3.19   Pushbroom scanner.

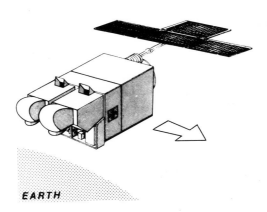

Figure 3.20   SPOT satellite with two HRV pushbroom scanners and attached solar panels

previously, in that it does not incorporate any moving parts such as scanning mirrors. In contrast, each line of the image is formed by measuring the radiances as imaged directly on to a one-dimensional linear array of small detectors located in the instrument's focal plane. Each line is then subsequently scanned electronically and the radiance values recorded onto magnetic tape. As before, successive lines of the image are produced by the forward motion of the satellite along its orbital path. This pushbroom concept is illustrated diagrammatically by Figure 3.19, and Figure 3.20 is an artist's impression of the satellite.

The main advantages of the pushbroom scanner are that it tends to be lighter, use less power, have a longer life expectancy and, most importantly, have a higher geometric fidelity than the equivalent optical-mechanical scanners.

Further significant orbital and sensor details relating to the SPOT system are given in Table 3.5. Figure 3.21 illustrates a simulated SPOT image which was produced using the Daedalus 1268 MSS scanner discussed in section 3.2.3.2.

A further salient feature of the SPOT system will be its capability to provide stereoscopic coverage of the earth's surface. A rotatable mirror in the SPOT sensor package will permit a given scene of the earth to be acquired over areas

Table 3.5 SPOT satellite system specifications

Orbital details	
Launch date	Early 1985
Altitude (km)	832
Period (min)	101
Equatorial spacing of orbits (km)	1084
No. of orbits/day	14.2
No. of days for repeat coverage	26
Equator crossing time	10.30
Swath width (km)	60
Sensor details	
High Resolution Visible (HRV) scanner —	
MSS mode	
No. of spectral bands	3
Spectral ranges (μm)	$\begin{cases} 0.50-0.59 \\ 0.61-0.68 \\ 0.79-0.89 \end{cases}$
No. of individual sensor detectors	3000
Ground resolution (m)	20
No. of grey levels	256 (8 bit)
Data rate (megabits/s)	25
Black-and-white mode	
No. of spectral bands	1
Spectral range (μm)	0.51-0.73
No. of individual sensor detectors	6000
Ground resolution (m)	10
No. of grey levels	128 (6 bit)
Data rate (megabits per second)	25

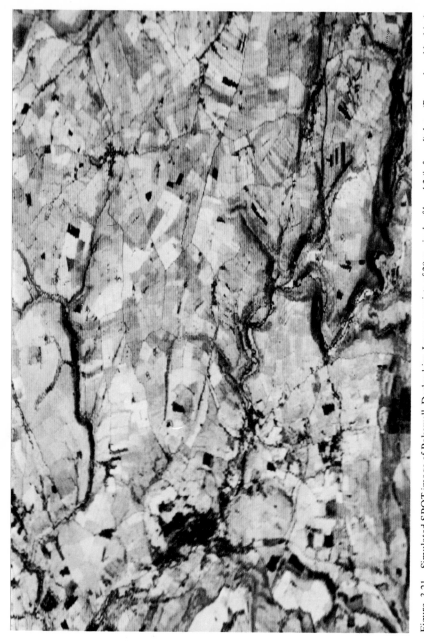

Figure 3.21   Simulated SPOT image of Bakewell, Derbyshire. Image consists of 20 m pixels of band 3 (infrared) data. (Reproduced by kind permission of National Remote Sensing Centre, Royal Aircraft Establishment.)

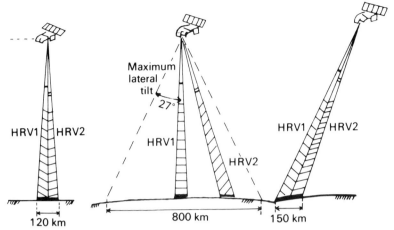

Figure 3.22   SPOT:rotatable mirror. The two HRV scanners can either be operated in a vertical position or tiltable mirrors can be used to point to areas located at some distance from the satellite ground track. (Adapted from Ducher, 1980.)

up to 400km left or right of the normal vertical vantage point of the satellite. Besides providing stereoscopic coverage, this feature will also permit much easier acquisition of high priority scenes. In addition, the two HRVs will be able to be operated jointly covering a swath width of 117km (3km overlap). These features are illustrated by Figure 3.22. It seems likely that SPOT will form the beginning of a new generation of high resolution earth observation satellites which should be of considerable benefit to the civil engineer. Further details relating to the SPOT system can be found in Chevrel et al. (1981) and Begni (1982).

MOMS (Modular Optoelectronic Multispectral Scanner) is a further example of the pushbroom design of scanner. This instrument, developed by the

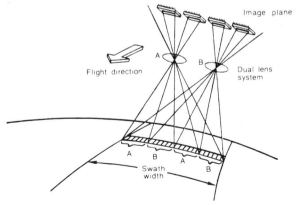

Figure 3.23   MOMS system: geometric arrangement of optical system.

Table 3.6 MOMS 01 system specifications

Orbital details	
Altitude (km) (on Space Shuttle)	300
Swath width (km)	140
Sensor details	
Lens focal length (mm)	237
No. of spectral bands	2
Spectral range (μm)	0.575–0.625
	0.825–0.975
No of individual	
sensor detectors/array	6912
Ground resolution (m)	20
No of grey levels	128
Data rate (megabits s^{-1})	40

German MBB company for the German Aerospace Research establishment (DFVLR), is suitable for use on both aircraft and satellite platforms. The first satellite-borne imagery was obtained with the system during the seventh Space Shuttle flight in June, 1983. The scanner has several unique design features of which the most significant are the dual lens system and the four linear arrays of 1728 pixels each which enable a continuous line of 6912 pixels to be swept out by the scanner (Figure 3.23). Details of the system specification are given in Table 3.6 and further discussion relating to MOMS may be found in Hofmann (1982). Plate 5 illustrates one particular example of the type of imagery obtainable from MOMS.

A second generation MOMS system is currently under development by MBB which will offer the possibility of obtaining stereoscopic imagery and which will also have an extended range of spectral bands. It is expected that MOMS-02 will be flown on board the Space Shuttle in 1986.

Further details relating to the mapping possibilities offered by both SPOT and MOMS are discussed in Chapter 6.

3.3 Active scanning systems

All the systems which have been discussed so far have been of the passive type, that is, they sense and measure the naturally occurring reflected or emitted radiation from a body. There is, however, another group of systems which supply their own source of energy to illuminate features. An image is subsequently produced by recording the reflections of the illumination signal from the feature being examined. For example, a typical active photographic system would be a camera when used in conjunction with some external illumination source, such as a flash unit. Similarly, a good example of an active non-photographic system, which is relevant to remote sensing, is radar.

3.3.1 *Radar*

Radar (Radio Detection And Ranging) was initially developed as a means of using microwaves to detect the presence or absence of an object and then subsequently to derive its range from the transmitter. This process was achieved by transmitting pulses of radiation and recording the reflection which occurred from features within the beam of the signal.

Most of us are familiar with the standard cathode ray tube (CRT) radar display, produced by a rotating antenna, such as is found on the majority of ships. The display is a record of the echoes received from ships or other objects within the area of interest. A photograph of this trace could therefore provide us with a 'radar image' if required.

Although this system could be used on board an aircraft or satellite for imaging purposes, two problems preclude its application. Firstly, it would be rather impractical to operate a rotating antenna on board an airborne platform. This, however, is not the main difficulty. The basic problem is one of resolution. The spatial resolution of a radar system is a function of several factors including the wavelength of the signal, the pulse length and the antenna length. The pulse length relates to the time interval between successive microwave pulses. This parameter can be altered and is therefore not a critical problem. Antenna length is, however, a more difficult problem, because it has a direct relationship with the antenna beamwidth, which in turn is directly related to resolution. Antenna beamwidth can be evaluated by the following expression:

$$\beta = \frac{\lambda}{L}$$

where β is the antenna beamwidth, λ is the wavelength of the transmitted pulses and L is the length of the antenna. Consequently, a longer antenna will have a smaller beamwidth and therefore be of higher resolution. It is this point which precludes the use of rotating antenna systems. For example, to achieve a 10 mrad beamwidth with a 50 mm wavelength radar requires a 5 m antenna and for a 1 mrad beamwidth, a 50 m long antenna! Clearly this is impractical.

The solution to the problem involves reducing the coverage of the system by mounting a fixed antenna to the side of the aircraft or satellite. A system such as this is known as Side Looking Airborne Radar (SLAR), and is illustrated by Figure 3.24.

3.3.1.1 *Side Looking Airborne Radar (SLAR).*

SLAR was first developed for military purposes, in the early 1950s. It was not however until the early 1970s that it became available commercially. The main impetus for the development of SLAR arose out of its two significant advantages over optical photographic or scanning systems: its ability to produce imagery both day and night and also its ability to 'sense' through haze, smoke, cloud and even rain.

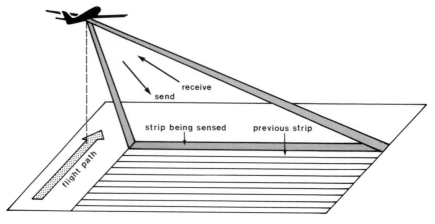

Figure 3.24   Side-looking airborne radar (SLAR). (After Rudd, 1974.)

Table 3.7   SLAR: common wavelength bands

Band designation	Wavelength (mm)
K	8 to 24
X	24 to 38
C	38 to 75
L	150 to 300

The main reason for these twin advantages stems from the SLAR system's use of microwaves as the imaging source. Several different microwave sources are commonly used with SLAR, as shown in Table 3.7, and all are capable of transmission through most atmospheric conditions. The shorter wavelengths tend to be attenuated by atmospheric conditions to a greater extent than the longer wavelengths.

The image which is produced by SLAR is very different from that produced by conventional optical systems. The view which is obtained is a record of the earth's reflective properties at microwave wavelengths. Consequently, the nature and intensity of the reflections by SLAR will be influenced by factors, such as ground conductivity and surface roughness, which are much less significant with optical systems. In addition, the geometrical properties of the image differ significantly from a conventional aerial photograph.

The main components of a typical SLAR system are illustrated in Figure 3.25. It can be seen that the basic principle of operation of a SLAR system involves the measurement of the time interval between the transmission and reflection of a microwave pulse. This indirectly provides the range from the aircraft to the ground feature. The information obtained is subsequently used in many systems to produce an image on a CRT display. The intensity of the returned signal controls the intensity of a bright spot

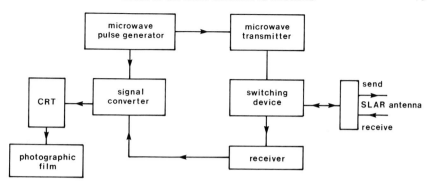

Figure 3.25   Components of a typical SLAR system.

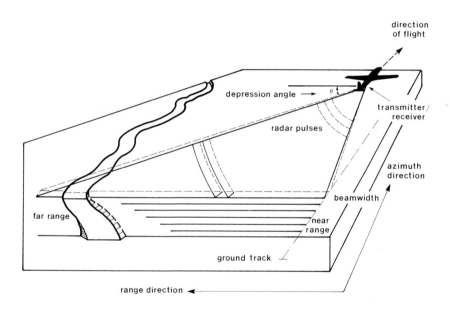

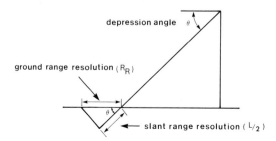

Figure 3.26   Geometry of a SLAR system.

moving across a CRT display at a velocity proportional to the aircraft velocity. Successive positions of the spot therefore correspond to successive ranges across the track. By this process a line of varying intensity is swept across the CRT with each pulse from the microwave transmitter. By synchronizing the velocity of a moving film to that of the aircraft, a continuous photographic image can be created.

A critical consideration in the design of a SLAR system is the question of ground resolution. As was mentioned previously, this is controlled by several factors, including wavelength. However, for a fixed wavelength system, the two most significant parameters are, as mentioned previously, firstly, pulse length and secondly, antenna beamwidth (with its associated parameter antenna length). Figure 3.26 indicates that the pulse length determines the spatial resolution in the direction of microwave propagation, that is, in the range direction.

Ground resolution in the range direction can be determined by the expression:

$$R_R = \frac{tv}{2\cos\theta}$$

where t is the pulse length e.g. $0.1\mu s$,

$\quad v$ is the velocity of a signal e.g. $3 \times 10^8\,\mathrm{ms}^{-1}$, and

$\quad \theta$ is the depression angle.

Resolution is therefore poorer in the near range than in the far range. In contrast, the antenna beamwidth dictates the resolution in the direction of flight or azimuth direction. The latter is the more critical parameter and has been one of the main limiting factors in the search for high resolution SLAR. However, in recent years new techniques have evolved in SLAR design which have led to the development of two distinct types of SLAR systems, namely Real Aperture Radar and Synthetic Aperture Radar systems.

The SLAR system whose components and geometry has been discussed so far in section 3.3.1 is conventionally referred to as a *real aperture*, 'brute force' or noncoherent radar system. The main distinguishing feature of this design of radar is the resolution limitation of the system in the azimuth direction. Figure 3.27 indicates the deterioration in resolution in the azimuth direction which is a consequence of the fanning out of the signal as the range increases. In this example the two objects close together in the near range position (a) will be discriminated as two individual objects since two separate signals will be reflected. At position (b), however, in the far range, the two objects the same distance apart will not be resolved, since they are both within the beam simultaneously.

This azimuth resolution limitation could be improved by using a longer physical antenna, which would result in a much narrower beamwidth and hence improve resolution in the far range. There is, however, a limitation to the length of antenna which can be mounted on the side of an aircraft ($\sim 5\,\mathrm{m}$) and

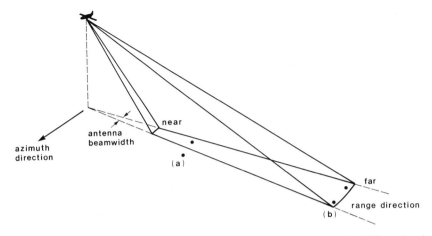

Figure 3.27   Azimuth resolution of a real aperture radar system. (Adapted from Lillesand and Kiefer, 1979.)

it is this problem which severely limits the application of real aperture radar.

An alternative design of radar which overcomes the azimuth resolution limitation of the previous system is the SAR (synthetic aperture radar) system. SAR systems are much more complex, both in operation and in subsequent data processing, than the equivalent real aperture radar systems. They are also much more expensive to operate. A detailed analysis of SAR is beyond the scope of this chapter; therefore the discussion will be restricted solely to the fundamental principles of operation of the system. For further details about SAR, see Jensen et al. (1977).

The main distinguishing feature of SAR is the much shorter antenna and hence wider beamwidth associated with the system when compared with the equivalent resolution real aperture system. This approach would appear initially to lead to a system of much lower resolution. However, by means of some complex data processing, the antenna is made to behave as if it were a very long antenna. The antenna is therefore electronically synthesized in order to effectively increase the antenna beamwidth and azimuth resolution. The procedure by which this is achieved is as follows.

A series of short microwave pulses are transmitted by the instrument, as with the real aperture systems. Due to the wide beamwidth, as the aircraft or satellite flies over the terrain, features will enter the antenna's beam, move through the beam and finally leave it after a relatively long time-period (depending on the range to the feature). The receiver on board the aircraft or satellite detects the delay between transmission and reception of each microwave pulse and is therefore able to determine the range to a particular feature on the ground. Signals from points on the surface that differ in range can therefore be discriminated on the basis of their arrival time at the antenna. However, for any given position of the aircraft, there will be many points which

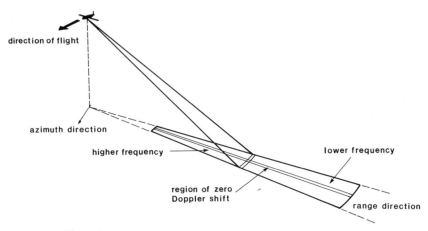

Figure 3.28   Resolution of SAR. (After Lillesand and Kiefer, 1979.)

will be at the same range from the antenna. In order to discriminate different points with the same range, the azimuth to all features is also measured. The azimuth details are determined by means of the Doppler shift in the return signals. The Doppler shift is the change in frequency of the return signal caused by the relative motion of the aircraft and target. For example, the echo from a point perpendicular to the flight path has a Doppler shift of zero, whilst points ahead of the perpendicular are shifted to high frequencies and those behind are shifted to lower frequencies, as shown in Figure 3.28. This Doppler shift information is obtained by comparing the reflected signals with a stable reference signal, generated internally by the system. The comparison is carried out by making the reflected signal interfere with the reference signal, so producing a radar interference pattern. This pattern is the radar equivalent of an optical hologram.

These 'radar holograms' may be recorded and processed, either photographically or digitally. In the case of photographic processing, a coherent light source, such as a laser beam, is normally employed in order to recreate the radar image. Digital processing is also possible. However, at present, it is very expensive and also rather slow. For example (see Elachi, 1982(b)), over one billion arithmetic and logic operations are required in order to digitally process the information recorded in one second from the SIR-A radar system (see section 3.3.1.3). Even when a processor such as the CRAY 1 (one of the fastest and most expensive computers currently in operation capable of over 100 million operations per s) is employed, over 500 seconds of processing are still required for each second of data capture.

Finally, the factors affecting the central problem of resolution must be reexamined. Firstly, the resolution of SAR is determined by the system's ability to accurately measure the minute differences in time delay and Doppler shift resulting from adjacent surface elements. Secondly, the azimuth resolution is further improved by the system's capability of synthetically producing a much longer antenna than the real antenna actually employed. This synthetic antenna is produced because the signals received by the SAR system are recovered over a relatively long time period. During this time period the aircraft motion translates the real antenna over a corresponding distance. It is this distance which in effect becomes the length of the synthetic aperture. By this process a small real antenna is therefore able to act as if it were much longer, with a consequent increase in azimuth resolution.

3.3.1.2 *Aircraft-based systems.* The development of aircraft-based SLAR systems is a very recent phenomenon (Table 3.8). One of the first large-scale projects using SLAR was a survey carried out by the Westinghouse Electric Corporation using a real aperture system developed for the US Army. This survey, of Darien, a cloud-covered province between Panama and South America, produced images which formed a mosaic covering 20 000km². A more ambitious project involving the use of SLAR was the production of mosaics covering the entire Brazilian Amazon basin, an area of some 4 000 000km². This project was known as Project Radam. Imagery was acquired by a SAR system installed in a Caravelle jet, which was operated by the Goodyear Aerospace Corporation. On the basis of the mosaics, tentative routes were selected for sections of the Trans-Amazon Highway.

A more recent airborne radar project, relevant to the United Kingdom, was the *SAR* 580 *Experiment.* The European SAR 580 experiment took place during the summer of 1981. A multiband synthetic aperture imaging radar system was operated aboard a Convair 580 aircraft, as part of a research project, jointly sponsored by the European Space Agency (ESA) and the European Joint Research Council (JRC). The main objective of the project was to evaluate the potential role of airborne SAR for the collection of high spatial resolution data over cloudy regions of Europe. A secondary objective, (Haskell, 1981) was to acquire a greater understanding of the design of SAR in order to aid the development of a satellite-based SAR system.

A selection of parameters relating to the system is given in Table 3.9.

Table 3.8 Specifications of aircraft-based SLAR systems.

System	Operator	Type	Band	Resolution (m)	Comments
Westinghouse	—	Real aperture	K	10–20	Ceased commercial operation in 1973
Motorola	MARS	Real aperture	X	20–40	—
Goodyear	Aero Service	Synthetic aperture	X	10	Operated in Caravelle
SAR 580	Intertech	Synthetic aperture	X, C, L	3	Dual polarization
IRIS	CCRS*	Synthetic aperture	C	6	Dual polarization Available 1985

* Canadian Centre for Remote Sensing.

Table 3.9   Characteristics of the SAR 580 system (adapted from Wright, 1982).

	X Band	C band	L band
Wavelength (mm)	32.0	57.0	235.0
Azimuth resolution (m)	2.5	2.5	2.5
Range resolution (m)	2.0	2.0	3.0

A further feature of the system was its ability to transmit and receive radiation which is either horizontally (H) or vertically (V) polarized. Thus, the image resulting when both the transmitted and the received radiation polarization planes are the same (HH or VV) is known as a 'like polarized' image. Conversely, when the polarization planes are different (HV or VH), a 'cross polarized' image is produced. The SAR 580 system was capable of producing both HH and HV images. Figure 3.29 illustrates a typical example of this type of imagery.

Although the SAR 580 experiment took place in 1981, there was a considerable delay in the production of processed images. This, unfortunately,

Figure 3.29   SAR 580 image of Northampton, X band, HH polarization. (Reproduced by kind permission of DFVLR.)

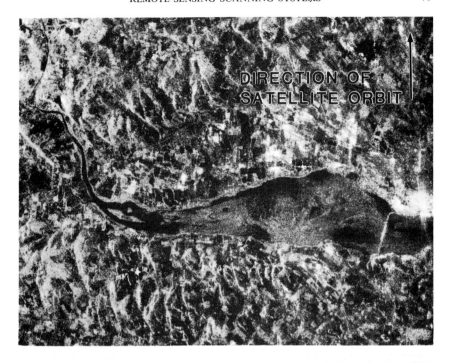

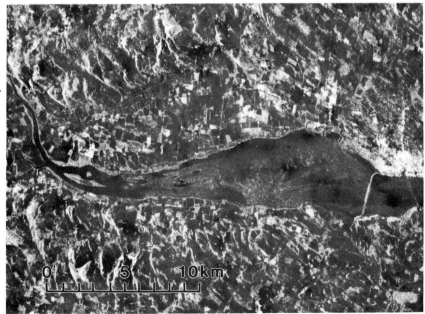

Figure 3.30   Seasat SAR images of River Tay/North Fife, Scotland, obtained in August 1978. (Scale approx. 1:250 000.) (Top) Optically processed image. (Reproduced by kind permission of NASA.) (Bottom) Digitally processed image. (Reproduced by kind permission of DFVLR.)

has led to a significant delay in the reporting of the conclusions of the experiment.

Further details relating to the coverage and availability of SAR 580 data can be obtained from the National Remote Sensing Centre at the Royal Aircraft Establishment (RAE).

3.3.1.3 *Satellite-based systems.* To date there have been two SLAR satellite programmes. Both were of the SAR type and were primarily designed for research purposes. During their operational lifetimes, a substantial amount of imagery was collected and this is now available for interpretive analysis.

The first of these systems to be launched was *Seasat.* Seasat was launched in June 1978 and was chiefly oriented towards oceanographic and geological research. The majority of the sensors on board Seasat were radar-based. Of these, the most important was the SAR system. The SAR operated in the L band ($\lambda = 230$ mm) and orbited at an altitude of 800 km. Each image path consisted of a 100 km wide band located between 230 km and 330 km to one side of the satellite groundtrack. The paths extended for over 400 km and had a resolution of 25 m. Figure 3.30 illustrates two examples of Seasat imagery obtained over Dundee, Scotland. Unfortunately, the Seasat system had an operational life of only 99 days, failing on 3rd October 1978. Nevertheless, during its lifespan, it acquired a significant amount of imagery, which gave a unique view of the earth's surface. Further details on the application of Seasat may be found in Elachi (1980), Foster and Hall (1981) and Allan (1983).

The *Shuttle Imaging Radar-A (SIR-A)*, launched aboard the second flight of NASA's space shuttle Columbia on 12th November 1981, was an experiment which again had as its primary objective the investigation of spaceborne imaging radars for geological mapping. In common with Seasat, SIR-A employed a SAR, which operated in the L band ($\lambda = 230$ mm). The antenna, 9.4 m long, was fixed to produce a 50° incidence angle at the centre of the swath. This 50° incidence angle alleviated one of the most serious problems encountered in the analysis of Seasat SAR data in areas of high relief. In this type of terrain Seasat suffered from extreme foreshortening and layover, which was caused by its low incidence angle (24° at centre). The larger incidence angle associated with SIR-A therefore reduced this significantly, resulting in images which were more geometrically correct.

SIR-A operated from an altitude of 250 km over selected parts of the earth's surface from latitude 41° N to 36°S. Figure 3.31 indicates the areas of the world for which coverage is available. Data were recorded optically on to signal film carried in a cassette on board the Shuttle. The imagery was subsequently optically processed on to film with a swath width of 50 km and a resolution of 40 m. The scale of the imagery was 1:500 000. Figure 3.32 illustrates as example of this type of imagery. For further details see Elachi (1982) (*a*), (*b*) and Holmes (1983).

A successor to SIR-A, SIR-B, will be flown in the near future. The SAR

Numbers are Data Take References.   Swaths are 50 km across.

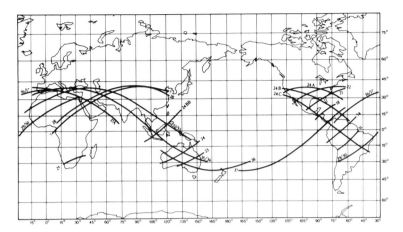

Figure 3.31   Coverage of Shuttle Imaging Radar-A (SIR-A). (After NASA.)

Figure 3.32   Shuttle Imaging Radar-A (SIR-A) image of Brasilia. (By kind permission of Hunting Geology and Geophysics Ltd.)

used will be a modified version of SIR-A. The principal modification is the incorporation of the facility to mechanically rotate the radar antenna in order to obtain imagery at different incidence angles, typically between 15° and 60° as measured from the gravitationally defined vertical. Digital rather than optical techniques will be used in order to produce the imagery.

Two future SAR satellite systems currently under development which are worthy of mention are the *ERS-1 system* and the *Radarsat project*.

ERS-1 (ESA Resource Satellite-1) is the first of a series of European remote sensing satellites which will come into operation in the late 1980s, and operate throughout the 1990s. Planned for launch in 1987 and operating in a 750 km near polar orbit, ERS-1 will carry on board several sensors, of which the most significant from a civil engineering point of view will be the Active Microwave Instrumentation (AMI).

The AMI, operating in the C band, will combine the functions of a SAR imaging system, a wave scatterometer and a wind scatterometer. The principal aim of this package of sensors is to provide high-resolution images of coastal zones, ice areas and land areas together with data about the surface condition of the sea. Two areas where the data could be of use are the fields of coastal and offshore engineering. In the former case the SAR imagery could be used to complement the optical data provided by other satellites such as Landsat 5 and SPOT, whilst in the latter case the continuous monitoring of sea states could provide useful statistical data on wave and wind conditions for the engineering design of oil platforms and other offshore structures.

The second SAR satellite system under consideration is Radarsat. Radarsat is a Canadian system which is planned for launch in 1990. The primary aim of the project is the development of a system to provide information about ice conditions for selected Arctic and coastal regions of Canada.

The overall concept of Radarsat is illustrated by Figure 3.33. The satellite is planned to operate in a near-polar orbit at an altitude of approximately 100 km. It is proposed that SAR data over a 150 km swath will be transmitted to a ground receiving station where the data will be converted digitally into imagery. The image data will then be relayed via a communications satellite to an ice information centre, where other data such as aircraft SAR and weather satellite data will be included to provide an ice forecast. This forecast will then be relayed direct to users such as offshore drilling rigs, ships and so on within the area of interest.

3.3.2 Lidar

Lidar (Light Detection and Ranging) is a further example of an active remote sensing system. Whilst much less common than radar the fundamental principle of operation is very similar and involves the determination of range by measuring the time interval between the transmission and reception of a pulse of EM energy. In this case, however, the source of energy is a laser, rather

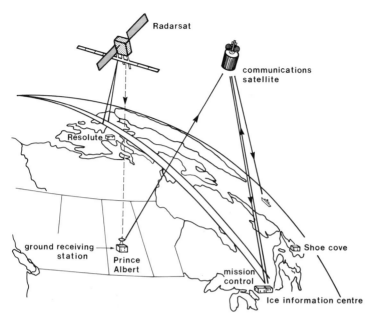

Figure 3.33   Radarsat (adapted from Raney, 1983).

than a pulse of microwaves. Lidar systems can be broadly classified as either those which operate in a profiling mode, or those which operate in a scanning manner. In both cases, however, the primary aim is to measure range rather than the production of imagery. The components and functional arrangement of a typical lidar profiling system are illustrated by Figure 3.34.

Accurate profiling of water depth is accomplished by transmitting a pulsed coherent laser light source from the sensor platform to strike the water at right angles. A strong reflected light signal is received from the water surface, followed closely by a weaker reflected signal from the floor of the water body. The calculation of water depth is carried out by determining the time of travel of a given laser pulse for the round trip from aircraft to water bed to aircraft minus the return round trip travel time from aircraft to water surface. Further details relating to the practical application of this technique to bathymetry are discussed in Chapter 11.

A recent development of the lidar technique is the scanning lidar. One example of this approach is the Larsen-500 system currently under development by the CCRS for use by the Canadian Hydrographic Service. The main components of the system are illustrated by Figure 3.35.

As with the profiling system range data are continuously being acquired by the system. In this case however the scanning facility enables large areas to be covered much more efficiently. The final processing is carried out on the ground at which time the lidar depth data is integrated with acoustic

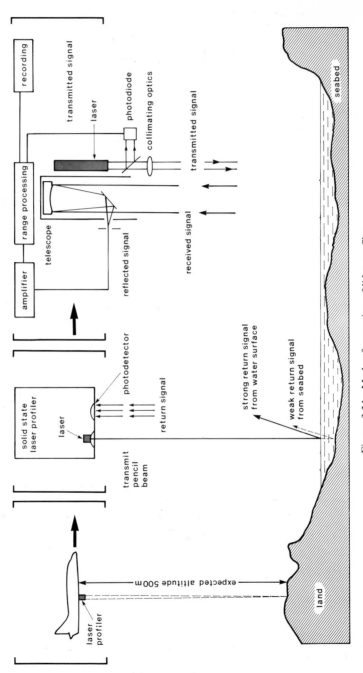

Figure 3.34   Mode of operation of lidar profiler.

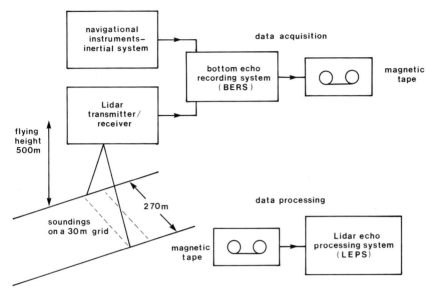

Figure 3.35   Components of the Larsen-500 Lidar Scanning System.

soundings, archived data, aids to navigation and so on to create a final hydrographic chart.

3.4   Conclusions

Remote sensing scanning systems of the type discussed in this chapter may be considered both as an alternative and as a means of complementing the conventional photographic systems which were discussed in Chapter 2. Whilst, in general, the spatial resolution of scanning systems is not as good as that obtainable using photographic processes, they do nevertheless offer several major benefits. Firstly they offer the user the facility to record over a much wider spectral range, and to sense regions of the EM spectrum which are 'invisible' to conventional photographic processes. Secondly the ability of active systems, such as SLAR, to produce imagery in all weathers, regardless of the time of day is a major advantage in many regions of the world. However the principal benefit of the scanner approach is the opportunity to digitally process the remotely sensed data in order to enhance and classify the information content of the imagery. Further details relating to this aspect of remote sensing are dealt with in Chapter 4.

References

Allan, T. D. (1983) 'A Review of Seasat', in *Satellite Microwave Remote Sensing*, Allan, T. D. (ed.), Ellis Horwood, Chichester, 526 pp.
Anon. (1983) Exploration: new scanning system augments remote sensing techniques. *Mining Journal*, September.

Barnett, M. E., Bird, A. C. and Dawes, M. C. (1984) Multiband thermal infrared imagery as a discriminant for surface rock types. *Int. Journal Remote Sensing* 5(2) 511–515.

Begni, G. (1982) Selection of the optimum spectral bands of the SPOT satellite. *Photogrammetric Engineering and Remote Sensing* 48, 1613–1620.

Benny, A. H. and Dawson, G. J. (1983) Satellite imagery as an aid to bathymetric charting in the Red Sea. *The Cartographic Journal* 20(1) 5–16.

Berg, C. and McGinnis, D. F. (1980) 'Mapping of the 1978 Kentucky River flood from NOAA-5 satellite thermal infrared data', in *Proceedings of the 46th Annual Meeting of the American Society of Photogrammetry*, St Louis, Missouri, pp. 106–111.

Bullard, R. K. and Lakin, P. J. (1981) *First Steps in Remote Sensing*. Working Paper No. 3, North East London Polytechnic, Department of Land Surveying, 61 pp.

Chevrel, M., Courtois, M. and Weill, G. (1981) The SPOT satellite remote sensing mission. *Photogrammetric Engineering and Remote Sensing* 47, 1163–1171.

Ducher, G. (1980) Cartographic possibilities of the SPOT and Spacelab projects. *Photogrammetric Record* 10(56), 167–180.

Elachi, C. (1980) Spaceborne imaging radar: geologic and oceanographic applications. *Science* 216, 1073–1082.

Elachi, C., 1982(*a*) Shuttle imaging radar experiment. *Science* 218, 996–1003.

Elachi, C., 1982(*b*) Radar images of the Earth from space. *Scientific American* 247(6), 46–54.

Estes, J. E., Mel, M. E. and Hooper, J. O. (1977) Measuring Soil Moisture with an Airborne Imaging Passive Microwave Radiometer. *Photogrammetric Engineering and Remote Sensing* 43, 1273–1281.

Foster, J. L. and Hall, D. K. (1981) Multisensor analysis of engineering features. *Photogrammetric Engineering and Remote Sensing* 47, 655–664.

Haskell, A. (1981) 'The European SAR 580 Campaign as a preparation for the ERS-1 Satellite SAR', in *Matching Remote Sensing Technologies and Their Applications*, Remote Sensing Society, London, pp. 50–51.

Heilman, J. L. and Moore, D. G. (1982) Evaluating depth of shallow groundwater using HCMM Data. *Photogrammetric Engineering and Remote Sensing* 48, 1903–1906.

Hofmann, O. (1982) Digitale Aufnahmetechnik. *Bildmessung und Luftbildwesen* 50, 16–25.

Holmes, A. (1983) Shuttle Imaging Radar-A. 1983. Information and data availability. *Photogrammetric Engineering and Remote Sensing* 49, 65–67.

Jensen, H., Graham, L. C., Porcello, J. and Leith, E. N. (1977) Side looking airborne radar. *Scientific American* 237(6), 84–94.

Lillesand, T. M. and Kiefer, R. W. (1979) *Remote Sensing and Image Interpretation*. John Wiley and Sons, New York, 612 pp.

NASA, *Landsat Data Users Notes*, 1978–1983. U. S. Geological Survey, Sioux Falls, S. Dakota.

Raney, R. K. (1983) 'The Canadian SAR Experience', in *Satellite Microwave Remote Sensing*, Allan, T. D. (ed.), Ellis Horwood, Chichester, 526 pp.

Rudd, R. D. (1974) *Remote Sensing: A Better View*. Duxbury Press, N. Scituate, Massachusetts, 135 pp.

Schowengerdt, R. (1982) Enhanced thermal mapping with Landsat and HCMM digital data. *Proceedings of the 48th Annual Meeting of the American Society of Photogrammetry*, Denver, Colorado, 414–422.

Swain, P. H. and Davis, S. M. (1978) *Remote Sensing: The Quantitative Approach*. McGraw-Hill, New York, 396 pp.

Townsend, J. R. G. (ed.) (1981) *Terrain Analysis and Remote Sensing*. George Allen and Unwin, London, 232 pp.

Watson, K., Hummer-Miller, S. and Offield, T. (1982) Geological thermal inertia mapping using HCMM satellite data. *Proceedings of the IGARSS' 82 Symposium*, Munich.

Wright, R. (1982) Land Use Applications of imaging radar: retrospect and prospect. *Photogrammetric Record* 10, 697–703.

4 Digital processing of remote sensing data*

K. H. BAGOT

4.1 Introduction

This chapter is intended as an introduction to digital image processing and does not represent a comprehensive treatise on the topic. It is concerned with remote sensing data and hence the processes described are those most likely to be used within this limited field. Within the bibliography are several works which examine the subject in greater depth.

4.2 Background

Digital images in remote sensing are generally made from a collection of picture elements, which are normally referred to as pixels. This is like considering a photograph as a large number of successive lines where each line contains a large number of square pixels. A number representing the average intensity of the scene within the square is stored. Thus the image is a vast matrix of numbers. These images are very often held on magnetic tape and in particular on computer-compatible tape (CCT), and the simplest way to store the data is to write all the numbers corresponding to one line of the image on to the tape as a 'block' followed by a space and another block. This process is repeated until the last line in the image.

A digital image can therefore be read into a computer, line by line. Besides being viewed on image display systems attached to the computer, these images can also be 'written' to film writers. In this case, a light beam is caused to move in straight lines over a piece of unexposed film. The digital numbers along a line are used to modulate the light beam as it moves along one line on the film. The numbers from the next line in the image modulate the light beam as it passes over the next line on the film, and so on.

In order to understand the image processing functions in this chapter, it is necessary to know something of binary arithmetic. With decimal numbers there are ten characters, namely 0, 1, 2, 3, 4, 5, 6, 7, 8, 9, but in binary there are only two: 0 and 1. When counting using decimal numbers, the characters are used in order from 0 to 9. To proceed beyond 9 requires two characters starting at 10 and going to 99, after which three characters are required. Similarly in binary, after counting from 0 to 1, a second character is required, starting at 10 and going to 11, after which three characters are required, and so on.

This decimal and binary counting procedure is shown below, where, starting at 0, the number 1 is added to each successive line.

Decimal	Binary
0	0
1	1
2	10
3	11
4	100
5	101
6	110
7	111
8	1000
9	1001
10	1010
11	1011
:	:
98	1100010
99	1100011
100	1100100
101	1100101
:	:
254	11111110
255	11111111
256	100000000
:	:

Thus, to count to 255 requires 8 columns in binary. This binary number is said to have 8 'bits'. Most image processing machines are designed to deal with images where the range of intensity for a pixel is from black (level 0) to white (level 255), i.e. 8 bits are required in each binary number. Note that the characters in the leftmost column are more important or more significant. Thus in decimal, the numbers in the hundreds column carry more weight than the numbers in the tens column. In binary, the bit on the left is called the 'most significant bit' or MSB and the one on the right is the 'least significant bit' or LSB. The MSB is generally called bit 1, and the LSB, bit 8.

An electronic switch can be used to represent a single bit. A switch which is off represents 0, and on represents 1. An 8-bit number therefore needs 8 switches.

A small example of a digital image is shown in Figure 4.1. One pixel has the value 98. From the table above, the binary equivalent of this is 01100010. The eight switches required to hold this number are shown. Each pixel has a similar set of eight switches and the result is that all the MSB switches are collected in

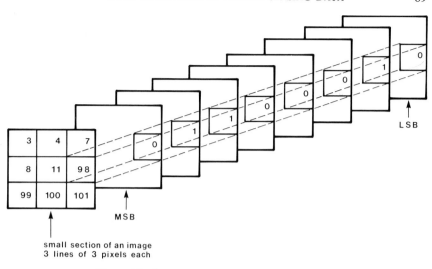

small section of an image
3 lines of 3 pixels each

Figure 4.1   Storage of pixels in a computer memory.

a plane, and likewise for the other seven bits. Image processing machines generally have stores which are from 256 pixels in 256 lines, up to 1024 pixels in 1024 lines. Each of these 'image planes' generally can cope with numbers from 0 to 255 and hence have 8 'bit planes' of the type shown in the example above.

4.3   Need for image processing

When one considers aerial photography, one might wonder what the advantages of digital images and image processing are. The following list illustrates some of the limitations of film, and of the human eye and brain.

(a) There are a limited number of grey levels that can be held on film. Due to the noise in the photographic material, it is only possible to have between 20 and 30 discrete and separable levels. Landsat MSS data has 64 grey levels, the Landsat Thematic Mapper has 256, the low orbit weather spacecraft have 1024, and some radar imagery has 8192. The human eye can separate only perhaps 10 to 15 levels, or about twice that if the grey levels are in fact in large patches touching each other in sequence, as in a 'grey wedge'. Thus not only is a film incapable of holding the information, but the human is unable to take in all the information to his 'image processor' in his brain.

(b) Film is limited in its spectral response to the visible part of the spectrum and just into the near infrared. Scanners exist which can observe much more of the spectrum and are currently using the near infrared, many regions in the mid infrared, (where the atmosphere does not absorb all the radiation), the thermal infrared where temperature can be monitored most accurately, and in the microwave region (where the systems can be insensitive to the weather).

(c) There is a limit to the number of spectral bands which can be put on to film and observed by eye. There are at most three layers on a photographic film and hence there can only be three independent images displayed together. Similarly there are only three primary colours and hence it is only possible to convey three images to the eye to be correlated. Landsat MSS has 4 spectral bands, the Thematic Mapper has 7, many aircraft scanners have 11, and some even have 24. An image processing system is therefore required to correlate this data.

4.4   Image processing systems

The simplest type of system for image processing is a computer. Images are read into the system, the required operation is performed using the software and the results are written out on to another tape, or to a film writer. This process, although highly flexible (since a new program can easily be written for a new operation), precise and repeatable, is inconvenient because of the time taken to produce results that the user can examine, i.e. film products.

A much more convenient system is one such as the GEMS which allows the user to display the results on a television screen (Figure 4.2). The organization of this machine, which is typical of the software-based systems, is shown in

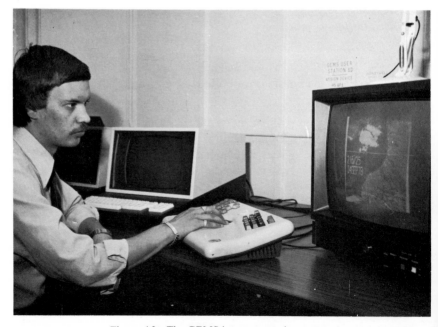

Figure 4.2   The GEMS image processing system.

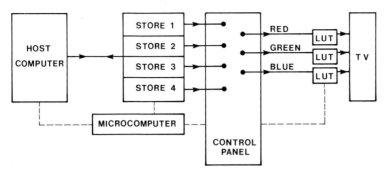

Figure 4.3   Organization of GEMS

Figure 4.3. The central component of the GEMS system is the store shown to the left in the diagram above. The host computer can load one or more images into the stores within GEMS and vice-versa. In GEMS there are 512 lines each one containing 512 pixels, making a total of 262 144 pixels in one image. There are so many pixels that the eye cannot see them as a collection of points, but rather as a continuous picture.

Four of these images can be stored and any one of these can be connected to any of the three colour guns of the television. Thus in Figure 4.3, within the box labelled 'control panel', a connection can be made from store 1 to red, simply by pressing a button. This set of three colour guns, red, green and blue, can be used to make any other colour. Thus if store 1 were also connected to green, the picture on the screen would be yellow. Connecting store 1 to blue as well, would result in a black and white picture. However, before the picture is displayed on the television, the data pass through a box labelled 'LUT'.

The concept of these 'look up tables' (LUT), is important and is used in many image processing systems. In the case of GEMS, each LUT is a box with 256 memory locations. Suppose initially that 0 is placed into memory location 0, 1 into location 1, and so on to 255 into location 255. The information in the image passes along the wires labelled RED, GREEN and BLUE, line by line. Remembering that each line is a collection of pixels, or numbers in the range 0 to 255, it can be seen that each number can be treated as an address to this memory bank of 256 locations. Thus if one pixel had an intensity of 42, then location 42 would be examined and the contents of that location (in this case 42) would be sent out from the box.

If now the LUT had the contents changed so that 0 was in location 0, 2 in location 1, 4 in location 2 etc., then in the case above, the number 84 would be sent out from the box. This simple operation allows the system to multiply each picture element by 2. Many more complex functions can be implemented using such a system.

The advantage of an LUT is that a slow cheap microprocessor or minicomputer can be used to put the correct numbers into the table which can operate at the very high rates required to process the data as it passes from the stores to the television screen.

There are a number of more complicated systems which are hardware based. Essentially, where the simple system has the LUT, the hardware system has a line of processing modules, many with LUTs within them. These long processing chains allow much more complex processes to be undertaken quickly. The simple systems would use the host computer to do the processing, which on a 512 × 512 image may take a few seconds to many minutes depending on the process. The advantage of the hardware systems is therefore speed, but the disadvantage is usually the extra cost of a relatively special-purpose system compared to a general-purpose computer.

Examples of the cheapest (costing around £10 000), slowest systems, include DIAD made by Nigel Press Associates, the LS-10 Image Processing System, by C. W. Controls, both in the UK, and ERDAS, ORSER, and an Apple-based system from other countries. These machines are based on microcomputer systems and the resultant limitations they have are in speed of operation, difficulty in dealing with large images (generally they have 256 × 256 pixels in an image) and, currently, the lack of peripherals suitable for storing large volumes of data. They generally require data on floppy discs which are not interchangeable with other systems, are slow and have very limited capacity.

Costing about five times as much in stand-alone form are, for example, the GEMS system made by GEMS of Cambridge, the American VICOM, COMTAL, GRINNELL, LogE/ISI, and the Canadian DIPIX. These are minicomputer-based systems, and may have considerably more hardware than the microcomputer machines. The general features are that they are faster, can deal with large images, and with a full range of standard peripherals are generally able to cope with the large quantities of data easily.

Costing perhaps another two or three times as much again, are the fast hardware systems such as the IDP3000 made by Plessey but no longer marketed, or the International Imaging Systems machines from America. These processors are similar to the ones in the previous group, but are much faster.

These guidelines are of necessity approximate, and, particularly in regard to cost, should be treated as such.

4.5 Digital image processing

4.5.1 *Contrast stretching*

Adjustment of contrast has been done on photographic images since the birth of photography, but the problem of contrast stretching is much more extreme in digital images. It is very difficult to display the subtle intensity detail in a digital image of say 200 grey levels, when the eye can only see 10 to 20. Contrast stretching simply to brighten up a dark image certainly does make an image

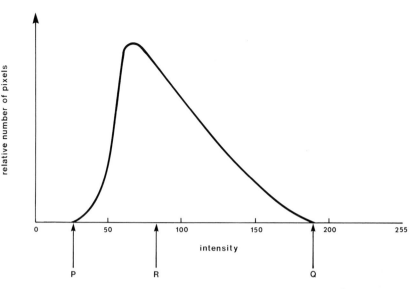

Figure 4.4   Typical histogram of intensity in an image.

more interpretable, but it may not highlight a great deal of detail that could be useful. More complex ones can help the user make the most of the data, visually.

Much use is made in this section of histograms of intensity. These are charts or graphs where the horizontal axis contains all 256 possible intensity levels, and the vertical axis shows the relative number of pixels from the scene at each intensity. Figure 4.4 shows a typical histogram.

As was mentioned earlier, the data from an image pass through a box labelled 'LUT' before being presented on the television screen. This is shown in Figure 4.5. The graph in Figure 4.6(a) shows what happens to the data initially. Data entering the LUT at level 80 leave the other side at level 80 as well. This graph is called a 'transfer function' since it shows how the input data are transferred to the output. In Figure 4.6(a) there is the 'unity' transfer function, or the one that does not change the data. In Figure 4.6(b), the transfer function has been changed so that data at level 80 leave the LUT box at level 85. However note that data at 30 or below all emerge at level 0, and data at 180 and above emerge at level 255. This would be a suitable contrast stretch for the data shown in the histogram in Figure 4.4, since there is virtually no information below 30 or above 180. Thus the range from 30 to 180 has been

Figure 4.5   Block diagram of the operation of a Look Up Table.

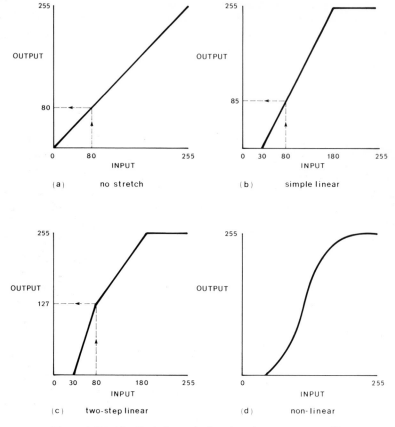

Figure 4.6(*a*)–(*d*)   Typical transfer functions for contrast stretching.

stretched to the range of 0 to 255. Hence the name for the process. Since the graph is a straight line, this is called a linear contrast stretch.

However the histogram shown in Figure 4.4 was skewed. In fact the median of the data (i.e. the level at which half the pixels are below and half are above) was at 80 (R in Figure 4.4). The linear contrast stretch moved this to level 85 as shown in Figure 4.6(*b*). So most pixels would leave the LUT box with an intensity of less than 127, or mid-grey. Thus the picture will appear fairly dark and difficult to interpret. The next stage in this sequence of contrast stretching is a two-step linear stretch as shown in Figure 4.6(*c*). Here the median data emerge at level 127, i.e. mid-grey. There are as many pixels above this level as below giving the picture a good balance. The next stage in the sequence of contrast stretching leads to much more complicated transfer functions as illustrated in Figure 4.6(*d*) and they are non-linear.

Most image processing systems use LUTs to perform contrast stretches. Even in a software program, it is often more efficient in time to use them.

However the best results are obtained using an interactive system, since the machine is used to present the best possible image (for the particular application) to the user, who uses his own image processing abilities which are extremely powerful for spatial and textural analyses.

Figure 4.7 illustrates the effect of the four transfer functions in Figures 4.6(a), (b), (c), and (d). It is difficult to see the image in Figure 4.7(A) since it is

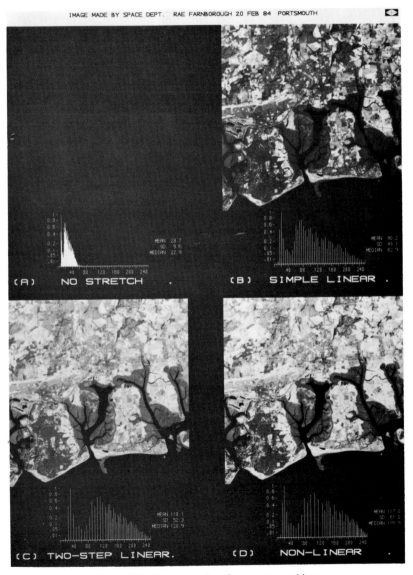

Figure 4.7   Four examples of contrast stretching.

so dark, and this is illustrated in the histogram shown below the image. The scene is of the Portsmouth area in England and was taken by the Thematic Mapper (band 4) on Landsat 4 on 4-Feb-83. A mid-morning image in winter in the UK is bound to be dark, and this picture demonstrates the need for contrast stretching.

The simple linear contrast stretch as shown in Figure 4.7(B) (corresponding approximately to the transfer function in Figure 4.6(b)), produces a satisfactory result. The histogram of the stretched image shows a good spread of the information over the whole display range of 0 to 255. Note the distribution appears to be bi-modal, the left hand peak corresponding to the water area, and the right-hand peak, to the land. The image might still be thought a little dark and the median at 82.9 (shown to the right of the histogram in Figure 4.7(B)), is well below mid grey at level 127. The result of a two-step linear contrast stretch (of the type in Figure 4.6(c)) is shown in Figure 4.7(C), where the median of the land data has been moved to mid-grey, although the overall median is at 120.9 due to the large number of dark sea pixels contributing to the statistics. Finally, in Figure 4.7(D), a non-linear contrast stretch has been applied on top of the stretch in Figure 4.7(C). The effect of this is to broaden the distribution (note that the standard deviation has increased from 52 in (C) to 61 in (D)), and this makes the image look more contrasty. It may be easier for the eye to see some features in the more contrasty image, but others will be lost in the highlights and shadows. This demonstrates that a single contrast stretch for all applications is a compromise and that the human eye can extract most information for a particular application by using an interactive image processing machine to produce a specific stretch.

Plate 9 illustrates the contrast stretch operation applied to three bands of a colour picture. The scene is of Northern Kenya, taken by Landsat MSS on 23-Jan-73, with band 7 in red, band 5 in green, and band 4 in blue.

4.5.2 Density slicing

Density slicing is another photographic operation that poses several additional possibilities and problems. The original idea was that every pixel in a black-and-white image could be colour coded. For example, all the pixels from black to dark grey could be made yellow, all those from dark grey to mid grey could be made green. Since, as was mentioned earlier, the number of intensity levels in a digital image is very large compared to the capabilities of the eye and film, this facility is much more necessary to enable the user to examine the subtle differences in tone in an image. The ease and the precision with which the density slice can be applied in a digital image is in marked contrast to the difficulty and imprecision of the photographic system.

It may be found in an image that every pixel between one level and another is associated with a particular type of ground cover. For example, in many images water appears very dark, and a simple density slice may isolate all the water areas. This is an example of a simple 'Classification', and the water would be a 'Class' of ground cover. Later, these ideas are developed further using more than one band of an image. However, this simple idea here should be understood before the more complex classifiers are examined.

Plate 7 illustrates the density slice operation applied to the same Portsmouth scene as in Figure 4.7. The first slice in blue from level 0 to 13, colours in the water area, and this simple process can be seen as classifying this area as water, very successfully. The second slice in dark red is from level 14 to 21 and picks out mud/wet sand areas above the water line. However, there are many other areas within the town of Portsmouth at the bottom left, that are also picked out, and thus this is a relatively inaccurate classification of mud/wet sand.

4.5.3 Classification

Classification using density slicing (above) is all very well, but this simple operation may result in many errors. In the mud/sand example, some areas of mud may lie outside the range dark grey to mid grey, and other features, such as shadows, may lie within the range giving errors of both types, i.e. excluding some of the required feature and including parts of other features. This density slice could be performed on a second spectral band where it may be found that the error areas are different. If the second slice is applied only in the areas sliced in the first band, there should be a reduction in the number of error areas. This process could be repeated for all the spectral bands but it would be very tedious. Classifiers allow the user to do this multiband selection with the minimum of effort.

To operate a classifier, the user normally will mark an area on an image displayed on a screen, with a box or by running a line round it. The user is telling the system that within the box is an homogeneous area of ground. Within this area the classifier examines the data in each of the spectral bands. For each band, the minimum and maximum values of the intensity are found and these are the limits that would be used in the density slice example earlier. Finally the image processing system examines all the pixels within the scene, tests whether they lie within the limits in each and every spectral band, and if they do, they are generally coloured in on the screen. Not only are the similar areas displayed on the screen for the user to examine, but the systems can generally count up all the pixels that have passed the tests and present the total area in a few seconds.

This classifier described so far is called the 'box' or 'parallelepiped' type. There are limitations which mean that it is not as discriminating as it might be. Other types of classifier including the so-called 'Maximum Likelihood' or 'Cluster' etc. types are more complex, take longer to run, but are generally better matched to the data and have better discrimination. However, the principles of operation as described, still apply.

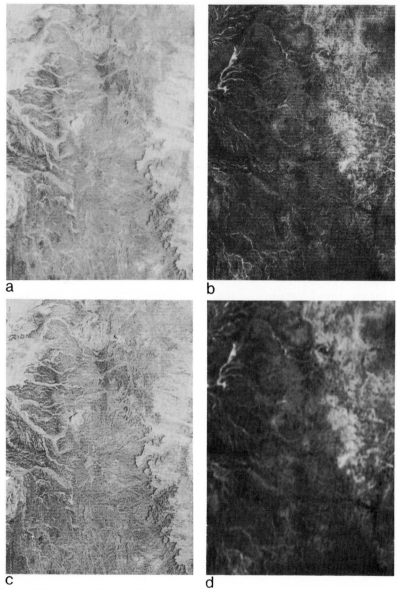

Figure 4.8(*a*) Landsat Band 7. (*b*) Ratio Band 7/Band 5. (*c*) Band 7 edge enhancement. (*d*) Smoothed ratio.

In practice, the user should have information from a field trip to one or more parts of the area in the image, so that when a box is put over a training area in the image, the user knows what is actually there on the ground. This known area is then used by the processor to classify the whole displayed image, and the user assesses the accuracy of the results by comparison with the areas for which he has ground data. Further training areas can be added until the classification best fits the ground data, where it exists. Thus, the classification process allows the user to extrapolate from known small test areas to a whole region, with some degree of confidence, and hence to produce maps, statistics, and so on. Plate 10, an extract from Plate 9 in Kenya, illustrates a single small training area in black, over a vegetated area, with the resultant classification shown in purple.

4.5.4 *Arithmetic operations*

Many arithmetic operations are performed on a pixel basis. Thus, suppose there are two images A and B which are to be added. Every pixel in every line of image A is added to the corresponding pixel in image B. Adding one image in one spectral band to another image of exactly the same area but in another spectral band, will result in an image where the intensity of a pixel will be the average of the two spectral bands. Adding images together in this fashion is also a way of reducing noise, or speckle in an image. Similarly if one image were subtracted from another of the same area, in the same spectral band, but taken at a different time, the regions of change will be highlighted. (e.g. an urban development, a change in vegetation state). Dividing one band of an image by another tends to show the spectral characteristics of land units irrespective of illumination conditions. For example grass on the sunlit side of a hill would appear much brighter than grass on the dark side, in the original image, but both sides of the hill would appear very similar in an image formed by the ratio of the two bands. In Figure 4.8 (*a*) there is a picture of part of Botswana taken in the near infrared. Vegetation reflects strongly in this part of the spectrum and hence some of the bright areas are vegetation, but some are bare rock. Notice also that there are deep shadows due to the hilly terrain. By taking the ratio of band 7 (the near infrared band) to band 5 (visible red),

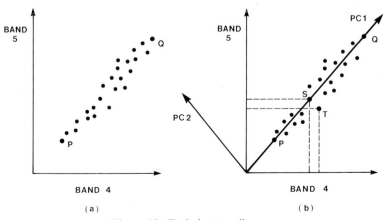

Figure 4.9 Typical scatter diagram.

vegetation turns out light and is therefore separable from the rocks, as in Figure 4.8 (b). Note however that the shadows have been largely suppressed in this ratio image.

Multiplication can be used for masking operations. Where the interest is in water alone, a density slice of Landsat band 7 could pick out the water areas as shown earlier. If in the sliced image, the land were set to 0 and the water to 1, then on multiplying any other band by this latter image, the water part would be unmodified, by the land would be set to 0, i.e. it would be masked out.

More complicated arithmetic functions can also be performed, e.g. one 'vegetation index' for Landsat MSS is (band 7 − band 5)/(band 7 + band 5).

These arithmetic operations can often be specified as though simple numbers were being considered, and not the very large arrays of numbers in the digital image.

4.5.5 *Principal components analysis*

One particular process of arithmetic combinations of different spectral bands is used in principal components analysis. Consider the plot in Figure 4.9(*a*), known generally as a scatter diagram. The intensity of a pixel P, in band 4 from Landsat MSS, has been plotted against the intensity of the same pixel in band 5. This has been repeated for the pixel Q, and all the other pixels within the image. However these bands are highly correlated. Thus a pixel which is dark in band 4 is also dark in band 5 (as at P) and similarly if bright in band 4 is also bright in band 5 (as at Q). Hence all the plotted points lie on or near the diagonal line between the axes of the plot. As far as the interpreter is concerned, the fact that the data are highly correlated, means that, having studied band 4, he gets little further information from looking at band 5. Figure 4.10 which is a Landsat MSS picture of Botswana (185/77) taken on 17-Jan-73, shows this point very well, in that there is very little variation in the four spectral bands.

Principal components analysis is designed to remove this high correlation by creating new bands, each of which is made by adding different proportions of the input bands. This is illustrated in Figure 4.9(*b*). A new pair of axes have been defined (PC1, PC2), created simply by rotating the original ones until PC1 lies along the direction of maximum variance of the data as shown. The method by which the image of the PC1 is produced is roughly as follows. The intensity of pixel S in the PC1 image is the sum of part of the intensity in band 4 and part of the intensity in band 5. If the PC1 axis has been rotated through 45 degrees, then the contributions of the two bands are equal. If the angle were less than 45 degrees, then band 4 would contribute more. Similarly, PC2 is made by subtracting the intensity of S in band 4 from band 5. Note that it is very difficult to see the difference between points S and T in bands 4, 5 and PC1. By projecting the points S and T onto these bands (as shown for bands 4 and 5 in Figure 4.9(*b*)), it can be seen that the separation of S and T is very small compared to the total range of the data in each of these bands. Thus this subtle

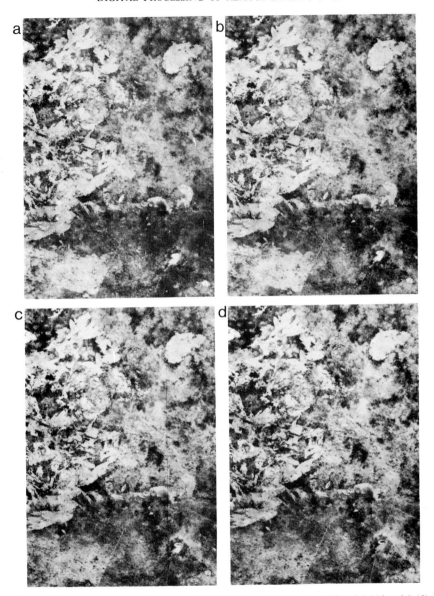

Figure 4.10   Landsat scene of Botswana (185-77) 17-Jan-73. (*a*) Band 4; (*b*) band 5; (*c*) band 6; (*d*) band 7.

difference in intensity could well be invisible to the eye. However, in PC2 the separation of S and T is about half of the total range of the data in this band and would therefore be easily visible. This serves to illustrate that principal components analysis can often show subtle variations in spectral response which would normally be invisible.

In this illustration, PC1 is the average of the two input bands, and PC2 is the

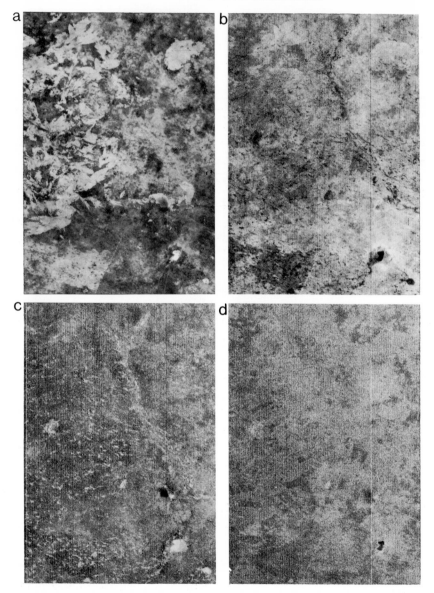

Figure 4.11   Landsat scene of Botswana (185-77) 17-Jan-73. (*a*), PC1; (*b*) PC2; (*c*) PC3; (*d*) PC4.

difference between them. This process can be applied to more than two bands, and the rules are as follows: PCl is along the direction of maximum variance; PC2 is at right angles to PC1, and subject to this, is along the next direction of maximum variance; PC3 is at right angles to both PC1 and PC2, and is along the next direction of maximum variance, and so on.

Figure 4.11 shows the principal components analysis applied to the four bands of Figure 4.10. From an examination of the relative contributions of the four input bands, PC1 is approximately the average of all four bands, PC2 is the difference between the visible and the near infrared bands (i.e. (band 4 + band 5) − (band 6 + band 7)), PC3 is the difference between the two visible bands (i.e. band 4 − band 5), and PC4 is the difference between the two near infrared bands (i.e. band 7 − band 6). The four principal component images all look different in Figure 4.11 and all show different information although PC3 and PC4 also have a great deal of noise. Note for example, how the strong black/white pattern (actually burnt rangeland) present in all four input bands (Figure 4.10) and in PC1 is absent in PC2, PC3, and PC4. By using mainly PC2, it is possible to find features irrespective of whether they are in burnt areas or not. Subtle geological subsurface structure can perhaps be seen better in PC2 and PC3. Further details relating to the interpretation of principal component images and false colour composite images in particular may be found in Chapter 9.

4.5.6 Spatial filtering

Two types of filter are considered here, edge enhancement and smoothing filters. Edge enhancement is used to make subtle edges more visible to the eye. This process is illustrated in Figure 4.12, where the intensity of the pixels are plotted along one scan line in the image. Suppose that all the pixels in a barley field at the left of the image are all at level 40, and those in the adjoining grass field are all at 43. This one scan line happens to pass through these two fields with pixel 84 along the line as the last pixel in the barley field, (see Figure 4.12(a), and pixel 85 as the first in the grass field. Note also that there is a 'noise' pixel at 92. This pixel should also be at level 43, but for some reason there is some noise which has increased the value.

At the top of Figure 4.12 (b) there is a 'window' or a 'filter', which is three elements by one. At the current position of the window, pixel 81 is multiplied by the first element in the window, pixel 82 by the second and pixel 83 by the third. These three results are then added together to produce pixel 82 of the output image. Thus the sum is

$$\text{output pixel } 82 = (\text{pixel } 81 \times -1) + (\text{pixel } 82 \times 3) + (\text{pixel } 83 \times -1) = 40$$

Thus in this case the filter has not altered the data at all. The window is now moved along one pixel to the right. Pixels 82, 83, and 84 are used in the same process to produce output pixel 83, and so on, producing the output line in Figure 4.12(b).

Whereas the step in intensity between the barley and the grass was only 3 in the original image and would be difficult for the eye to see in a range of say 255, the step has been increased to 9 (i.e. 46 − 37) in the output scene. This process, which has increased the difference over a boundary, makes the boundary easier to see, and is therefore called an edge enhancement. In areas where there are no edges, the data are not modified, but note that the noise pixel at 92 has been considerably enhanced. Edge enhancement should leave homogeneous areas unaltered and should sharpen edges, but unfortunately, will also enhance noise.

Filters do not have to be one-dimensional (and hence result in edge enhancement in one direction only) but can be in two dimensions and can be bigger. Figure 4.8 (c) shows the effect of a 5 × 5 edge enhancement filter applied to the image in Figure 4.8(a). The opposite of an edge enhancement filter is a smoothing filter, an example of which is shown at the top of Figure 4.12(c). If this filter is applied to the line image in Figure 4.12(a) in a similar manner, it gives rise to the output line as shown in Figure 4.12(c). The noise spike at pixel 92, which was 4 grey levels above the rest of the grass field and may have been visible, has now been reduced to 1 level above (strictly 1.33, but rounded down in an integer system) and may now be invisible. Smoothing filters thus reduce noise in images but also reduce the sharpness of edges as shown in Figure 4.12 (c) where the boundary between the fields has been made less distinct. As for edge enhancement, two-dimensional filters can be produced, and Figure 4.8(d) shows the effect of a 5 × 5 smoothing filter applied to the 'noisy' looking ratio image in Figure 4.8(b).

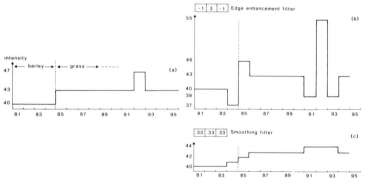

Figure 4.12 (a) Pixel intensity along a scan line. (b) Edge enhancement applied to line in (a). (c) Smoothing applied to line in (a).

Different filters are therefore used for different applications. Edge enhancement may be applied to a good image for the study of geological lineaments, but image noise will be increased. Smoothing filters may be applied in large estuaries when looking at suspended sediment patterns, since the images tend to be noisy and the loss of spatial resolution is unimportant due to the scale of the features.

4.5.7 Geometric transformation

This process is normally undertaken in 'background' on a large minicomputer or mainframe, since for a normal-size image it can take many minutes to many hours to complete. Essentially, the process is as follows. The image is examined for suitable 'ground control points' (GCP), which are easily identified objects that can be located highly accurately. Headlands in the sea, small islands in lakes, dams on reservoirs, the crossings of runways, roads, railways, etc., all make good GCPs. These points are also found on a map. In the computer, the image is distorted like a rubber sheet, so that all the GCPs in the image fit their corresponding points on the map. Perhaps 100 points are used to control this stretching operation with a good degree of certainty. Typically, a Landsat image (with pixels which are 57 m by 79 m on the ground) of an area in the UK can be transformed so that the error in the position of a pixel is about 50 m or less.

Having the ability to transform images allows a user to combine the remote sensing data with other forms of data, such as maps of soil type, climate, topography, etc., so that with the image processing, there is a much more powerful system. Correlation of the image data with 'ground truth' is made much easier. Maps of classifications can be produced directly from the computer. Given two or more images of the same area but taken at different times, they can be transformed to fit a map (and hence each other) so that changes over a period of time can be monitored. Having transformed two adjacent scenes, it is possible to mosaic them together so that work can be carried out over a very large area, such as might be required in the study of large-scale geological features.

4.6   The future

It is envisaged that two major developments will change image processing in the near future. One is that much cheaper interactive image processing systems will become available, thereby permitting more investigators to use digital images more fully, and secondly, the ideas expressed above concerning the use of map data and remote sensing data will evolve into 'geographic information systems' which will eventually handle enormous volumes of map and image data and have easy to use interactive terminals for interrogation.

Ultimately, these geographic information systems will accept a wide range of questions, will examine the 'database' for the relevant information and present the results to the user.

Bibliography

Bernstein, R. (1978) *Digital Image Processing for Remote Sensing* IEEE Press, New York, 473 pp.

Gonzales, R. C. and Wintz, P. (1977) *Digital Image Processing*. Addison-Wesley, Reading, Massachusetts, 431 pp.

Pratt, W. K. (1978) *Digital Image Processing*. John Wiley, New York, 750 pp.

Rosenfeld, A. (Ed.) (1976) *Topics in Applied Physics Vol. 11—Digital Picture Analysis*. Springer Verlag, New York, etc., 351 pp.

5 Remote sensing in civil engineering practice

T. J. M. KENNIE, M. C. MATTHEWS and P. J. BEAVEN

5.1 Introduction

The measurement and recording of data relating to the physical characteristics of the earth's surface is a critical phase of any major civil engineering project. The information which these 'terrain investigations' provide is an essential element of the initial planning stages of a project and it can also provide useful data in subsequent phases of a project. Remote sensing in the form of the photographic, scanning and processing systems discussed in earlier chapters is one of the most appropriate means of recording existing ground conditions, of assessing their potential for engineering projects and also of evaluating the effect, or potential effects, of the subsequent construction on the environment. It should however be stressed that remote sensing is only an aid to engineering investigations, providing information which is complementary to that obtained from field measurements, site visits and existing sources of data such as maps and project reports. Indeed, if maximum benefit is to be gained from remote sensing techniques it is essential that 'ground truth' information from external sources forms part of the survey in order to verify the results of the remote sensing investigation independently.

It is therefore the primary aim of this chapter to examine the role of remote sensing systems in terrain investigations for civil engineering projects. A secondary aim is to present a coherent summary of the present and future uses of remote sensing in civil engineering practice. Subsequent chapters will deal in specific terms with the application of particular remote sensing techniques to various branches of civil engineering practice.

5.2 The role of remote sensing in terrain investigations

Remote sensing methods are a highly cost-effective means by which the civil engineer can obtain complete, up-to-date and often repetitive information about terrain conditions. The data produced about the terrain may be in two

106

forms, either metric or interpretive. In the former case the information relates to the precise position of features, for example as provided by topographic maps produced by photogrammetric methods. In the latter case the information is primarily thematic in nature based on the subjective interpretation of the remotely sensed imagery, with much less emphasis on positional accuracy. Whilst this categorization is clearly not mutually exclusive it does nevertheless illustrate the broad distinction in the role which remote sensing plays in ground investigation.

5.2.1 Photogrammetry

The use of remote sensing imagery (almost totally photography) for the production of orthophotographs and topographic maps by photogrammetric means is a well established and highly sophisticated science. Whilst this aspect of the use of remote sensing in civil engineering is dealt with in greater detail in Chapter 6, it is useful to examine one particular example in order to illustrate the use of remote sensing in this role.

Route mapping for highway location and design is one of the most common forms of photogrammetric project in civil engineering. In this role the remote sensing data, typically in the form of medium to large scale black-and-white panchromatic aerial photography, enable the civil engineer to evaluate several alternative route alignments within a broad corridor of interest. In addition, by further restricting the area under consideration to a much narrower band of interest, more detailed preliminary design data can be examined before the final design data is produced for one particular alignment. By using different scales of aerial photography, as shown in Table 5.1, together with photogrammetric methods, topographic maps, digital ground models (DGM) and detailed design data can be produced. Further discussion of remote sensing in this particular role can be found in Leatherdale (1975) and Adolfsson (1972). More details regarding the further use of remote sensing in highway engineering can be found in Chapter 9.

Table 5.1 Typical specifications for route/highway mapping by photogrammetric methods

Stage of investigation	Photographic scale	Flying height (assuming wide angle lens)	Map scales	Contour interval (m)
Route location	1:30 000	4 600	1:20 000– 1:10 000	5
Preliminary design	1:10 000	1 500	1:2 500	1
Final design	1:3 000	460	1:500	0.5

5.2.2 *Interpretation*

A second and vitally important role of remote sensing in terrain investigations is as a source of data on various themes of engineering significance. In this case the information provided by remote sensing involves either subjective human interpretation or automatic computer classification of the available imagery. Examples of the specific forms of thematic information which can be provided by remote sensing techniques include geology, geomorphology, geotechnical information such as site history, extent of reclaimed land and location of landslips, together with additional information, including drainage patterns, groundwater potential, urban/rural development, transportation patterns, energy monitoring and pollution control.

Whilst the interpretation of remote sensing data can be an extremely useful tool for the civil engineer, it is essential before embarking on a terrain investigation involving remote sensing to consider the following points. Firstly, consideration should be given to whether remote sensing is appropriate. This will depend largely on the extent of existing material and, if material does exist, on the reliability of that information. If remote sensing is considered a suitable technique the question of choosing the most appropriate system(s) arises. This also raises questions about further matters such as the most suitable method of viewing and interpreting the imagery, the means of verifying the results of any interpretation, and of obvious importance, the costs which will be incurred in a project of this nature.

The choice of the most suitable technique to use depends on several factors including (a) the scale of the project (regional or local), and (b) the stage of the investigation, (reconnaissance, feasibility, design, construction or post-construction). Both factors also tend to be related to the stage of development of a country. In general terms the distinction can be made between regional investigations concerned with the reconnaissance and feasibility stages of a civil engineering project, and more local investigations where the primary role of remote sensing is as an aid at the design, construction and post-construction stages of a project. In the former case the projects tend to be almost exclusively located in developing or Third World countries, whereas in the latter the projects are more predominant in the developed world.

Several reasons account for this situation. In developing countries the major economic needs are likely to involve the development of transportation, drainage and agriculture and also the exploitation of natural resources. Projects undertaken in such areas are therefore likely to be on a regional scale. In addition the basic information in the form of topographic and geological maps is likely to be limited or in some instances non-existent. Hence there is an immediate requirement at the reconnaissance stages of such projects to obtain an overview of the ground surface. This can be gained rapidly and at reasonable cost only by using remote sensing techniques. The resolution of the techniques which are used need not be very high, and hence Landsat MSS and

TM imagery and high-altitude aerial photography may be quite suitable. In some areas where the earth's surface is continually obscured by cloud the use of airborne or satellite-based radar (SAR) systems may be the only means of obtaining the necessary information. More detail relating to the application of Landsat imagery, in particular, for regional planning studies of this nature may be found in Chapter 7.

In contrast, within developed countries the majority of construction projects are of a more local nature. In addition since the demand for land may be high and the amount of land take restricted on economic or environmental grounds, the scope for selecting the most suitable sites for construction is much more limited. Also the amount of background information about the project area in the form of topographic maps, geological survey reports, site investigation reports, records of mines and mineral deposits, hydrological information and aerial photography is likely to be high. Much greater emphasis is therefore placed on investigating the ground conditions at a local level, particularly for design purposes. Further discussion relating to the interpretation of aerial photography for localized projects of this type may be found in Chapter 8.

5.3 The use of remote sensing for projects in the developing world

The range of development and economic status of countries outside Europe and the USA is diverse. However they all share the need to expand their civil engineering infrastructure in order to support development projects in areas such as agriculture, urban development, mineral extraction and forestry. All projects of this nature generate the need for terrain investigations for planning purposes. These are generally undertaken on a national scale, although more detailed investigations may also be necessary subsequently, when a particular project is agreed upon. The relative importance of the engineering terrain investigations depends primarily on the objective of the project, and specifically on whether it involves a planning or design study. A feature common to all such projects is that they tend to cover a very large area, and also have to be carried out within strict budgetary limits. Under these circumstances it is essential to employ techniques that can rapidly examine large areas at relatively low cost. Hence, the interpretation of remote sensing can make a significant contribution to improving the effectiveness of regional engineering investigations of this type.

It has already been noted that the use of background information such as maps of geology, topography, soil or climate can aid considerably in the accuracy of an interpretation. In addition the use of terrain evaluation techniques enables the engineer to focus the interpretation on to the significant parts of the terrain, further increasing the efficiency of the interpretation. The objective of a terrain evaluation is to subdivide an area of ground in such a way that it is possible to record the terrain properties of interest to a particular investigation (see Mitchell, 1973).

The basis of any terrain evaluation involves the classification of the ground into distinct mapping units, selected to meet the following criteria.

(i) The units must divide up the terrain in a way that is relevant for the user of the map.
(ii) The units must be reasonably homogeneous in terms of the purpose that they are intended to serve.
(iii) The units must be convenient to map, in terms of the effort required and the resources available.

These criteria must be considered before deciding which mapping units are most appropriate. The mapping scale is largely determined by factors (ii) and (iii).

The end result of a terrain evaluation study is usually a thematic map, which may be purely geological or soil-type, but should preferably be of more direct relevance to the project in hand. The Geological Society (1982) has produced a comprehensive report on terrain mapping which outlines the various systems and recommends the use of air-photo interpretation based on a framework of terrain classification or geomorphological terrain mapping. The most widely used system of terrain classification for land resource mapping is the land system/land facet concept, devised for use in both engineering and agricultural surveys (Beckett et al., 1972). The advantage of this joint technique is that data gathered by one group can be used by others. For example the maps and reports edited by Hill (1978) for the Land Resources Development Centre have provided the basis of many engineering studies in Nigeria.

The type of terrain classification used in these surveys is based upon the fact that terrains can be divided up in a hierarchical fashion, in which large units are made up of associations of smaller units, in a manner similar to soils. The largest units in the classification occupy many thousands of square kilometres; the smallest may cover only a few square metres. Land systems and land facets occupy a position of central importance in a scheme that includes more generalized as well as more specific levels. A land system is a large area of terrain having characteristic landforms, drainage pattern and associations of materials, developed on a single geological unit or sequence. It is typified by a distinctive scenery, land use and social pattern, and it can generally be mapped at about 1:250 000 to 1:1 000 000 scale. Land systems form distinctive air photo patterns caused by their arrangement of drainage, topography and land cover. The component parts of a land system, called land facets, are defined in a similar way, but they are smaller and less variable, so that an engineer would normally expect a single design to be appropriate for sections of road built on each facet. The number of land facets in a land system is generally between three and six, but they always occur in the same relationship. Land facets can be subdivided into land elements (the smallest members of the classification hierarchy) if these small features are considered to be important, as they often are in engineering studies. The relation between land system, land facet and land element is shown in Figure 5.1. Terrain classification studies have been carried out in Africa (Scott *et al.*, 1971) and the Far East (Lawrance, 1978; CSIRO, 1976) as well as other areas of the world.

5.3.1 Selection of appropriate techniques

The interpretation of remote sensing imagery represents a technique that can be used to varying degrees in all types of survey. Its relative importance will depend on the scale of the survey, and also on the availability of other material. The availability of background material is different for every project and in some cases a reconnaissance survey is commissioned to collect data needed for planning. In addition the facilities available to an expatriate consultant may be different to those available to a local Ministry, e.g. the time scale of a project may make it impossible to seek out and collate data which is suspected to exist.

The importance of the interpretation of Landsat imagery for planning studies is set out in Chapter 7, with reference to a wide variety of surveys. Most of the studies described were carried out from Europe or America; one reason for this is that digital imaging processing techniques were used in several studies, and at present most of the equipment needed for this is both expensive and sophisticated and thus less readily available in developing countries. However photographic processing of Landsat data provides an effective source of imagery as demonstrated by the prints produced at the Regional Centre for Services in Surveying and Mapping in Nairobi. In addition the development of microcomputers and associated accessories means that small robust image processors are now being produced which give high-quality images suitable for interpretation in engineering surveys. In this way it will be possible to take the equipment to the country being surveyed, and by making the interpretation during the course of the project, demonstrate its usefulness locally and also enable more rapid correlation between interpretation and field checking. The theme of appropriate equipment is also discussed in Chapter 9 describing the use of light aircraft to take specialist photography for the interpretation of specific features. Although related to highway engineering, the techniques described are appropriate to many other types of survey. In addition to specialist surveys, this chapter describes the interpretation of satellite imagery and conventional air photography for highway projects ranging from a planning survey through feasibility and design studies to post-construction monitoring.

5.4   The use of remote sensing for projects in the developed world

Engineering projects in the developed areas of the world are associated primarily with the improvement and expansion of the infrastructure of that country. In such projects remote sensing techniques may be employed in a variety of applications including topographic mapping, site investigations,

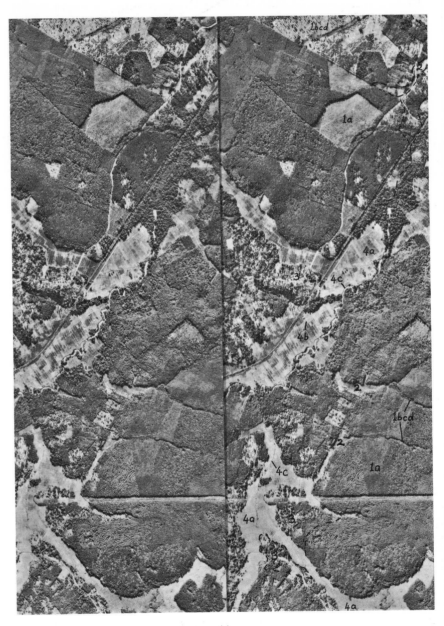

(a)

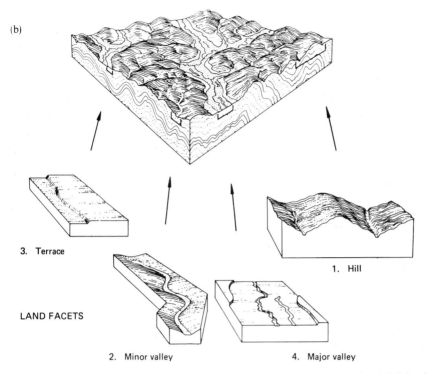

(b)

3. Terrace

1. Hill

LAND FACETS

2. Minor valley   4. Major valley

Figure 5.1   Stereopair and block diagrams showing the land facets of the Alor Gajah land system. (Air photos by courtesy of the Director of National Mapping, Malaysia, Government of Malaysia copyright reserved: DNMM 21.16/60).

and environmental engineering studies (e.g. energy conservation and pollution monitoring).

In topographic mapping applications much use is made of conventional black-and-white aerial photography. The demands on accuracy set by this application necessitate specialized equipment and skills. Expensive survey cameras of the types described in Chapter 2 are used to obtain the photographs and complex stereoplotting instruments are used in order to determine accurate three-dimensional coordinate data. The photogrammetric operations required for such processes are discussed in Chapter 6.

In contrast, the use of remote sensing for site investigations demands a much lower degree of accuracy with respect to the measurement process. In this case emphasis is placed on the interpretation of the imagery to locate features of geotechnical significance. The size of the project area will generally be small (from a fraction of a hectare to the order of one or two hundred hectares). In Europe and the USA small- and large-scale maps and documentary information are usually readily available, providing useful background information about the project area. However, the wealth of data may, in some instances, obscure the impact of some factor of vital importance, either because it is too localized or specialized to be included in these data sources. A definitive image of the ground from an elevated platform can clearly provide comprehensive information which complements that obtained from other sources. The resolution of this imagery should however be compatible with the dimensions of the features of interest and hence at present aerial photography is the primary source of imagery for projects of this nature. Currently the spatial resolution of satellite-borne sensors is not sufficiently high to enable the detection of ground features likely to be of engineering significance in such investigations. The availability of existing aerial photography is limited largely to black-and-white panchromatic obtained for topographic mapping purposes. However, the type of photography used for this purpose need not be restricted to conventional black-and-white vertical photography, and may involve the interpretation of oblique photographs and those obtained using colour and 'false' colour infrared emulsions. Indeed, the increase in interest in small-format photographs obtained using remotely piloted aircraft (RPA) (Tomlins, 1983) and microlight aircraft (Graham and Read, 1984) may make the commissioning of oblique and colour or 'false' colour infrared photography a cost effective approach for small projects.

The benefits which can be derived from incorporating the interpretation of aerial photography into a site investigation project can be substantial. For example the information obtained by the aerial photography may be used for the following:

(a) The planning of the distribution of site investigation work in the field. Gates and breaks in hedges or fences, together with an overview of the general terrain to be covered, can be seen on photographs taken at the appropriate scale. This can be of great assistance in planning the movement of drilling rigs and other equipment over the site.

(b) The location and usage of fill, aggregates and other construction materials. The interpretation of the geology of the site and its environs will often provide this information.

(c) The identification of catchments, the evaluation of run-off, the pattern and density of streams and the location of spring lines and seepages. This information is normally clearly visible on aerial photographs and may be more comprehensive than that obtained from topographic maps.

(d) The identification of instability. Landslip activity whether recent or not can often be identified. Examination of photographs taken over a period of time may be used to define the most active zones in landslip areas. Also air photographs may be used to identify areas of potential instability.

(e) The determination of site history. Examination of the photographs may reveal evidence of the past use of the site or natural changes which may have affected the site. This may include the identification of landfill, areas of tree removal, and areas subject to occasional flooding. In coastal areas the rate of cliff recession may be apparent from a sequence of aerial photographs. The use of aerial photography as a means of assessing site history is described in Dumbleton (1983).

(f) The identification of localized features of geotechnical interest. For example this may include features such as sinkholes, land drains, infilled trenches and natural drainage channels, disturbed drainage, gullies and abandoned mine shafts.

(g) The identification of general topographic and geological features in and around the project area.

Remote sensing also has an important role to play in environmental engineering. By using scanning systems it is possible to obtain data about objects outside the visible spectrum. This is particularly useful for energy conservation studies where heat loss is often an important area of interest. Thermal infrared techniques can be used very cost effectively to detect heat loss from structures and also from buried services (e.g. steam lines). Thermal and multispectral scanning systems may also be used for pollution and sediment transport studies. Clearly a high resolution is necessary for such investigations, and this, with a few exceptions, precludes the use of satellite-mounted systems. Hence the systems are generally mounted in an aircraft. More discussion relating to the use of thermal infrared imagery to environmental engineering in particular may be found in Chapter 10.

5.5 Future developments

Many of the recent and future developments in remote sensing have been discussed in the earlier chapters of the book. It is, however, worth examining how some of these technological advances may influence their future application in civil engineering.

One of the most significant advances which has occurred with satellite-based scanning systems has been the dramatic improvement in spatial resolution. This is clearly illustrated by Figure 5.2 which shows the progressive improvement which has occurred in the last decade.

For various reasons, both technical and political, it seems highly unlikely that there will be a major improvement in this area in the near future. Nevertheless one can envisage that substantial interest will be generated in satellite remote sensing when the full impact of the Landsat TM and SPOT data becomes apparent. Indeed the improved resolution and stereoscopic viewing facility of SPOT should prove to be an extremely useful aid for both reconnaissance and feasibility level investigations.

Turning attention to aircraft-based systems, it is possible to identify two major areas of future development. Firstly, from a photogrammetric viewpoint the possibility may exist in the near future for the use of data from high-resolution digital framing cameras which utilize solid-state areal arrays (Petrie, 1983). A radical development of this nature would have dramatic

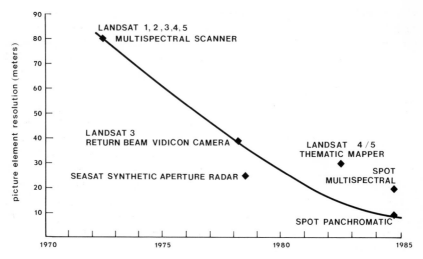

Figure 5.2 Improvement in resolution of satellite-based scanning systems. (Adapted from Settle, 1983).

repercussions on both the storage requirements for such data (e.g. video discs), and also on the measurement techniques which would be suitable (the video stereocomparator). The development of such a system would offer many benefits to mapping for civil engineering projects, some of which are currently applicable to analytical plotters. These include improved accuracy, greater flexibility both in terms of data input and also of output, generation of data for inclusion in geographic information systems, and finally decreased time and cost. A second future development related to airborne systems, specifically the scanner systems, will be an increase in the spatial and spectral resolution. Furthermore, as experience is gained in the analysis of high-resolution MSS imagery and coverage is extended and becomes more readily available the use of this source of data will become more widespread. Indeed it is quite possible that eventually imagery of this type will become a standard source of information for local site investigations and act in a complementary manner to conventional aerial photography.

Undoubtedly, however, the main advance which can be identified in the future, and one which will benefit both spaceborne and airborne systems, is the continued drop in the cost of computer memory and the increased speed of operation of computer systems. This will continue the movement of remote sensing away from analogue photographic methods to systems which make much greater use of digital technology. Two developments which are relevant in this respect are the development of low-cost image processing systems and also of geographic information systems. Brief mention has been made of the low-cost image processing systems in Chapter 4. This development will have enormous impact on remote sensing and in particular on the expansion of remote sensing into fields such as civil engineering. The opportunity to use, at relatively low cost, only a few of the processing techniques discussed earlier will enable the user to make much greater use of the vast information content of most remotely sensed imagery than is possible by simple visual inspection. Finally brief mention should be made of geographic information systems (GIS). A GIS is a computer system designed specifically to accept large volumes of spatial data, derived from a variety of sources including remote sensing. The system is able to store, retrieve, analyse and display these data according to the requirements of the user and to create both tabular and cartographic output which reflects these requirements. Currently these systems are in their infancy and many problems have to be solved before they become widely available. They do, however, seem to offer an opportunity to make optimum use of remote sensing data by combining its unique attributes with those of other sources of spatial data. Further discussion of GIS may be found in Marble and Peuquet (1983).

5.6 Conclusions

Remote sensing systems whether mounted in an aircraft or a satellite provide a comprehensive overview of the ground surface and are thus a cost effective source of data for engineering investigations. These data, which are normally displayed in the form of an image, may be used either for the precise determination of planimetry and height or for the qualitative analysis of ground type and condition. The former application is restricted largely to the use of vertical aerial photography, whilst the latter commonly involves the examination of all forms of remotely sensed imagery.

Five stages of engineering investigation have been identified: reconnaissance, feasibility, design, construction and post-construction. In developing countries projects tend to be on a regional scale, often with limited background information, hence greater emphasis is placed on the reconnaissance and feasibility level investigations. In such cases small-scale aerial photography and/or satellite imagery is applicable. In contrast the needs of the industrialized nations are different and hence greater emphasis is placed on the design, construction and post-construction stages. In terms of remote sensing large-scale aerial photography and airborne scanning systems are the most appropriate forms of imaging.

The chapters which follow provide a state-of-the-art review of past and current applications of remote sensing in civil engineering. It is hoped that this will prove to be an interim review and that as future remote sensing systems become operational and the costs of processing and storing images are reduced, so the range of applications and their general usage will increase accordingly.

References

Adolfsson, B. (1972) 'The adaptation of photogrammetric techniques to road design needs', in *Computer Systems in Highway Design* (ed. Turner, A. K.) Proceedings NATO Advanced Study Course, Copenhagen, Denmark, pp. 52–64.

Beckett, P. H. T., R. Webster, G. M. McNeil and C. W. Mitchell (1972) Terrain evaluation by means of a data bank. *Geographical Journal* 138(4) 430–456.

CSIRO (1976) *Lands of the Ramu-Madang area, Papua New Guinea.* Land Research Series 37, Commonwealth Scientific and Industrial Research Organisation, Australia.

Dumbleton, M. J. (1983) *Air Photographs for Investigating Natural Changes and Present Conditions of Engineering Sites.* Dept. of the Environment, Dept. of Transport, Transport and Road Research Laboratory Report 1085, Crowthorne, Berks.

Geological Society Working Party (1982) Land surface evaluation for engineering practice. *Q. J. Eng. Geol.* 15, 265–316.

Graham, R. W. and Read, R. (1984) Small format aerial photography from microlight platforms. *J. Photographic Science* 32, 100–110.

Hill, I. D. (ed.) (1978) *Land Resources of Central Nigeria.* Ministry of Overseas Development, Land Resource Study 29, Land Resources Development Centre.

Lawrance, C. J. (1978) *Terrain Evaluation in West Malaysia, Part 2, Land Systems of South West Malaysia.* Dept. of the Environment, Dept. of Transport, Transport and Road Research Laboratory Report SR 378, Crowthorne, Berks.

Leatherdale, J. W. (1975) Surveys for engineering design. *The Consulting Engineer...*

Marble, D. F. and Peuquet, O. J. (eds.) (1983) 'Geographic information systems', in *Manual of Remote Sensing*, Vol. 1 (ed. Colwell, R. N.), American Society of Photogrammetry, pp. 923–958.

Mitchell, C. W. (1973) *Terrain Evaluation*, Longman, London, 165 pp.

Petrie, G. (1983) 'The philosophy of digital and analytical photogrammetric systems', in *Proceedings of the 39th Photogrammetric Week*, University of Stuttgart, W. Germany.

Scott, R. M., C. J. Lawrance, R. Webster and F. H. T. Beckett (1971) *Atlas of the Land Systems of Western Kenya.* Military Engineering Experimental Establishment, Christchurch, Hampshire.

Settle, M. (1983) 'Current trends and research challenges in land remote sensing', in *Proceedings Alpbach Summer School, European Space Agency Report* ESA SP-205, 3–9.

Tomlins, G. F. (1983) Some considerations in the design of low cost remotely piloted aircraft for civil remote sensing applications. *The Canadian Surveyor* 37, 157–167.

6 Remote sensing and topographic mapping

G. PETRIE

6.1 Introduction

Topographic mapping is based almost wholly on the use of remotely sensed imagery to provide the basic information both for the construction of the maps themselves and the other coordinate information about terrain features which is generated during mapping. Only at the very largest scales of mapping (1:1000 and larger) and over comparatively small areas is it possible for *field survey methods* to compete economically with those methods which are based on the measurement and interpretation of remotely sensed imagery. However, it is most important to realize that, even when based on such imagery, no topographic mapping with any claim to usefulness and reliability can be carried out without a certain amount of field survey work to establish ground control; to collect names and information on boundaries, which are an integral part of a topographic map; to classify features which cannot be identified on the imagery; and to complete the mapping of features which are obscured by vegetation, buildings or shadows. This field component may only amount to 5% of the total effort involved in a mapping project but the information which it provides is the vital ingredient which makes the map a reliable and acceptable product to the user. This is too often forgotten by some enthusiasts for remote sensing.

Since the other applications of remote sensing discussed in this book are concerned with the mapping of data and distributions appropriate to specific themes, it will be useful to set out the main differences between such thematic maps and the topographic maps which are the concern of this chapter, in the context of remote sensing. These are summarized in Table 6.1 below.

The topographic map and its modern equivalent consisting of a set of digital coordinate information is not only a highly valued product in its own right but it acts as the base on which other types of thematic map can be compiled from remotely sensed imagery. The sheer scale of the activity is often not grasped by those outside the industry. In the UK alone, large government mapping

119

Table 6.1

Thematic maps	Topographic maps

1. The objects to be mapped are often of large areal extent—e.g. fields, forests, lakes, wetlands, etc. A synoptic view is often required or preferred.
  Scale and resolution requirements of the imagery are therefore moderate.
	Very fine point and line detail is required—e.g. streams, bridges, wells, secondary roads and tracks, individual buildings, pylons, etc.
	  Large scale and high resolution imagery is frequently required.

2. Good use can be made of multispectral images for visual or machine-based interpretation and classification.	Little help is obtained from multi-spectral images or from image analysis techniques (e.g. density slicing, band ratioing, digital image classification, etc.). Many objects are point objects or fine line features.
3. Collateral information is available from topographic maps to help detection and interpretation and to provide a base for the thematic mapping.	Little collateral information is available. Almost always, there is a need for a systematic pre-plotting or post-plotting field completion.
4. Users are often satisfied with a relatively low planimetric (positional) accuracy and with a comparatively low level of completeness.	Very high demands are set for the planimetric accuracy of the objects mapped and even more so for the completeness of the mapped information. High resolution imagery and a thorough field completion are needed.
5. Normally purely planimetric (2-D or x/y coordinates) mapping is being carried out. Mapping from single images is often acceptable.	Accurate spot heights and contours (3-D mapping or $x/y/z$ coordinates) are required. Thus overlapping stereoscopic coverage and a large base:height ratio (i.e. good 3-D geometry) are a necessity.

agencies such as the Ordnance Survey and the Directorates of Overseas and Military Surveys employ many thousands of people on topographic mapping and there is also a large private sector which is geared particularly to supplying the mapping needs of engineers, planners, architects, public utilities, oil and mineral exploration companies, and others. All of these employ remote sensing imagery extensively in one form or another. This chapter will attempt to cover this activity in three parts which correspond to the three main types of imagery which could be used for topographic mapping—photographic, scanner and side-looking radar imagery. All are employed for the purpose but some are more useful than others, though sometimes only for a specific purpose or range of scales or in certain special circumstances.

6.2 Topographic mapping from photographic images

Consideration will be given first to topographic mapping using aerial photographic images since this is a thoroughly proven and highly developed field of activity. This will be followed by consideration of the possibilities of mapping from space photography which is about to commence on an experimental basis.

6.2.1 *Mapping from aerial photography*

As mentioned in previous chapters, photographic remote sensing systems are still the most common means of sensing the visible and near infrared parts of the electromagnetic spectrum. This applies with particular force to the field of topographic mapping whether it be carried out at *small scales* for reconnaissance purposes, overall feasibility studies or project design, or at *large scales* for surveys of specific sites and detailed design and planning. The photogrammetric technology and methods used to convert the aerial photographic images taken with a calibrated camera into maps or coordinate data are highly refined and very well established. In terms of both resolution and accuracy they give results which cannot be approached by any other type of imagery. This is not to say that other types of remote sensing imagery cannot be used for topographic mapping—they can, but the tendency is to use them principally for reconnaissance and small-scale mapping, as map substitutes, or for map revision.

Another important point is that the type of photographic image commonly used for topographic mapping is that recorded on *black-and-white panchromatic and infrared emulsions* which, when used in combination with modern distortion-free lenses, give resolutions of 40 to 60 line pairs per mm — equivalent to 0.1 metre at 1:5 000 scale. The use of these monochromatic emulsions is not due to conservatism on the part of photogrammetrists, but results from the experience that, for topographic mapping in most types of terrain, there is little improvement in the interpretation and in the amount of detail that can be plotted when *colour or false-colour photography* is utilized for the purpose. Furthermore, the slight benefits achieved are greatly outweighed by the difficulties and extra expense incurred in using and processing colour photography. If, however, the needs of specialist interpreters, e.g. those requiring information on geology, soils and vegetation, require the use of colour or false-colour photography, then this can and will be used also for the topographic mapping operations without any need to modify the photogrammetric equipment or procedures used for the task.

6.2.2 *Geometrical considerations*

An aerial photographic image is essentially 'map-like' in appearance yet even a cursory comparison with a map shows that the photograph contains substantial positional displacements and variations in scale due to the effects of terrain relief and aircraft tilts which are always present. It is these *relief and tilt displacements and scale variations* which prevent mapping from being a purely tracing operation and require photogrammetric methods to be

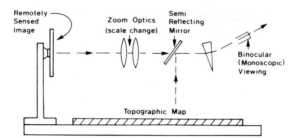

Figure 6.1   Bausch & Lomb Zoom Transfer Scope (ZTS) allowing the simultaneous viewing and superimposition of a remotely sensed image on to an existing map. The detail present on the image can be drawn by the operator directly on the map.

employed to ensure that the features shown on the image are plotted in their correct (map) position (see section 2.3.1.1).

Inexpensive instrumentation does exist which can remove some of these errors including

— *the sketchmaster* (which utilizes single photographs and removes tilt displacement);
— *the radial line plotter* (which uses stereo-pairs and removes relief displacement);
— *the mirror stereoscope and parallax bar* (which allows rough height measurements).

All of these are approximate solutions, so the final results are none too accurate. At the same time, the procedures associated with their use are extremely laborious and time-consuming. The result is that these instruments and methods are only used for map revision or the transfer of specialized information from the photograph to an existing topographic map. However, the most useful instruments for such tasks are *optical transfer devices* such as the Bausch and Lomb Zoom Transfer Scope (ZTS) (Figure 6.1) and the OMI Stereo Facet Plotter which are easily operated by engineers or field scientists. They have the distinct advantage that their zoom optics and correction devices also enable them to transfer details from scanner and side-looking radar imagery on to existing maps. However they cannot be used for original mapping or for the measurement of accurate heights and contours.

6.2.3   Stereo-plotting machines

As far as original topographic mapping is concerned, this is based almost universally on the use of *stereo-plotting machines*. Large numbers of these instruments have been installed in the UK and they are in widespread use both by national survey and mapping organizations such as the Ordnance Survey which provide basic topographic map coverage and by commercial air survey companies providing a service to engineers, planners, and others, requiring the

Figure 6.2 A 3-D stereo-model is formed from two overlapping photographs and is measured in all three dimensions (x, y, and z) using the measuring mark located in the centre of the tracing table. In this way, both the plan detail and contours are measured and compiled to form the topographic map.

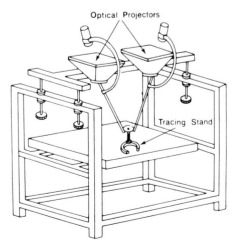

Figure 6.3 A stereo-plotting machine based on the *optical projection* of each photograph and forming an *optical model*.

provision of maps at a specific scale and contour interval for a particular project. Unlike the use of aerial photography for interpretation purposes which can relatively easily be mastered and carried out by engineers, the equipment used in stereo-plotting is expensive and the procedures highly specialized, hence the need to employ the services of the companies mentioned above.

The basic principle of a stereo-plotting machine is that it recreates an exact 3-D *stereo-model* of the terrain from the aerial photographs (Figure 6.2). The photogrammetrist then measures this stereo-model very accurately instead of going out into the terrain to carry out the measurements using surveying instruments. The savings in time and cost of doing so are quite enormous.

The models measured in the stereo-plotting machine may be either optical or mechanical in nature. *Optical models* are formed by optical reprojection of the two photographs making up a stereopair (Figure 6.3). A measuring device is then used to measure and map the objects and features present in the model in all three dimensions (*x*, *y* and *z*). *Mechanical models* are formed by replacing the optically-projected rays by their mechanical equivalents in the form of rods (Figure 6.4). The use of optical models (in the so-called optical projection machines) is still common in North America, but the use of mechanical projection machines is almost universal in the UK and most countries in Western Europe. The former are simpler and less expensive but less flexible in the types of photography that can be accommodated. The latter are more complex and more expensive but also more accurate and more flexible.

There also exist *analytical stereo-plotting machines* (Figure 6.5) in which the optical or mechanical models are replaced by an equivalent mathematical solution which is executed in real-time using a suitably programmed computer which also controls the viewing/measuring devices of the instrument being used by the photogrammetrist. Only two or three of these instruments have

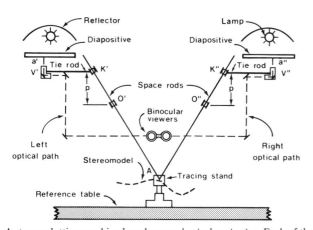

Figure 6.4   A stereo-plotting machine based on *mechanical projection*. Each of the two corresponding optical rays which intersect to locate a point in the model is replaced by a mechanical space rod. Hence a *mechanical model* is formed and measured.

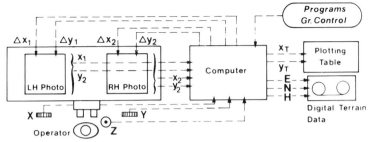

Figure 6.5   A computer-controlled *analytical stereo-plotter*. The X, Y and Z positions of a point measured by the operator are passed to the control computer which computes the corresponding positions of the same point on each photo of the stereopair in real time. Thus the point being measured can also be viewed by the operator in 3-D since the viewing optics are also controlled by the computer. The latter also controls the output which may be in the form of a map or purely digital data.

been installed in the UK to date and these are used on specialist tasks. As yet, none have been installed in government or commercial mapping organizations in the UK, but the first examples are now on order. Their importance for topographic mapping from remote sensing imagery can hardly be overemphasized, since the control computer may be programmed to simulate and correct any type of image no matter how complex it is in geometrical terms, and in a manner which no optical or mechanical projection stereo-plotting instrument can attempt to duplicate.

All topographic mapping from remote sensing imagery requires the use of *ground control points* so that the individual images or stereo-models may be correctly related to the terrain both in position, i.e. located on the National Grid or in geographical coordinates (latitude and longitude), and in height (relative to mean sea level). In the case of stereo-models, the minimum requirements for a single such model are two suitably located points of known position (i.e. with known x and y coordinates) and three points whose height (z) values are known. These points have to be provided either by field surveyors using theodolites and electronic ranging devices or by a complex photogrammetric operation termed *aerial triangulation*. This requirement distinguishes all topographic mapping of an original nature, compared, for example, with the registration or transformation of small-scale Landsat MSS imagery in the UK, where the positional information may be conveniently scaled from an existing accurate topographic map produced photogrammetrically.

6.2.4   *Output from stereo-plotting machines*

The output from stereo-plotting machines may be provided in any one of three forms:

(i) in *graphical form* in the shape of the familiar type of *topographic map* with lines, symbols, and so on to represent planimetric detail and spot-heights and contours to give the height and shape of the terrain;

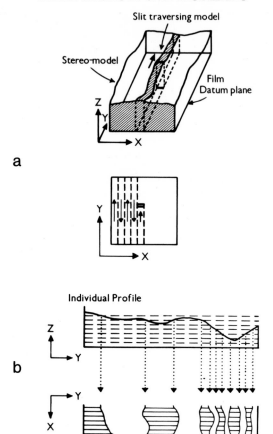

a

b

Figure 6.6 (*a*)   The 3-D stereo-model may be scanned systematically in a raster scan pattern with a slit. During each scan, the operator keeps the slit continuously at the height of the stereo-model and all the detail is recorded orthogonally on the film below to produce the orthophotograph. (*b*) Each individual scan also produces a continuous profile of the terrain which cuts a number of contour surfaces. The information from a series of these adjacent profiles can be used to form the actual contours.

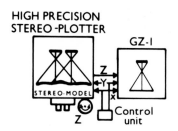

Figure 6.7   A stereo-plotter may also be attached to an additional rectifying projector which produces the orthophotograph.

(ii) in *photographic form* in the shape of an *orthophotograph*. This is a correctly-scaled photographic image from which all relief and tilt displacements have been removed, the image being generated during the scanning of the stereo-model (Figure 6.6) either by optical projection (Figure 6.7) or by optical transfer (Figure 6.8);

(iii) in *digital form*, all the three-dimensional measurements made in the stereomodel being digitized by the use of suitable measuring devices to give x, y and z coordinates (Figure 6.9) for the creation of a *digital terrain*

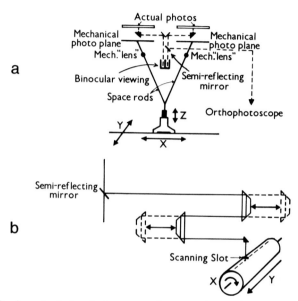

Figure 6.8 (*a*)   A mechanical projection stereo-plotter may have its image tapped off and taken by optical transfer to an orthophotoprinter. (*b*) the rectification, *e.g.* the scale corrections, take place in a unit at the side of the stereo-plotting machine.

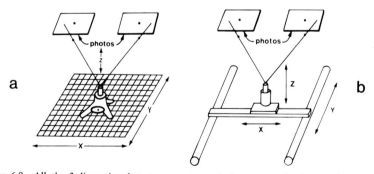

Figure 6.9   All the 3-dimensional measurements made in a stereoplotting machine may be digitized either (*a*) using a measuring tablet equipped with x and y position wires in the form of a grid or (*b*) by mounting the measuring mark on a suitable carriage or cross-slide system and encoding each of the axes (x, y and z).

model or as input to a digital mapping system or a geographically-based data bank or information system.

The scale of the final map or orthophotograph, the possible contour interval and the accuracy of the final product (including both positional and height accuracy) are dependent on various interrelated factors but chiefly

(a) the *scale and resolution* of the aerial photography;
(b) the *flying height*;
(c) the *base: height ratio*; and
(d) the *accuracy of the stereo-plotting equipment* used for measurement.

Taking the standard format (23 × 23 cm) wide-angle photogrammetric camera equipped with a lens of 15 cm focal length (i.e. $f = 0.15$ m) and aerial photography taken with 60% forward overlap (giving a base: height rate of 0.6), Table 6.2 summarizes the relationship between photographic scale and resolution on the one hand and the resulting mapping scale and contour interval on the other.

Table 6.2

Photographic scale	Ground resolution @ 40 lp/mm.	Flying height (m)		Mapping scale	Enlargement Factor (photo: map)	Contour Photograph interval
1:3000	0.075m	450	→	1:500	6 ×	0.5m
1:5000	0.125m	750	→	1:1000	5 ×	1m
1:10000	0.25m	1500	→	1:2500	4 ×	2m
1:25000	0.625m	3750	→	1:10000	2.5 ×	5m
1:50000	1.25m	7500	→	1:50000	1 ×	10m
1:80000	2.0m	12000	→	1:100000	0.8 ×	20m

These figures represent a rough yardstick of current practice by British air survey companies employing high-precision stereo-plotting machines on mapping contracts in the UK and abroad. It will be noticed that the ratio between photographic scale and map scale declines markedly as one goes from large-scale mapping for engineering purposes (where enlargement factors of 4 to 6 are normal) to small-scale topographic mapping (where only slight enlargements or reductions are common). This is due to the fact that, even on small-scale maps at 1:50 000 and 1:100 000 scales, it is necessary to detect, interpret and map features of rather small dimensions such as individual buildings, secondary roads, rivers and streams. If the scale and ground resolution of the photogrammetric imagery becomes too small, then the completeness of the map will suffer, leading to a large expense being incurred through the necessity for extensive field completion work by surveyors.

6.2.5 Mapping from space photography

The various factors discussed above which are associated with mapping from aerial photographs remain extremely relevant when the possibilities of topographic mapping from space photographs are being considered. Many individual photographs of specific sites or limited areas have been taken during manned space flights, mostly using hand-held small-format (70 mm) Hasselblad cameras. These individual photographs have achieved considerable publicity through their use in field science textbooks and scientific journals. However, relatively few areas have been photographed in a systematic manner with topographic mapping in mind. By far the most important are those taken during the manned *Skylab missions* in 1973 using cameras designed or modified for mapping.

The first was the *S-190A* Itek multi-spectral camera system (Figure 6.10) which comprised six individual small-format (70 mm) cameras coupled together to provide four simultaneous monochrome (black-and-white) exposures covering adjacent bands of the visible and near infrared parts of the spectrum plus two further simultaneous colour and false colour exposures. The second camera was the *S-190B* Actron medium-format (12.5 × 12.5 cm) *Earth Terrain Camera* (*E.T.C*) (Figure 6.11) which took overlapping stereophotographs using high-resolution panchromatic and colour films (Welch, 1976).

Some 15 years after they were first proposed (Petrie, 1970; Doyle, 1973),

Figure 6.10   Skylab S-190A multi-spectral camera.

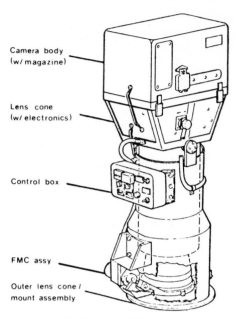

Camera body
(w/magazine)

Lens cone
(w/electronics)

Control box

FMC assy

Outer lens cone /
mount assembly

Figure 6.11 Skylab S-190B earth terrain camera.

large-format photogrammetric cameras are now being deployed in space for the first time, making use of the *Space Shuttle* as the camera platform. The first is a European Space Agency (ESA) project using a *Zeiss Oberkochen RMK camera* with a standard 23 × 23 cm format and equipped with an $f = 30$ cm lens (Ducher, 1980). This has been mounted and operated from within the Spacelab, the exposures of the Earth being made through a special glass window located in the roof of the capsule (Figures 6.12 to 6.15). The flight took

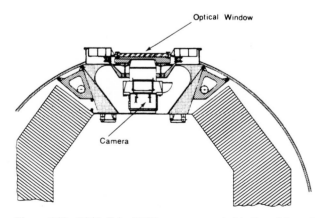

Optical Window

Camera

Figure 6.12 ESA's Zeiss RMK camera mounted in Spacelab roof.

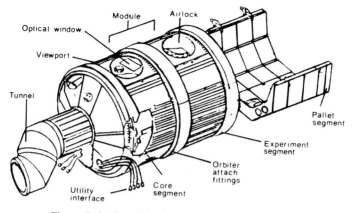

Figure 6.13   Spacelab with optical window in the roof.

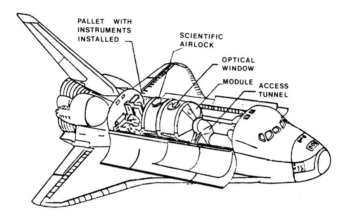

Figure 6.14   Spacelab in the Space Shuttle.

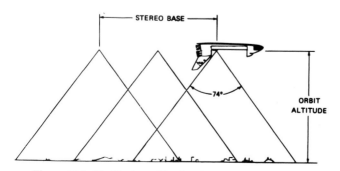

Figure 6.15   Upside-down Shuttle taking space photography.

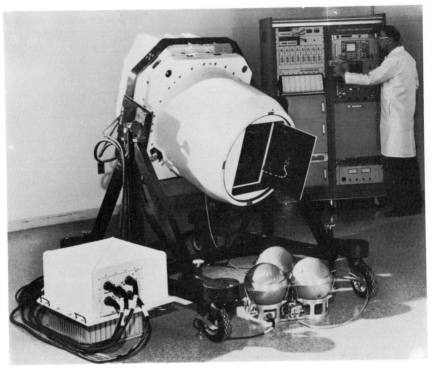

Figure 6.16   NASA's Itek LFC camera. (Reproduced by kind permission of the Itek Corp.)

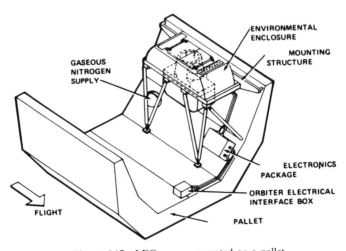

Figure 6.17   LFC camera mounted on a pallet.

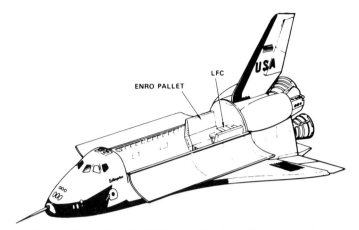

Figure 6.18 Pallet with LFC installed in Space Shuttle cargo bay.

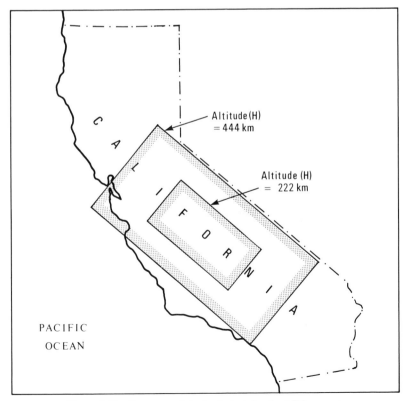

Figure 6.19 Coverage of single photo taken by LFC camera.

place in November 1983. This will be followed by a NASA project utilizing an *Itek Large Format Camera (LFC)* with a 23 × 46 cm format and also equipped with an $f = 30$ cm lens (Doyle, 1979). This camera will be mounted directly on an exterior pallet located in the Shuttle's cargo bay (Figures 6.16 to 6.19). The characteristics of these two cameras are as shown in Table 6.3.

Table 6.3

Camera	Focal length (cm)	Format (cm)	Coverage (km)	Scale	H (km)	Expected resolution (m)	Orbital inclination
NASA-LFC	30	23 × 46	225 × 450	1:1 000 000	300	15	28.5°
ESA-RMK	30	23 × 23	190 × 190	1:820 000	250	20	57°

The scale and ground resolution of the photography which will be produced by these two cameras will not be very different; the main distinction lies in their respective *format sizes*. The *Itek LFC Camera* is derived from a long line of specially-built American military mapping and reconnaissance cameras which utilize the 23 × 46 cm format. These can be operated either cross-track to ensure a greater terrain coverage or along-track to give a better geometrical arrangement. The latter arrangement is being followed in the Shuttle flight. When used with the $f = 30$ cm lens, a wide-angle (74°) coverage results in the along-track direction with a base: height ratio of 0.6 (for 60% overlap). By comparison, the *Zeiss RMK camera* utilizes the standard 23 × 23 cm format of most photogrammetric cameras. When used with a lens of the same focal length as the LFC ($f = 30$ cm), it gives a normal-angle (41°) coverage and a base:height ratio of 0.3 for the same 60% overlap.

The importance of these two projects in assessing the possibilities of producing topographic maps from space can hardly be exaggerated. While the actual results should be available soon, nevertheless it is possible even now to make some predictions and assessments as to the possibilities of this type of mapping using the earlier Skylab S-190B photography taken with the Earth Terrain Camera (ETC). Its scale (1:950 000) and ground resolution (15 to 30 m at low contrast) are of the same order as those of the two Shuttle missions, so that the planimetric accuracies and the completeness of the detail that can be extracted from the images should be similar. However, the focal length ($f = 46$ cm) and format size (12.5 × 12.5 cm) of the S-190B camera are quite different so that the resulting base:height ratio (0.1) will be poorer, thus affecting the accuracy with which spot heights and contours may be measured.

6.2.6 Experimental mapping from S-190B (ETC) photography

A large number of tests have been carried out on the S-190B photography at the Universities of Glasgow, Scotland, and Georgia, USA, using test areas located in Illinois, USA, and Belleville, Canada. One test covering the Urbana area in Illinois was concerned with *plan or positional accuracy* (in *x* and *y*). A network of ground control points was established from large-scale maps using well-defined points such as road intersections. The same points were then measured on the photographic image using a high precision stereo-measuring instrument. The measured coordinates were transformed into their terrain values and compared with their known positional values. This showed that the overall planimetric errors are of the order of ± 20 to 25 m, equivalent to ± 20 μm at the image scale. A second test involved the *completeness of detail* that could be extracted from the S-190B images (Welch, 1982). Both 1:50 000 and 1:250 000 scale map sheets were available for the Belleville test area. The latter depicted two-lane and four-lane main roads, railway lines, power lines, airfields, main woodlands, urban areas, and water features such as lakes and main rivers. These basic categories were also present on the former (1:50 000 scale) map but were supplemented by considerable additional detail such as smaller streams and woodlands and specific cultural features such as golf courses and hospitals. Plots of all the required features were then made from the S-190B photography and also from Landsat RBV and digitally enhanced false-colour composite MSS images of the same area and compared with the existing 1:50 000 scale maps. The results are shown as comparative plots (Figure 6.20). The superiority of the S-190B (ETC) images over the Landsat images for topographic mapping is clearly shown.

In addition, all the plots from these images were digitized as were all the details present on the two existing maps. The amounts of detail that could be

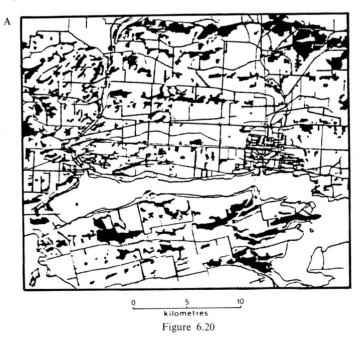

0   5   10
kilometres

Figure 6.20

B

```
0        5        10
    kilometres
```

C

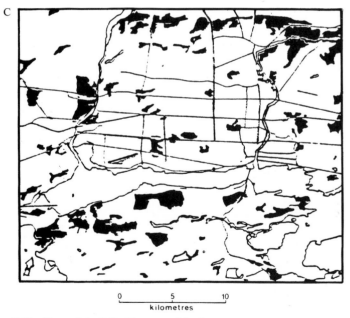

```
0        5        10
    kilometres
```

Figure 6.20   Maps of the Belleville area (originally at 1:100 000 scale) prepared from
A.   S-190B ETC photograph;
B.   Landsat-3 RBV image; and
C.   Digitally enhanced Landsat 3 MSS image.

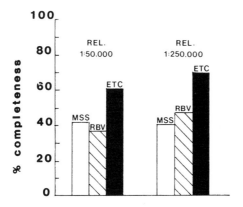

Figure 6.21   Completeness relative to 1:50 000 and 1:250 000 scale topographic maps

plotted from each type of image were then compared and ratioed as a percentage of the data present on the two map sheets. The results are given in Figure 6.21. Relative to the 1:50 000 *scale map*, the MSS and RBV image data provided only some 40% of the detail required by the map specification, whereas the S-190B (ETC) images yielded over 60%. Improved percentage completeness figures were obtained when comparisons were made with the 1:250 000 *scale map*, to nearly 50% with the RBV image and to 70% with the S-190B (ETC) image. The features which were missed with the S-190B images included the smaller woodlands and streams and many specific cultural features though the highways, railways, airfields and the limits of the urban areas were well defined. With the RBV images, the main highways and the urban areas were well mapped but railways and vegetated areas were often omitted and streams were usually missing. The digitally enhanced false-colour MSS image gave good results with urban areas (bright green) and forest lands (bright red) where the spectral component helped to offset the poor spatial resolution. But many roads, railways and settlements were missing.

6.2.7 *Topographic mapping from the space shuttle photography*

With regard to *planimetric accuracy* of the plotted detail, on the basis of the S-190B tests, this should be quite adequate for mapping within the range of scales 1:50 000 to 1:250 000. As far as the *map content* is concerned, since the scale and resolution are directly comparable, the results of the S-190B tests given above should again offer a good idea as to the type of feature and the completeness of detail likely to be discerned and mapped from the Shuttle photography. The possible difficulties over the omissions of numerous small but important cultural features will be apparent. Also the sheer effort required to detect, interpret and plot features from this very small-scale, high resolution space photography is very much greater than that experienced with the normal small-scale (1:50 000 to 1:80 000 scale) aerial photography used for plotting topographic maps at 1:50 000 and 1:100 000 scales. All of these various difficulties suggest that *orthophotographs* may well be the most suitable form of output from this type of high-resolution space photography (Doyle, 1971). All the planimetric detail would be retained, the effort of plotting would largely be eliminated and the interpretation would be shifted substantially on to the backs of the users! However some prior experimentation combining such photo-images with lines, symbols and names is a requirement before such a suggestion is implemented. The placing of these in such a way that they do not obscure photographic detail is a most difficult problem to solve and needs much cartographic skill and judgement.

Turning next to a discussion of the possible *height and contour* values obtainable from the Shuttle photography, one notes that the geometrical characteristics of the NASA-LFC camera are very much more favourable for height determination than that of the S-190B photography. However, non-military users have as yet had no experience of using this photography or of testing it. The figures attainable with the ESA-RMK normal-angle photography would normally not be expected to be quite as good as those from the LFC wide-angle photography. However, information on the accuracy achievable with the Zeiss photography is readily available; Stark (1976) gives the *spot height accuracy* obtained in testing RMK 30/23 photography over the Reidt test-field in West Germany with high precision equipment as $\pm 0.069‰\ H$, i.e. 1/14 000 of the flying height for the Zeiss Planimat stereo-plotting machine and $\pm 0.054‰\ H$ (1/18 500 of the flying height) using the Zeiss PSK-2 stereocomparator. Applying these figures to the alternative Shuttle orbital altitudes of (i) $H = 300\,\text{km}$ and (ii) $H = 250\,\text{km}$, Table 6.4 is obtained (Petrie, 1979).

How one should go on from spot height figures obtained in special tests using specially targeted and signalized points to making an estimate for the *detailed contouring of the terrain* is a matter of opinion. Optimists will select a low multiplying factor; pessimists will adopt a larger one. A realistic one will lie somewhere between. Selecting a factor of 4 to 5×, then this indicates possible contour intervals of between 50 to 100 metres. Unfortunately this is not particularly useful to very small-scale topographic mapping except in areas of high mountainous terrain.

Table 6.4

Measurement accuracy (m_h)	Spot height accuracy (m)	
1/14 000	(i) 21	(ii) 18
1/18 500	(i) 16	(ii) 13

6.2.8   *Future possibilities for mapping from space photography*

Looking beyond the Space Shuttle photography, if the scale and ground resolution of the photographic images produced by the ESA-RMK and NASA-LFC prove to be inadequate for topographic mapping at small scales, then the solution is to use longer focal length lenses to increase the scale and resolution from orbital altitudes—albeit at the cost of a reduction in the area covered by a single exposure. As the diagram (Figure 6.22) shows, photographic scales in the range 1:1 000 000 to 1:300 000 with ground resolutions in the range 10 m down to 3 m are possible if ultra-high resolution (100 lp/mm) camera/film combinations were to be deployed at low orbital altitudes.

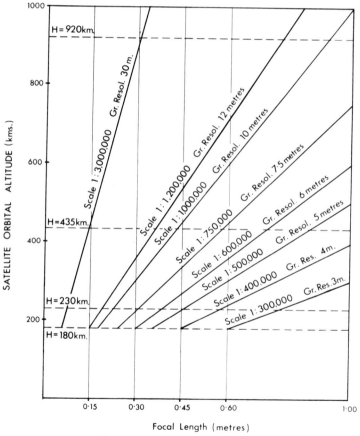

Focal Length (metres)

SCALE AND GROUND RESOLUTION FOR
TYPICAL RECONAISSANCE CAMERA
(RESOLVING 100 LINES/M.M.)

Figure 6.22.

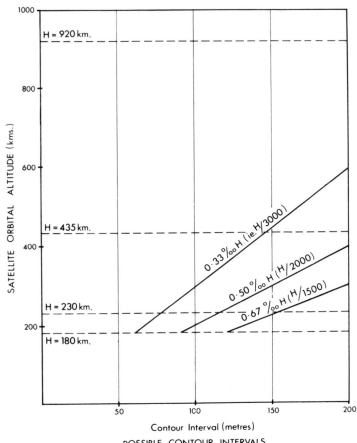

Contour Interval (metres)

POSSIBLE CONTOUR INTERVALS
FROM ORBITAL ALTITUDES

Figure 6.23.

It is however more difficult to envisage *heights and contours* being measured from space. Taking first-class contouring carried out on high accuracy stereo-plotting machines, the smallest possible contour interval is usually assessed in current photogrammetric practice as being $1:2\,000$ of the flying height ($H/2\,000$) which leads to intervals of $100\,m$ from low orbital altitudes. Even if the measuring accuracy could be improved to $1:3\,000$ of the flying height ($H/3\,000$), this still points to 60 to 80 m as the minimum possible contour interval (Figure 6.23).

6.2.9   Mapping from Landsat RBV imagery

Since the Landsat **RBV** cameras are from the geometrical point of view almost identical to a photographic camera, they may be dealt with here. It will be

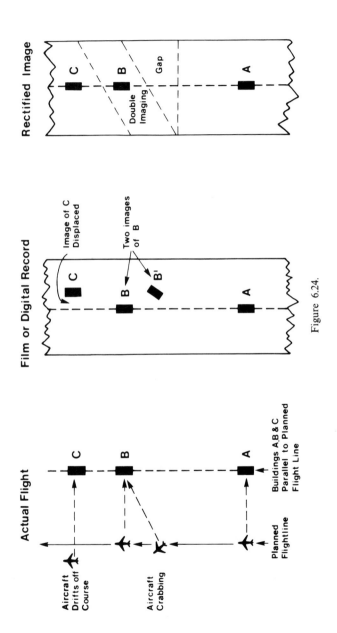

Figure 6.24.

apparent that the mapping that can be carried out from Landsat RBV imagery will be purely of the *plan detail* —the extreme orbital altitude and the narrow-angled coverage precluding any possibility of making useful stereoscopic measurements of heights and contours. As can be seen from Plate 8, the imagery produced from the RBV cameras operated from Landsat-3 has a smaller pixel size (30 to 40 m) and better spatial resolution than that produced by the Landsat MSS. Indeed it is only a little poorer than that of the Thematic Mapper (TM) newly operational on Landsats 4 and 5, with a pixel size of 30 m. However, these figures are considerably worse than the 15 m resolution achieved with the images from the S-190B ETC camera.

The results of topographic mapping achieved with Landsat 3 RBV imagery have been outlined above. A further test comparing the potential of RBV and MSS images for mapping in developing countries will be discussed later.

6.3   Topographic mapping from scanner images

As with photographic cameras, so *optical-mechanical scanners* may be mounted either in aircraft or satellites. However, while basically there are no differences in the photogrammetric techniques used for topographic mapping from airborne or spaceborne cameras, the situation regarding mapping from airborne or spaceborne scanners is quite different.

Scanner imagery is formed by a line scanning system in which the individual point images along a single line are recorded sequentially while the forward motion of the platform allows the exposure of successive lines to build up a single strip image of the terrain. As discussed in the introductory chapters, the resulting geometrical characteristics include scale compression towards the edges of the image and the relief displacement always being perpendicular to the flight line. However, with *airborne scanner imagery*, important additional characteristics are the scale variations due to aircraft velocity and altitude changes and the effects of aircraft motion (pitch, roll, yaw and drift). The latter are particularly difficult to deal with since they result in gaps and double imaging being present even if rectification of the scale compression, and other corrections have been carried out (Figure 6.24).

With *satellite-borne scanners* these difficulties are usually quite minor since the satellite is orbiting in the near-vacuum of space and is not subjected to the arbitrary and unpredictable aircraft motions caused by atmospheric turbulence. Therefore the scanner can be operated in a much more stable manner in space. Since almost all spacecraft carrying scanners operate from very high orbital altitudes (920 km in the case of Landsat), the resulting imagery also exhibits little or no relief displacement, which again serves to lessen the geometrical problems. Thus in practice, after digital processing to rectify the basic geometry, satellite scanner imagery is normally treated as corresponding closely to a map in geometrical terms. Therefore, in practice, maps made from satellite scanner images are normally compiled by direct tracing to produce line maps or by photographic enlargement to produce photomaps. ⊭

Although in principle it is possible to take overlapping scanner images with a view to achieving *stereoscopic coverage* and the measurement of heights and contours, in practice, the various difficulties outlined above preclude this possibility, so the mapping that can be carried out from scanner imagery is normally purely planimetric in nature. However, these statements will need qualification in future when satellite images begin to appear from *pushbroom scanners* such as MOMS and SPOT. Scanners of this type equipped with linear arrays allow the simultaneous exposure of points along a line and so have a different geometry to that of a conventional optical-mechanical scanner equipped with a scanning mirror or lens such as the Daedalus airborne scanner or the Landsat MSS satellite scanner. Furthermore, the SPOT scanner is designed specifically to acquire overlapping stereoscopic coverage.

6.3.1 *Mapping from aerial scanner imagery*

As will be apparent from the discussion above, topographic mapping of an original nature has not been attempted using aircraft scanner imagery. Most mapping that is carried out from this type of image involves the transfer of thematic information from the image to an existing topographic sheet. The use of an optical transfer device such as the Zoom Transfer Scope (ZTS) to fit the image to the detail on the topographic map piece-by-piece is quite typical.

6.3.2 *Topographic mapping from satellite scanner imagery*

Since *Landsat MSS images* form the bulk of the space imagery which is available to engineers and to the topographic mapping community, inevitably it must be considered in some detail. The work carried out on Landsat imagery to date falls into two main categories—accuracy, testing and actual mapping.

6.3.2.1. *Accuracy tests.* These tests are of course concerned almost exclusively with *planimetric accuracy*. A great variety of approaches have been tried. Different mathematical models have been adopted—e.g. interpolation methods using polynomials of different types or piece-wise polynomials or splines; parametric methods solving for orientation elements, etc.—a comprehensive survey is given by Konecny (1976).

Generally the approach to testing has been to select and measure a test field of control and check points from large-scale topographic maps, then to measure the corresponding image coordinates on the Landsat MSS imagery and to transform and fit these to the control points, so deriving the unknown coefficients in the polynomial equations. These coefficients are then used to transform the image coordinates of the check points into terrain coordinates which are compared with their known values. Root mean square error values for planimetry are then calculated.

Table 6.5

Type of transform	Imagery used	No. of points	Root Mean Square Errors (m)			Source
			m_x	m_y	m_{p1}	
Uncorrected	Bulk	181	215	195	290	Wong (1975)
Linear	”	181	94	67	115	” ”
Affine	”	64	74	67	100	” ”
”	”	64	—	—	70	Trinder (1975)
12 term polynomial	”	64	—	—	66	” ”
16 ” ”	”	?	42	39	57	Forrest (1975)
20 ” ”	”	181	37	44	57	Wong (1975)
21 ” ”	CCT	?	36	46	58	Forrest (1979)
Parametric	Bulk	—	—	—	61	Trinder (1979)
”	CCT	—	57	54	79	Forrest (1979)
”	”	16 (14)	—	—	53	Bernstein (1976)

A summary of some of the main tests for the accuracy of such procedures on Landsat MSS imagery is given in Table 6.5.

The results are satisfactory in most cases and almost startlingly good with the more sophisticated and elaborate models. However, one must be clear that these are purely numerical methods producing coordinates of a limited number of hopefully well-identified points. No map results from these operations. But still they show that the mathematical models and procedures exist to reduce the geometrical errors in the MSS imagery of Landsat 1, 2 and 3, down to the sub-pixel level. If they can be applied to control the operation of a suitable computer-controlled output device such as a film writer or laser-beam recorder, then precision processing is assured.

6.3.2.2. Mapping and interpretation. Topographic mapping, whether using conventional aerial photography or other types of imagery, still relies almost entirely on purely *visual interpretation* of film transparencies, paper prints, and other photographic media to detect, interpret and identify topographic detail. In the case of Landsat MSS images, often these will have been produced from digitally enhanced images such as the EDIES images available from the EROS Data Center. These incorporate geometric and radiometric corrections and contrast and edge enhancements. Undoubtedly these improve the general image quality required for topographic mapping. Unfortunately, however, digitally-based *image analysis techniques* such as density slicing, ratioing, texture analysis and the many land cover classification procedures have not as yet been found useful for topographic mapping. Whereas many other scientists and engineers are concerned with the classfication of land areas where these techniques may be useful, to a large extent topographic mapping is concerned with the detection, identification and mapping of boundaries, different types of communications, settlements and other man-made structures and much fine cultural detail. So far, digital image classification techniques have not offered much assistance with the mapping of such features.

Even with visual methods, the biggest single difficulty with producing topographic maps from Landsat MSS imagery is the fact that the *spatial resolution* is much too poor to allow the detection and interpretation of most of the point and line features required for even the smallest-scale topographic map. Although the MSS pixel size is 79 m and high-contrast linear images such as canals and motorways can be detected with widths considerably less than this, the ground resolution for low-contrast images is often of the order of 250 m (Welch, 1973). As Doyle (1975, 1976) mentions, this resolution is quite inadequate even for 1:250 000 scale topographic mapping except where terrain morphology is the prime cartographic feature and cultural features are absent.

The amount and type of detail which can be interpreted and mapped from Landsat MSS imagery will of course depend greatly on atmospheric conditions and season but it will also vary enormously with the type of landscape being mapped and the pattern of development present in the area. Leatherdale (1978) of Hunting Surveys, reporting on his experience with several mapping projects carried out mainly in *Africa and the Middle East* mentions that

> coast lines, mud flats, lakes, reservoirs, very large canals and swamps are the features which can be interpreted most consistently from the infra-red bands anywhere in the world. In mountainous and broken country, Landsat gives a good visual impression of relief which can be used as a photomap. The interpretation of drainage is very variable and, except in obvious cases, it is not easy to define the watershed between drainage basins correctly. Since rivers less than about 40 metres wide are generally not visible, drainage has to be inferred from the relief pattern or associated vegetation which is difficult or impossible in areas of low relief, uniform vegetation or complex land use. However, the simple agricultural land use, vegetation and geomorphological classifications normally shown on topographic maps—such as forest, moorland, rough pasture, rock or sand desert and cultivated areas—can in general be defined adequately.... It is the *man-made infrastructure*—settlements, communications, bridges, dams, administrative and recreational facilities, land marks and historical monuments—which the user is most likely to want to be complete and up-to-date. These are the most difficult features to detect from Landsat or any other imagery. Even on enhanced Landsat imagery, remarkably few settlements and communications can be identified direct and even when their locations are known from other sources the success rate is disappointing. Only very wide highways, railways and canals with very pronounced contrast to the surrounding land can be detected on Landsat. Desert towns built of local materials are perfectly camouflaged except where ringed by cultivation.

Trinder and Nasca (1976) appear to have had more success in detecting *new* roads, railways, pipelines, etc. on Landsat MSS imagery in *Australia* and see it as making a useful contribution to the revision of the nation-wide

1:250 000 topographic series recently compiled from aerial photography. *Canada* is similarly a country of huge areal extent which has also completed its 1:250 000 scale topographic series. Again, Fleming (1976) quotes examples of new mostly linear features—wilderness roads, transmission lines—being detected from Landsat imagery. The two latter features were shown up by the cleared swath which much exceeded the narrow width of the features themselves and formed a distinct contrast to the surrounding background image.

Apart from such examples of the revision of existing sheets, there are only one or two really satisfactory and successful examples of topographic mapping of an original nature from Landsat MSS imagery. A notable example is the set of 1:250 000 scale reconnaissance maps produced by the Directorate of Overseas Surveys (DOS) for part of *Antarctica* (Swithenbank and Lane, 1975; Read and Lane, 1976). 99% of the surface detail in the areas mapped comprised snow and ice features which are revealed by a variety of grey-scale distinctions, the remaining detail including coast lines, mountain ranges and nunataks. The maps have therefore been produced both as a half-tone reproduction of Band 7 MSS imagery with added graticule, symbols, spot heights and place-names and as an interpreted line map. The reaction of the users (glaciologists, geologists, aircraft pilots and navigators) has been favourable.

A second major series covers the whole of *Libya* (2 000 000 km^2) comprising 127 sheets at 1:250 000 scale, each sheet covering 1° latitude by 1.5° longitude. These photomaps have been produced by the Earthsat Corporation in the United States from 100 digitally produced and enhanced Landsat MSS colour images. Given the huge sparsely populated areas of the country and the almost total lack of topographic map coverage, this photomap series has been well received by those Libyan government agencies responsible for regional resource planning and development.

6.3.3 *Topographic and land use mapping from Landsat imagery for developing countries*

In view of these very varied experiences of topographic mapping from Landsat MSS images, a number of tests have been carried out at the University of Glasgow in collaboration with the Sudan Survey Department to evaluate the feasibility of producing a series of topographic maps at 1:250 000 for the *Sudan*. Reports of prior mapping work, primarily of a thematic character, were encouraging (e.g. Mott and Chismon, 1975; Mitchell, 1975). Also the country desperately needs such a series. The existing maps at that scale were compiled many years ago largely from rapid route and sketch surveys, supplemented by compilation from World War II tri-metrogon aerial photography, and are now badly out of date. Thus there was and is a situation of real need in this developing country with its huge areal extent and comparatively limited

Table 6.6 (i) Summary of detectability and interpretability of topographic details on Landsat imagery of Sudan, Khartoum area

Element mapped on 1:250,000 scale maps	Landsat 2 MSS		Landsat 3 RBV	
	Detected on imagery	Identified on imagery	Detected on imagery	Identified on imagery
1: *Lines of Communication:*				
Hard surfaced roads	Sometimes	Not	✓	✓
Unsurfaced roads	Not	Not	Not	Not
Tracks	Not	Not	Not	Not
Footpaths	Not	Not	Not	Not
Streets	Not	Not	✓	Not
Bridge location	Not	Not	Not	Not
Ferry location	Not	Not	Not	Not
Railroads	Sometimes	Not	Depends on	surroundings
Railroad stations	Not	Not	Not	Not
2: *Culture:*				
Cultivated land	✓	✓	✓	✓
Big cities	✓	Not	✓	✓
Towns	Not	Not	✓	Not
Villages	Not	Not	Not	Not
Ruins	Not	Not	Not	Not
Towers	Not	Not	Not	Not·
Lighthouses	Not	Not	Not	Not
Electrical substations	Not	Not	Not	Not
Pipelines	Not	Not	Not	Not
Powerlines	Not	Not	Not	Not
Wells	Not	Not	Not	Not
Storage tanks	Not	Not	Not	Not
Cemeteries	Not	Not	big ones only	Not
Quarries	Not	Not	Not	Not
Airports	✓	✓	✓	✓
Landing ground	Not	Not	Not	Not
3: *Hydrology:*				
Rivers	✓	✓	✓	✓
Falls	✓	Not	✓	Not
Food plains	✓	✓	✓	✓
Canals	✓	✓	✓	✓
Irrigation channels	Not	Not	Not	Not
Water bodies	✓	Not	✓	Not
Dams	✓	✓	✓	✓
Reservoirs	✓	Not	Not	Not
4: *Hydrography:*				
Tidal flats	Require repeated coverage			
Reefs	Require repeated coverage			
Rocks	✓	Not	Not	Not
Near shore bathymetry	Not	Not	Not	Not
Water depth	Not	Not	✓	✓
Marsh	✓	✓	✓	✓

Table 6.6   (*Contd.*)

Element mapped on 1:250,000 scale maps	Landsat 2 MSS		Landsat 3 RBV	
	Detected on imagery	Identified on imagery	Detected on imagery	Identified on imagery
Harbours	√	√	√	√
Small harbours (marsas)	√	Not	√	√
Shore line delineation	√	√	√	√
Islands	√	√	√	√
5: *Relief and Surficial Material*				
Sand dunes	√	Sometimes	√	Sometimes
Gravel beds	Not	Not	Not	Not
Elevated ground	√	√	√	√
Escarpments	Not	Not	Not	Not
Contours	Not	Not	Not	Not
6: *Vegetation:*				
Woodland	√	Not	√	Not
Scattered trees	Not	Not	Not	Not
Scrub	Not	Not	Not	Not
Orchards	√	Not	√	Not
7: *Other Information*				
International boundary	Not	Not	Not	Not
Provincial boundary	Not	Not	Not	Not
Council boundary	Not	Not	Not	Not
Rest houses	Not	Not	Not	Not
Chiefs' court	Not	Not	Not	Not
Tribal homes	Not	Not	Not	Not
Triangulation pillars	Not	Not	Not	Not

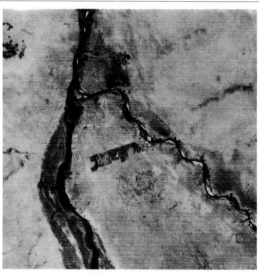

Landsat MSS Band 5

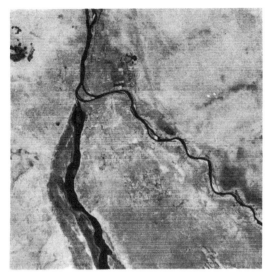

Landsat MSS Band 6

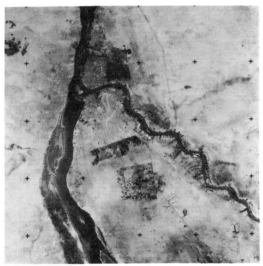

Landsat RBV

resources for mapping. Suitable test areas existed both in the Red Sea Province and around Khartoum where 1:100 000 scale sheets have recently been produced by the Directorate of Overseas Surveys (DOS) and the Sudan Survey Department. A check list of all the features contained in the specification for the 1:250 000 scale series was compiled and attempts were made to detect these. The results over the area of three Landsat MSS frames were varied. On the one hand, there was, even when reduced scale film positives of the new 1:100 000 scale maps were overlaid on images, an almost complete failure to find the point and line features (e.g. roads, railways, towns, villages, and the many smaller but important features—water tanks, bridges) which form the most important planimetric detail in the area. On the other hand, a generalized pattern of the relief and many of the drainage features could be discerned, as could the chequerboard land use pattern of large irrigation projects such as the Gezira scheme.

The summary tables (Table 6.6) showing the *detectability and interpretability* of the topographic details required by the standard specification for the 1:250 000 scale topographic map series of the Sudan are given below for both Landsat MSS and Landsat RBV imagery.

The difficulties in mapping the lines of communication and the cultural features are immediately obvious. Other shortcomings such as the lack of completeness of certain hydrological vegetation and relief features are also apparent.

Further tests of Landsat MSS and RBV images for land use mapping have also been carried out at the University of Georgia (Welch and Pannell, 1982) for three test areas in *China*, two of them covering the cities of Peking and Tientsin, the third covering a large intensively farmed agricultural area at the confluence of the Huang Ho and Wei rivers. Each area had been covered by recently produced 1:250 000 scale topographic maps. Supplementary 1:25 000 and 1:50 000 scale sheets were also available for the two city areas. The degree of completeness of the mapping carried out from black-and-white images of Bands 5 and 7 of the Landsat MSS coverage and from the Landsat-3 RBV imagery is given in Figure 6.25 which shows the percentage completeness for each individual land use class.

Figure 6.26 gives a comparison of the completeness scores as interpreted from black-and-white film transparencies of MSS Bands 5 and 7 and RBV images and from digital MSS data displayed as a false colour composite on a colour CRT terminal. Mapping from a hard copy transparency of the colour CRT images produced a 10% higher score than those from the MSS black-and-white images. Finally, Figure 6.27 shows the overall completeness scores

PERCENT COMPLETENESS BY LAND USE CLASS

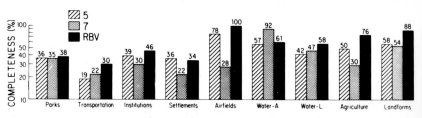

Figure 6.25.

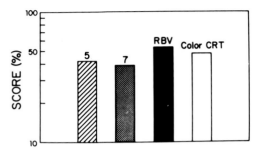

Figure 6.26   Comparative PI scores.

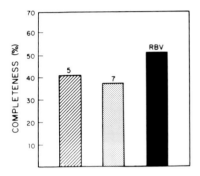

Figure 6.27   Completeness of detail from Landsat images as percentage of features on 1:250 000 maps.

of 41, 37 and 51 per cent respectively for the MSS Bands 5 and 7 and the RBV images based on the percentage of features present on the 1:250 000 scale maps of the study areas.

These findings confirm the view that the spatial resolution of Landsat MSS and RBV image data is inadequate for the compilation of 1:250 000 scale land use and topographic maps to acceptable standards of completeness.

6.3.4 The topographic mapping potential of forthcoming satellite scanners

In view of the current deficiencies of satellite scanners for topographic mapping, largely centered around their lack of spatial resolution, the most important development over the next few years will be the deployment of sensors of much improved resolution and geometrical arrangement which will allow a much more thorough assessment of the potential of space scanner imagery for topographic mapping. On the recently launched Landsats 4 and 5, there is of course a much improved optical-mechanical scanner in the shape of the *Thematic Mapper* (TM). With this device the number of spectral bands have been raised to seven, mostly in the infrared part of the spectrum, and the pixel size is 30m. Because of the very large increase in the data resulting from the increased number of channels and the smaller pixel size, the data processing is more complex, more time-consuming and more costly. This has meant that very little TM imagery has reached the users so far and to date no results of tests of its suitability for topographic mapping have been published. The improved resolution resulting from the decrease in pixel size to 30 m must lead to an increase in the detectability and interpretability of objects. However, even with this improvement, it is obvious that it will certainly not place the TM image data in the class of the various types of photographic imagery available from the S-190B and Space Shuttle cameras.

Instead the attention of the topographic mapping community in respect of satellite-borne scanners is centred on the development of *linear arrays* of silicon diodes (also called Charge Coupled Devices, or CCDs). These simultaneously image a complete line on the terrain instead of sweeping it out sequentially as with the familiar MSS device. The arrays have no moving parts, hence they are more likely to be reliable. Also they will be lighter in weight, have a better geometric fidelity, and consume less power. The technology is reasonably mature, having originally been developed for use in military reconnaissance aircraft. The ground coverage is produced in the usual manner by the forward motion of the scanner platform, the overall mode of operation being known as the '*pushbroom*' *mode* (as discussed in section 3.2.3.3 — see p. 52). The basic technology has mostly been developed in the United States, from which the initial proposals for mapping satellites (Stereosat, Mapsat, and others) using this technology have also originated. However, these have not been funded by NASA so attention is currently focused on the *German MOMS* device and on the *French SPOT* project.

The two-channel MOMS scanner discussed in Chapter 3 has been orbited with spectacular success on the SPAS pallet deployed from a Shuttle flight in the autumn of 1983 with the comparatively high spatial resolution of 20 m pixel from the Shuttle orbital height of 300 km. The possibilities of mapping from this imagery are currently being investigated by Professor Bodechtel at the University of Munich. While this prototype MOMS scanner gives a conventional monoscopic linescan image, proposals exist for a Stereo-MOMS (Figure 6.28) with three sets of linear arrays, one pointing vertically down-wards, the second forwards and the third backwards as originally proposed for the Stereosat and Mapsat projects (Figure 6.29). If implemented, Stereo-MOMS will allow high-resolution stereo-scanner imagery to be obtained with an excellent base:height ratio (1.0) from satellite altitudes. This would give possibilities for measuring heights and contours for small-scale topographic mapping which are akin to and may even exceed those attainable with a conventional photographic camera orbited in space.

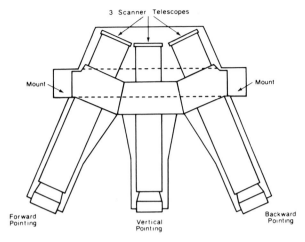

Figure 6.28   Stereo MOMS scanner.

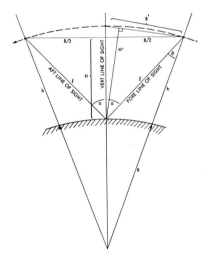

Figure 6.29   Geometry of stereo scanner imagery.

The SPOT satellite also discussed in Chapter 3 has been designed specifically for mapping applications. It can be operated in a purely vertical direction and also provides the possibility of using pointable mirrors to point to areas off the ground track of the satellite. This feature of pointable mirrors leads to the exciting possibility for mapping of acquiring overlapping across-track coverage (weather permitting) to give *lateral stereopairs* with

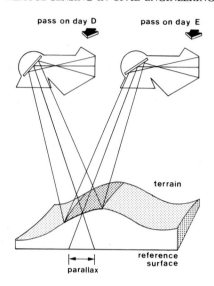

pass on day D   pass on day E

terrain

reference
surface

parallax

Figure 6.30   The arrangement of overlapping images to provide lateral stereoscopy and a good base: height ratio for parallax measurements for height determination.

base:height ratios of 1.0 for maximum opposite tilts of $\pm\, 27°$ (Figure 6.30). The processing of the SPOT image data will be carried out by CRIS (Centre for Rectification of Images from Space) jointly controlled by CNES, the French Space Agency, and IGN, the French national topographic mapping agency. Ducher (1980) of the IGN envisages two main applications:—

(i) In well-mapped countries, where existing topographic map coverage is good and digital terrain models (DTM) are already available, or can easily be generated, the main emphasis will be on the *revision of small-scale maps* (at scales of 1:100 000 for example) to speed up the frequency of such revisions and keep the maps up to date.

(ii) In unmapped or poorly mapped areas, the SPOT imagery will be used to generate original *line maps and orthophotographs* at 1:200 000 and 1:100 000 scales—and even, Ducher suggests tentatively, at 1:50 000 scale. In view of the results achieved in the tests with S-190B photographic imagery over the Belleville area, this will of course be difficult to achieve.

In view of the excellent base:height ratio (1.0) of the lateral stereopairs an increase in *heighting accuracy* should be possible leading again (Ducher suggests) to a possible minimum contour interval of 40 m. Undoubtedly operational and practical difficulties will arise, but nevertheless SPOT is by far the most promising project for topographic mapping applications using scanners since its spatial resolution and geometry are more compatible with mapping specifications and requirements.

6.4. Topographic mapping from side-looking radar images

The main application of side-looking radar (SLR) to mapping has been to those poorly mapped areas of the world where it has been very difficult to acquire images using optical sensors such as cameras and scanners. In particular, it has been applied extensively for small-scale reconnaissance-type mapping in the tropical equatorial areas of the world which are continuously covered by cloud.

Both real-aperture and synthetic-aperture radars have been used for the purpose. The *real-aperture type* is simpler and less expensive and the image can be recorded directly on film on board the aircraft. This offers immediate post-flight development and printing of the images to check that there is no loss of image due to rain or system malfunctioning. Also this means that the images are immediately available to the users. Real-aperture radar is limited to short-range, low altitude operation if a resolution is to be achieved which is useful for mapping. Thus it is only practical to use a real-aperture SLR from an aircraft. Again because of the resolution requirements, the use of short (millimetre) wavelength is normal with real-aperture radars.

By contrast, *synthetic-aperture radars* (SAR) are much more complex and correspondingly more expensive. Furthermore, an image is only produced after subsequent processing of the recorded data which, for non-military missions, is usually carried out on the ground. This delays the production of the image for the users and raises the costs still higher. But synthetic-aperture radars do offer improved resolution at much longer ranges than are possible with real-aperture radars and so they have been operated both from aircraft and from satellites. They are commonly operated at longer (centimetre) wavelengths where backscatter from rain is less of a problem, so that long-range all-weather operation is facilitated.

The *post-flight processing of synthetic-aperture image* data is a major consideration for mapping. Coherent *optical processing* is most usual, the processor exploiting the analogy between the microwave hologram recorded on the image data film and its optical equivalent. Only a few of these complex and expensive optical processors exist in non-military establishments and almost all are located in North America, mainly in research establishments such as ERIM, CCRS and JPL, though commercially operated optical processing is carried out also by Goodyear. *Digital processing* is important when the SLR image data cannot be recorded on film and recovered for processing, as is the case with satellite-borne radars. The time and cost required for such digital processing is enormous and it is confined to a few laboratories such as those at RAE Farnborough, DFVLR (West Germany) and JPL (USA). Results of the two techniques are shown in Figure 3.30.

The mapping products from SLR imagery are almost invariably photo-maps with varying degrees of annotation to show thematic information, names, and other detail. *Radar mosaics* are common, especially in developing countries (Leberl, Jensen and Kaplan 1976). Many are uncontrolled or semi-controlled mosaics with a poor correlation to their true position in terms of geographical or grid coordinates. Numerical radargrammetric block adjustment methods have been successfully devised by Leberl (1975) to overcome this difficulty but so far these have not been used extensively. In the UK and other well-mapped countries, ground control points are available from existing maps so that the relationship of the radar image to the National Grid can be established accurately.

6.4.1   *Mapping from side-looking airborne radar*

The mapping carried out using side-looking airborne radar (SLAR) has been very extensive, individual projects often covering large parts of a single country. The coverage of the Darien Province of Panama (Crandall, 1969) and of parts of Indonesia and the whole of Nicaragua were early examples using *real aperture radar*. More recently, the American Motorola organization (which manufactures X-band real-aperture radars) has produced coverage of the whole of Nigeria ($967\,000\,\text{km}^2$), the $1:250\,000$ scale radar mosaics being based on the existing US Joint Operation Graphics (JOG) sheets. A vegetation and forest survey based on these mosaics has been carried out for the Nigerian Government by Hunting Technical Services, information from conventional aerial photography and Landsat MSS imagery also being incorporated in the final map product (Parry and Trevitt, 1979).

In the early 1970s, *synthetic-aperture radars* were finally released for non-military applications and since then have been used extensively for mapping purposes. In particular, a consortium of Goodyear (manufacturers of synthetic aperture radars) and the Aero Service Corporation have used the Goodyear GEMS-1000 equipment mounted in a jet aircraft equipped with an inertial navigation system to give extensive coverage of the Amazon Basin in South America. The areal coverage is astonishing—$4\,500\,000\,\text{km}^2$ of the Brazilian part of the Basin alone produced by Project RADAM (van Roessel and Godoy, 1974). In addition, large parts of the eastern part of Peru, and southern parts of Colombia (Leberl, 1974, 1975) and Venezuela falling within the Basin have been covered.

Recently, experimental flights using an airborne SAR set have been made over Western Europe using the Canadian *SAR-580 system*. Topographic mapping experiments have been included in the programme but the difficulties experienced in the processing of the data (acquired in 1981) have meant that the imagery has still not been made available to most participants and so far no results from the topographic mapping experiments have been published, though undoubtedly they will become available in due course.

From the discussion above, it can be seen that the type of topographic mapping carried out from SLR imagery is very small-scale and reconnaissance in type with a low spatial resolution. So far, large-scale mapping has not been attempted due to the present limitations in resolution. However, this does not in any way lessen its value to the countries concerned for which conventional mapping from optical sensors is quite impracticable. Thus one can see that, in general, it is the all-weather capability of side-looking radar (SLR) which is primarily being exploited, rather than the special responses of the SLR at microwavelengths. To a large extent the radar imagery is being used as a *map substitute*, acting as the small-scale topographic base for recording forest, vegetation, geological and other information needed for planning and development purposes. The techniques used for the rectification and mapping are often very simple or sometimes non-existent, but given the reconnaissance nature of the mapping, the lack of an alternative base and the urgency with which even these crude maps are needed, the results appear to meet the needs of the many users.

6.4.2 *Mapping from side-looking spaceborne radar*

By contrast to the well-established case of airborne radar, the use of spaceborne radars has been limited so far to two examples—those orbited in the Seasat satellite and the Space Shuttle (the Shuttle Imaging Radar-A or SIR-A), and discussed in section 3.3.1.3 (see p. 80). The Shuttle Imaging Radar will again be flown in a forthcoming flight of the Space Shuttle which will be termed the SIR-B project.

A number of experiments to assess the suitability of satellite SAR imagery to topographic mapping have been carried out at the University of Glasgow and elsewhere on both optically and digitally processed images.

6.4.2.1. Accuracy tests. Since the test images are non-stereoscopic in character, accuracy testing has been confined to planimetric accuracy only. Small areas in Fife (Scotland), East Anglia and Pembrokeshire were selected in which large-scale maps and accurate ground control points were available for the purposes of the testing. The tests showed that the *optically processed* Seasat images had a low geometric fidelity in the form they are delivered to users. The application of an affine transformation improved the results greatly, a correction which could in fact have been applied in the optical processor. The use of more complex mathematical transformations such as high order polynomials reduced the magnitude of the errors still further. The *digitally processed* images were of a superior geometric quality and the application of complex polynomial transformations improved the results only a little. In both cases, the effects of terrain relief on the accuracy of the final results was noticeable. The results showed planimetric errors of about ± 40 m on RAE digitally processed images.

6.4.2.2 Mapping and interpretation. The major difficulty in utilizing the Seasat satellite SAR imagery lies in the marked deficiencies in its *image quality*. Great difficulties were experienced in detecting and interpreting the features required for topographic mapping. With linear man-made features such as roads, railways, power lines, and so on the orientation of an individual feature with respect to the flight line is important, often decisive, in determining whether or not it will appear and, if so, will be recognized. Linear features running parallel or near-parallel to the satellite track often show up well. However, if such a feature bends away or is oriented in another direction, it will not appear in the image. All of this makes for marked inconsistencies in terms of whether or not a particular object will appear on the SAR image and thus on the resulting map. Other factors such as the reflectivity of particular features relative to their surroundings can often play a part in deciding whether or not an areal feature such as a lake or a forest will appear. Thus there is a certain arbitrariness as to the content of the SAR image and the resulting map which is not found in other types of imagery used for mapping.

A particular feature of the Seasat SAR imagery which causes great difficulty in interpretation is the *background clutter* present in all the images but especially the optically produced examples. While much reduced with the digitally processed examples, still the clutter is quite troublesome and one must hope for a distinct improvement in this respect is progress is to be made in mapping from satellite SAR images. If this can be achieved, then the matter of the orientation of the object with respect to the SAR system is likely to be the limiting factor in conducting mapping operations from radar imagery. This is a more fundamental matter for which there is no solution in sight at present.

6.5   Summary and conclusion

Topographic mapping has specific requirements regarding high spatial resolution and the geometrical arrangement of the imagery from which this type of mapping can be undertaken. In the area of large- and medium-scale mapping at scales from 1:500 to 1:50 000 or 1:100 000 the use of *aerial photographic imagery* in combination with stereo-plotting machines accounts for 99% of all topographic mapping. The use of airborne scanner and side-looking radar (SLR) imagery is mostly confined to thematic or special purpose mapping which can utilize the information contained in the special signatures or responses recorded on these images. This is usually carried out on the basis of existing topographic maps which act as the base upon which the data is mapped. However, airborne side-looking radar has found a very specific application in the very small-scale (< 1:200 000) topographic mapping of tropical equatorial forests for which its all-weather capability is the chief attribute. Huge areas have been covered in this way. Acceptable height accuracy cannot be achieved from current airborne scanner and SLR imagery which yield purely planimetric information. Thus the measurement of heights and contours is a monopoly of aerial photographic imagery.

As far as *spaceborne sensors* are concerned, the main use of Landsat MSS imagery in the field of topographic mapping has again been to very small-scale purely planimetric mapping, typically at 1:250 000 scale. However, tests show that such maps derived from Landsat images exhibit a low level of completeness of the detail to be mapped due principally to lack of spatial resolution. But even such poor maps as can be derived from Landsat imagery will be acceptable to users if the alternative is no map. Spaceborne radar imagery also exhibits several negative characteristics, especially the difficulties in interpretation arising from the strong background clutter and the arbitrariness of the content recorded on the image which is strongly related to the look angle of the SLR. In turn this leads to a major shortfall in the completeness of the details appearing in the map derived from such images. However, mapping from space imagery is about to enter a fresh phase with a series of new projects—especially the Space Shuttle cameras and the MOMS and SPOT scanners—which are designed specifically for small-scale topographic mapping and promise results of an accuracy and completeness which have not previously been available.

References and bibliography

1. *Topographic mapping from photographic images*

Derenyi, E. E. (1981) Skylab in retrospect. *Photogrammetric Engineering and Remote Sensing* 47(4) 495–499.

Doyle, F. J. (1971) 'The orthographic view from space', in *Proc. Int. Symposium on Orthophotographs and Orthophotomaps*, Paris.

Doyle, F. J. (1973) Can satellite mapping contribute to topographic mapping? *Journal Research, U.S.G.S.* 1 (3) 315–325.

Doyle, F. J. (1975) 'Cartographic applications of satellite imagery', in *Proc. Conf. Comm. Survey Officers*, Paper K1.

Doyle, F. J. (1976) 'Space photography'. Invited Paper, *Comm. I, I.S.P. Congress*, Helsinki.

Doyle, F. J. (1979) A large format camera for Shuttle. *Photogrammetric Engineering and Remote Sensing*, 45(1) 73–78.

Ducher, G. (1980) Cartographic possibilities of the SPOT and Spacelab projects. *Photogrammetric Record* 10(56) 167–180.

Keller, M. (1976) Analytical aerotriangulation utilising Skylab earth terrain camera (S-190B) photography. *Photogrammetric Engineering* 42 (11) 1375–1383.

Petrie, G. (1970) Some considerations regarding mapping from earth satellites. *Photogrammetric Record* 6(36) 590–624.

Petrie, G. (1974) 'Mapping from earth satellites'. Paper XI, *Proc. P.T.R.C. Symposium*, Warwick.

Petrie, G. (1979) The status of topographic mapping from space imagery. *Remote Sensing and National Mapping*, 1–16.

Stark, E. (1976) 'The effect of angular field on horizontal and vertical accuracy in photogrammetric plotting', in *Proc. 35th Photogrammetric Week*, Stuttgart.

Stewart, R. B. (1975) 'Mapping from satellite photography', in *Proc. Conf. Comm. Surv. Officers*, Paper K2.

Welch, R. (1976) Skylab S-190B ETC photo quality. *Photogrammetric Engineering* 42(8) 1057–1060.

Welch, R. (1982) 'Image quality requirements for mapping from satellite data', in *Proc. I.S.P.R.S. Comm. I International Symposium on Primary Data Acquisition, Australia*, pp. 50–54.

2. *Topographic mapping from scanner images*

Bernstein, R. (1976) Digital image processing of earth observation sensor data. *I.B.M.J. of Research and Development*, 20(1) 40–57.

Colvocoresses, A. P. (1974) 'Evaluation of the first Earth Resources Technology Satellite (ERTS-1) for Cartographic Application'. Presented Paper, *I.S.P. Comm. I Symposium*, Stockholm.

Colvocoresses, A. P. (1976) 'Status Report on Landsat as a Source of Cartographic Data'. Presented Paper, *Comm. IV, I.S.P. Congress*, Helsinki.

Doyle, F. J. (1975) 'Cartographic applications of satellite imagery', in *Proc. Conf. Comm. Survey Officers*, Paper K1.

Doyle, F. J. (1976) 'Space photography'. Invited paper, *Comm. I.I.S.P. Congress*, Helsinki.

Ducher, G. (1978) Le satellite français SPOT. *Bull. Soc. Française de Photogrammetrie* 67, 19–20.

Fleming, E. A. (1976) 'The use of satellite photography in the National Mapping Program of Canada'. Presented Paper, *Comm. II, I.S.P. Congress*, Helsinki.

Forrest, R. B. (1975) Geometric correction of ERTS-1 MSS images. *Proc. I.S.P. Comm. III Symposium*, Stuttgart, 340–357.

Hofmann, O. (1981) Digitale Aufnahmetechnik. *Bildmessung und Luftbildwesen* 50(1) 16–32.

Konecny, G. (1976) 'Mathematical models and procedures for the geometric restitution of remote sensing imagery'. Invited Paper, *Comm. III, I.S.P. Congress*, Helsinki.

Leatherdale, J. (1978) 'The practical contribution of space imagery to topographical mapping'. Presented Paper, *I.S.P. Comm. IV Symposium*, Ottawa.

Mitchell, C. W. (1975) The applications of Landsat 1 imagery to the Sudan Savannah Project. *J. British Interplan. Soc.* 28(9 & 10) 659–672.

Mott, P. G. and Chismon, H. J. (1975) The use of satellite imagery for very small scale mapping. *Photogrammetric Record*, 8(46) 458–475.

Read, D. and Lane, C. J. B. (1976) Two slanted views of Antarctica. *Photogrammetric Record* 8(48) 726–747.

Swithenbank, C. and Lane, C. J. B. (1975) 'Mapping the Antarctic from satellite imagery'. In *Proc. Conf. Comm. Surv. Officers*, Paper K3.

Trinder, J. C. and Nasca, S. U. (1976) Tests on the mapping application of Landsat imagery. *Unisurv. G 24*, (24) 47–70.

Welch, R. (1973) *Cartographic Evaluation of ERTS-1 Image Quality*. Final Report to U.S.G.S. under Contract No. 14-08-0001-13167.

Welch, R. and Pannell, C. W. (1982) Comparative resolution of Landsat 3 MSS and RBV image data of China. *Photogrammetric Record*, 10(59) 575–586.

Wong, K. W. (1975) Geometric and cartographic accuracy of ERTS-1 imagery. *Photogrammetric Engineering* 41(5) 621–635.

3. *Topographic mapping from side-looking radar images*

Crandall, C. J. (1969) Radar mapping in Panama. *Photogrammetric Engineering* 35(7) 641–646.

Derenyi, E. E. (1974) SLAR Geometric Test. *Photogrammetric Engineering* 40(5) 597–604.

Derenyi, E. E. (1975) 'Topographic accuracy of sidelooking radar imagery', in *Proc. I.S.P. Comm. III Symposium*, Stuttgart, 244–250.

Derenyi, E. E. and Szabo, L. (1980) 'Planimetric accuracy of synthetic aperture radar imagery', in *Proc. I.S.P. Congress, Comm. IV*, Hamburg, B3, 142–148.

Graham, L. C. (1975) 'Geometric problems in sidelooking radar imagery', in *Proc. I.S.P. Comm. III Symposium*, Stuttgart, 199–206.

Jensen, H. (1975) 'Deformations of SLAR imagery — results from actual surveys', in *Proc. I.S.P. Comm. III Symposium*, Stuttgart, 230–234.

Leberl, F. (1971) Metric properties of imagery produced by sidelooking airborne radar and infrared linescan systems. *I.T.C. Publications Series A* No. 50, 125–151.

Leberl, F. (1974) Evaluation of SLAR image quality and geometry for PRORADAM. *I.T.C. Journal*, 4, 158–546.

Leberl, F. (1975) 'Radargrammetric point determination PRORADAM', in *Proc. I.S.P. Comm. III Symposium, Stuttgart*, 207–215.

Leberl, F. (1975) Sequential and simultaneous SLAR block adjustment. *Photogrammetria* 31(2) 39–51.

Leberl, F. (1976) Imaging radar applications to mapping and charting. *Photogrammetria* 32(1) 75–100.

Leberl, F., Jensen, H. and Kaplan, J. (1976) Sidelooking radar mosaicing experiment. *Photogrammetric Engineering* 42(8) 1035–1042.

Leberl, F. (1980) Preliminary assessment of Seasat-A SAR images. *Mitteilungen der Geodätischen Institut der Technischen Universität in Graz.*

Lodge, D. W. S. (1981) 'The Seasat-1 SAR: introduction, data reception and processing', *Ersel Post-graduate Summer School on Remote Sensing Applications to Oceanography, Meteorology and Hydrology,* Univ. of Dundee.

Parry, D. E. and Trevett, J. W. (1979) Mapping Nigeria's vegetation from radar. *Geographical Journal* 145(2) 265–281.

Van Roessel, J. N. and de Godoy, R. C. (1974) SLAR mosaics for Project RADAM. *Photogrammetric Engineering* 40(6) 583–595.

Yuritomo, K. (1972) 'Methods and instruments for the restitution of radar pictures'. Invited Paper. *Comm. II, I.S.P. Congress, Ottawa.*

7 Interpretation of Landsat satellite imagery for regional planning studies

T. E. BEAUMONT

7.1 Introduction

In recent times the requirement for regional planning studies has grown significantly in order to help resolve the magnitude and complexity of problems which confront both developed and developing countries faced with expanding populations and finite resources. To achieve optimum benefits for society, one of the major planning objectives is to allow for controlled growth of population by matching land use with land capability, and by matching specific utilization to appropriate natural conditions, so as to provide adequate food and materials supplies within ordered infrastructure and economic development without significant damage to the environment. If such objectives are to be fulfilled, a wide cross-section of economic sectors has to be considered for most regional studies which in essence, attempt to integrate the physical or spatial dimensions of planning with the socio-economic.

The realization that successful economic and social advancement can often be attributed to effective, coordinated planning is furthering a growing awareness and appreciation within current engineering practice as engineers become increasingly involved with environmental issues and are called upon to participate more fully in all aspects of development studies required by overseas countries. Similarly, the interdependence between infrastructure and economic development has tended to result in a growing trend for the engineering component to take on a greater prominence within regional planning studies. A corresponding need for continuity of data collection, and in some instances for great rapidity of data collection and analysis, has also become more manifest in recent years with increased understanding of the impact that environmental factors have on the development process and on human welfare.

Consequently, as the engineer in the future is likely to become more involved in planning activities, a comprehensive understanding is essential of

162

the expanding potential for remote sensing technology to provide efficiently the vital prerequisite and relevant information on the physical properties of the terrain and the socio-economic activities it supports. Currently, the interpretation of Landsat satellite imagery provides one of the best remote sensing methods whereby preliminary information may be acquired for regional planning purposes. In this chapter it is the intention to review the engineering applications of Landsat satellite imagery in regional planning studies, the various interpretation techniques available to acquire information relevant to engineering investigations and the future developments which are likely to affect the beneficial use of satellite data in engineering studies. As the value of this source of regional planning information can only truly be evaluated through practical experience, a range of case studies has also been included to illustrate some of the varied uses of Landsat data which have been achieved on recently completed projects.

7.2 Landsat data and regional development planning

In most undeveloped regions the primary base for economic development lies in exploitation of the available natural resources. A lack of comprehensive knowledge about the nature, quantity and location of these resources is frequently the main factor which prevents them being harnessed effectively for development purposes. Similarly, in many countries available information on landforms, geology, soils, hydrology and other features related to agricultural and engineering studies is limited, dispersed, and on the whole less than adequate for sound planning. The rapid acquisition of such knowledge is vital however, if those concerned with regional development are required to undertake project feasibility studies with the object of providing a basis for investment decisions. It is in response to these information needs that the use of satellite imagery is now becoming widely accepted as a means of initially providing a baseline inventory of a physical resource over a large region, and for studying physical characteristics of the terrain, such as geology and the drainage network, which will ultimately influence engineering decisions.

Traditionally in all countries, resource information has been acquired by a variety of means from different sources, and often maintained in separate agencies. National planners therefore, for these and other reasons, have rarely incorporated current and accurate resource information and environmental factors in their planning processes. For example, resource information generally only enters indirectly into the economic analysis and plan formulations of those countries that engage in central planning at the national level. Concerned traditionally with the allocation of financial resources, central planning authorities tend to base their calculations on broad economic, financial, population and other statistical variables. The particulars of resource information are attended to at lower levels under the aegis either of data collection agencies or of mapping organizations such as a geological survey, cartographical unit, or soils survey. Consequently, information from such sources is frequently integrated into planning for discrete development projects for which data requirements are generally more rigorous and sharply defined. These packaged project development schemes are then incorporated into the framework of a national plan.

The reasons for such shortcomings and frequent planning deficiencies can be attributed to various factors including a lack of coordination and common frame of reference between physical and economic planners, a lack of awareness amongst many economists of developments in the use of new data collection technologies, the long time scales of economic plans, and the responsibilities for resource management being lodged in sectoral ministries and technical services uncoordinated with respect to the priorities of the development programme. These types of problems are even more difficult to overcome where there is a demand for resource and environmental data required on a transnational scale to meet regional objectives such as crop yield forecasting, environmental monitoring, river basin development and disaster relief programmes. For all these purposes, and in many engineering considerations, the need exists for more comprehensive ways of evaluating the resource base of a region, and for improved means, both technical and managerial, of making resource information, such as the availability of engineering construction materials, count in development planning and resource management.

In recent years a few countries have begun to recognize the value of an integrative approach to resource management and have established centralized data collection, analysis and planning services, including geographical information systems, that incorporate the conventional administrative units. This innovation is still rare however in both developing and industrialized countries where the collection and use of resource data predominantly reflects the traditional sectoral compartmentalization. The history of land use, soils and other thematic mapping in the United Kingdom clearly substantiates this point. A further illustration within engineering is often encountered overseas where various administrative authorities concerned with the different aspects of water supply and development are uncoordinated and frequently unaware of the other organizations' activities and sources of relevant information. Similarly, it is not unusual in some countries for development studies to be undertaken solely to collate and review existing dispersed sources of relevant information.

As there have been no appropriate demands from central planners, and support has been lacking due to the parochial interests of sectoral data collection authorities, there has been little incentive or effort to produce an easily accessible, comprehensive, and integrated representation of a nation's resource base as a decision-making tool for regional or national development. The arrival of a technology, increasingly manifest in the imagery available from the Landsat satellites, that can serve at once as a new mode of data collection, management and display is quite likely in the future to induce significant change in planning practices.

7.3 Planning and regional engineering studies

Engineering involvement in regional planning studies usually concerns the acquisition and evaluation of information on the nature and physical properties of the terrain and various components of the socio-economic activities it supports so as to provide a sound basis for investment and associated engineering decisions concerning either the development or maintenance of infrastructure.

In order to obtain the best or most cost-effective option within the overall constraints of a particular project, the process of engineering survey and design is normally subdivided into three broad stages of reconnaissance, feasibility and detailed design. The objectives of the reconnaissance or prefeasibility study are to identify needs and assess both construction costs and ensuing economic benefits. Specific areas may also be selected where more detailed studies are likely to prove rewarding. Feasibility surveys provide more detailed calculations of costs and benefits to determine economic or social viability and often involve final alignment or site selection together with recommendations for appropriate design standards and timing of construction. The final design stage is concerned with detailed topographic and other relevant surveys, leading to precise location and design on the ground with calculations of quantities and costs for the preparation of contract documents. In developing countries, it is significant that there are often fewer constraints on engineering construction and projects may be on a larger scale which collectively result in more extensive areas of ground needing to be carefully investigated to ensure best site selection. This consequently places much greater emphasis on the planning activities which precede the final design study.

Unfortunately, much evidence exists to suggest that planning and site investigation procedures used in Britain and other developed countries are not sufficiently modified to take account of these factors when projects are undertaken overseas. In most industrialized countries there is an adequate amount of background information to serve the purpose of feasibility studies, so most investigatory effort is put into the detailed work required for the design stage. Where little information exists in undeveloped regions however, the earlier stages of survey are often relatively more important, since they determine the major decisions on the location and ultimately the total cost of the project. The dangers of ignoring this strategy are best illustrated by the fact that in the 1970s spending in the USA was well over $100 million annually to correct all types of highway landslides, most of which, it is acknowledged, could have been avoided by more thorough terrain surveys and site investigation before selection of the final route alignments.

Another important factor affecting planning and regional engineering studies in developing countries is the acquisition of data relevant to the derivation of engineering design and construction specifications which are appropriate for local conditions. The absence of suitable engineering standards, guides and recommendations can often result in a waste of resources where use is made of inappropriate foreign standards and codes of practice taken from industrialized nations where the range of climatic conditions and stage of economic and social development are different.

In recent years these problems have been highlighted in the design and construction of unsurfaced gravel roads, where higher investment is required in materials due to the incorporation of lower geometric standards and corresponding decreased costs for earthworks and structures. The most cost-effective construction, and subsequent lower maintenance costs, can only be achieved on these types of road by reducing haulage distances, which form the major item of expense, through making the best use of locally available materials. Locally occurring materials are however, often not used as extensively as would be possible due to the adaptation of specifications for road building materials that have been derived in industrialized countries with temperate climates and different geology. These specifications often prove to be inappropriate for natural gravels, weathered rock, and concretionary materials found in the tropics, many of which can be used successfully for constructing lightly-trafficked roads. In recognizing the importance of developing appropriate criteria for the selection and use of locally available materials, the engineer must primarily locate and map their occurrence on a local, regional or national basis through the use of suitable remote sensing and terrain evaluation methods (Beaumont, 1979a).

The interpretation of black-and-white aerial photographs has for many years proved to be one of the main sources of information for regional engineering planning studies. Acquisition of data on the physical properties of the terrain for engineering purposes has been most successfully achieved on a regional basis by making use of terrain evaluation methods. These techniques are based on the use of aerial photographs in a physiographic approach to studying terrain, whereby the ground conditions and associated engineering considerations are related to a land classification scheme where homogeneous units of land are initially identified by their distinctive airphoto patterns (Dowling and Beaven, 1969; Mitchell, 1973). Using such methods, information obtained about the ground for one site can be transferred, with some degree of confidence, to a site within a similar terrain unit wherever it recurs in the landscape. The ability to extrapolate data from known to unknown but similar sites is of particular benefit in the planning stages of engineering projects and can substantially assist in providing a better understanding of the ground conditions throughout wide regional areas of interest.

Although aerial photographic surveys have proved invaluable as a source of planning information, many shortcomings have been exposed as imagery has become available from new types of sensors combined with a space platform. Problems related to the limitations of aerial photographic surveys which have now been overcome through the availability of Landsat satellite imagery include the following:

— the small area that can be covered in any one photographic scene;
— high cost per unit area and hence significant expense incurred in covering very large areas;
— difficulties of obtaining complete coverage of large areas in short time frame, especially in humid tropics where cloud cover is frequent;
— recording of data in only one broad spectral range limits ability of interpreter to discriminate between ground features exhibiting similar photographic tone;
— photographic record more difficult to subject to computer-based, quantitative analytical interpretation and automatic feature classification procedures;
— seasonal operation of aerial surveys may not coincide with time of maximum interest for interpretation purposes;
— times of acquisition vary throughout the day, and the consequent variety of lighting conditions can impede temporal comparison of some features;
— limited availability of existing coverage and variability in scale of coverage worldwide.

It is evident from this summary of the restrictions affecting aerial photography that the main advantages provided by Landsat satellite imagery for regional engineering planning studies lie in the synoptic view to be realized of a large area of the earth's surface at a single point in time and space which may be interpreted to provide a variety of relevant physical and cultural information. Procedures for acquiring information through interpretation are also facilitated by the capability of the sensing devices to simultaneously record radiometric images in different spectral bands of the same area, which can additionally be monitored through the ability of the satellite to acquire sequential coverage at regular time intervals. These unique characteristics of Landsat data provide the basis for a whole range of expanding computer processing, interpretation and analytical techniques which enable specific information often to be acquired in more detail and at much greater speed.

The large regional views recorded by the sensor systems on board the Landsat satellites may now be interpreted to provide a wide range of information relevant to most of the different aspects of regional engineering study required in planning activities. Some of the major engineering uses of Landsat data can most suitably be considered under specific sectors of planning application.

7.3.1 Highway planning

As the planning of a highway project progresses from the stages of reconnaissance and feasibility survey through to design and construction, the need for accurate geotechnical appreciation of the terrain increases. Although the alignment chosen may be influenced to some degree by political and social factors, the final design is only achieved after a detailed examination has been made of the landforms, drainage, soils and materials to be found within the route corridor. On this basis the selected alignment may deviate from the shortest distance route in order to reduce construction and vehicle operating costs. Construction costs in the main are minimized by reducing earthworks, bridge and drainage structures; by selecting the strongest soil foundations and locating conveniently sited sources of durable road building materials; and by avoiding, where possible, ground hazards such as swamps, shifting sands, landslides and areas prone to erosion.

Landsat data offers unique advantages for highway planning in that information on all the factors which influence route selection, such as those mentioned above, may be initially acquired at the regional level through an interpretation of single and multidate imagery. Limitations in the ground resolution of multispectral scanner (MSS) imagery usually determine that the acquisition of useful information is restricted to the reconnaissance and feasibility stages of highway planning. However, even at the detailed design and construction phases, information may be derived on specific features such as the extent of black clay soils or the location of lines of drainage and geological faults. The opportunity of quickly being able to examine features relevant to detailed design in their regional setting is also often of considerable advantage, as for example in the evaluation of the catchment area of a line of drainage which the alignment must cross that is not totally covered in the route corridor aerial survey photography.

Useful image products can now be acquired up to scales of 1:100 000 after computer processing, and even larger scales are feasible where image quality is good and both atmospheric and ground conditions are suitable. Where Landsat Return Beam Vidicon (RBV) and Thematic Mapper (TM) data are available, the improved resolution and scale enlargement of the imagery enable much greater detail to be interpreted. As this progress in sensor technology and computer processing methods is continued, information derived from satellite imagery will become increasingly important in highway planning for the stages of detailed design and construction.

Repetitive coverage of land surface areas by satellite imagery provides a means of monitoring on a regional basis time-dependent changes in surface features (Howarth and Wickware, 1981). This may be useful for the highway engineer in monitoring, for example, the seasonal or periodic incidence of flooding, the movements of desert sands, the progress of erosion, or the visible induced benefits and changes in land use brought about by a road construction programme. A fuller discussion of the use of Landsat data in highway engineering is given in Chapter 9. In concluding this consideration of highway planning, however, it is important to note that one of the main advantages of the ready availability of Landsat imagery is realized in the commercial sector of engineering practice by consultants and contractors who have to respond quickly for tender submissions on projects in remote areas. On many overseas contracts only a very limited amount of time can be available from receiving notice of the project to submission of final tender documents which precludes the possibility of any detailed study of aerial photographs, topographic maps and other sources of locally available engineering data. Information acquired from the interpretation of Landsat imagery can assist in overcoming these problems (Beaumont, 1980) and at least ensure provision of an up-to-date base map and that any possible reconnaissance ground investigations in the time available are concentrated into the most rewarding areas.

7.3.2 Transportation planning

Much of the information acquired from the interpretation of Landsat imagery for highway engineering purposes is relevant to transportation planning due to the significant overlap existing between these fields of study. However, in the socio-economic investigation of road networks and other forms of transport, Landsat data may also be interpreted to provide relevant planning information on land use, agricultural practices, land capability, natural resource inventories and regional analyses of population and settlement patterns. The lower the level of development in a country, the more important it becomes for transport planners to investigate existing land use categories and land potential in relation to physical and cultural features and other natural resources in order to determine generated traffic. In planning transport facilities, the availability of up-to-date Landsat data is particularly valuable in the remote and least accessible areas where existing map coverage is limited (Beaumont, 1983). The monitoring capability of the Landsat system is also very relevant to developed countries where regular information on land use changes, expansion of urban areas and so on is of value to those both planning and managing transport facilities.

Regional planning studies often require investigations of the interplay between different transport modes. In providing coverage of such large areas of terrain, Landsat imagery can often provide much useful information in this context, as for example in examining different aspects of the integration of river, road and rail transport or the development of hinterland transport links in relation to selection of a suitable port site. Landsat imagery may also be interpreted to provide a wealth of information relevant to coastal engineering and sea transport, as the different spectral bands can reveal in specific situations, water depths, sedimentation patterns, coral reefs and other navigational hazards, tidal patterns, and oil slicks after appropriate processing and analysis. Similarly, as with the selection of route alignments for highways, it is possible to interpret physical and cultural features of the ground surface from Landsat data so as to plan and select suitable sites for airport locations and new town development or expansion. In summary, Landsat imagery has become invaluable for transport planning through its ability to provide an up-to-date picture of a large area of the earth's surface at a single point in time.

7.3.3 Urban planning

The planning and provision of engineering services associated with water resources and supply, drainage, sewerage, and other aspects of urban infrastructure development often involve studies covering large areas. Similarly, these may also extend to specific regional considerations of the municipal engineering, traffic and transport requirements of different population centres. Reference has previously been made to the role of Landsat data for acquiring regional information such as on resources, settlement characteristics or land use etc., and through terrain evaluation for site development location. As the resolution capabilities of satellite sensing systems improve, and research continues with computer processing and analytical techniques, satellite imagery is being increasingly used for purposes of census enumeration, urban area measurement and population estimates over large areas (Ogrosky, 1975; Lo and Welch, 1977). Significantly in recent years a wide variety of different urban measurements have been successfully accomplished within metropolitan areas from an analysis of Landsat data (Jensen et al., 1983) and the newly acquired imagery from the Landsat TM and SPOT satellite simulation programmes clearly reveals the potential for such studies in the future.

One of the most impressive of recent studies has utilized Landsat data acquired over Sydney, Australia with supporting ground data and multiple linear regression analysis to develop predictive equations for surface reflectance and a number of urban measurements, including surface cover proportions, housing density, relative average house values based on size, and a residential quality index (Forster, 1983). The monitoring capability of the Landsat system also proves to be most useful for planners wishing to evaluate the expansion of urban areas through a period of time and associated changes in population distribution, environmental characteristics and urban land utilization (Toll et al., 1980; Jensen et al., 1981).

The value of Landsat imagery for urban planning and housing surveys in overseas countries affected by inadequate map coverage has been further emphasized by the recent announcement of the Ministry of Public Works and Housing in Saudi Arabia of the intention to analyse Landsat data by computer to make the first overall location and measurement of all sedentary human settlements throughout the Kingdom. This initial task will establish a sample base for subsequent housing surveys to obtain for chosen cities the total number of dwellings, their basic characteristics and those of their inhabitants. The need for such data has arisen from a rapid development of the housing sector since 1974 when a substantial increase in the disposable incomes of

information, especially when subject to the criteria of international funding agencies. In developing countries the use of Landsat satellite imagery for initially providing a baseline inventory of a physical resource over a large region, and subsequently monitoring its development, exploitation or conservation, is now becoming widely accepted (NAS, 1977). This awareness of the value of Landsat data is becoming increasingly important to those engineers working in teams where technical staff from different disciplines are required on a project to link one set of data with another. Integrated use of resource information is desirable and can be achieved in the design and execution of a regional development project, even in countries where such information remains fragmented at the national level.

In the rural sector the successful planning and implementation of regional development involves much more than improving the basic techniques in any sector in order to increase production based on natural resources. Experience has shown that virtually all sectors of activity are closely interrelated in natural resource appraisal, regional planning and rural development programmes. Economic, agricultural, physical and social development must be planned so that they can be achieved together. Landsat satellite imagery, and associated larger-scale remote sensing data, can provide a useful framework for attaining this objective, whereby on the basis of image interpretation, different specialists can be coordinated within a fully integrated programme.

7.3.6 Hazard studies

The interpretation of Landsat imagery can provide useful geotechnical and associated information on the terrain relevant to regional engineering studies concerned with various aspects of natural hazards and disasters caused by earthquake, geological and volcanic activities, flooding, avalanching, glaciers, cyclone and hurricane damage, mass movements and landslides, sea erosion and damage. Similar studies may also be extended to hazards induced by the activities of man such as mining subsidence, seismicity (Pavlin and Langston, 1983), poorly constructed waste tips and landfills, toxic waste disposal, pollution, dam failure or gully erosion. Landsat imagery also provides one of the quickest means of acquiring regional assessment of damage to the physical and cultural features of the land surface after a specific disaster (Richards et al., 1983) and may often be able to monitor the development of the hazard as it occurs, as for example in cases of flooding (Deutsch and Ruggles, 1978, 1981).

Hazards causing disasters, such as river and coastal flooding, earthquakes, fires and hurricanes, pose special problems because of the difficulties of data collection. The sequential monitoring and synoptic capabilities provided by Landsat data can assist emergency services in establishing both the extent of the damage and the risk to human life, and thus aid the optimal disposition of relief activities. In regions of tectonic instability, as on the west coast of the USA, geologic hazard mapping is particularly relevant to engineering planning studies. The identification of large-scale lineaments on Landsat imagery indicative of faults, fractures, brittle deformations, jointing, and shear zones, which are often not evident on the ground or from aerial photographs due to the limited area of coverage that can be observed at one time, or the deep-seated nature of the feature, often provides a valuable contribution to the understanding of regional geological structure and tectonic movements that may affect engineering structures through seismic, volcanic or mass movement activity (Hays, 1981; Glass and Slemmons, 1978). Regional mapping of geologic lineaments is thus very important in relation to the siting of engineering structures and developments such as nuclear power stations, dams, or toxic waste disposal centres which involve high risk to public welfare if failure occurs.

Although the ability to predict natural and man-made hazards on a regional basis through the analysis of satellite data is unlikely for many phenomena, the provision of a wide range of information by these means at the very least enables earth scientists, engineers and planners to obtain a better understanding of the natural and human processes which affect the environment. It is only through acquiring such knowledge that adequate planning measures can be undertaken, wherever feasible, to safeguard against and minimize the adverse consequences of possible natural and man induced hazards.

7.4   Interpretation of engineering data from Landsat imagery

Although Landsat data may be analysed by both manual and computer-assisted procedures, acquisition of useful information is still dependent on the fundamental principles of interpretation, whereby detection and identification of features and processes is based on recognition of characteristic image pattern elements which include: tone/colour, size, shape, texture, pattern, height, shadow, site and association. Landsat imagery is significantly different to aerial photographic products, however, in that the recognition of pattern elements is also dependent upon the spectral characteristics of the ground features recorded within each specific image wavelength band. The ability to discriminate features through an analysis of their spectral response in different wavelength bands or 'multispectral signature' has meant that much greater emphasis has been placed on tone and colour in the interpretation of Landsat imagery, although the elements of texture, site and association are more extensively used as research continues in image processing techniques. To obtain the best results and maximum information from Landsat imagery it is essential, nevertheless, for the engineering interpreter to obtain a full understanding of the range and nature of the spectral data which will be subject to analysis (Beaumont, 1977, 1979b).

Digital image processing and interpretation techniques have experienced phenomenal growth in recent years, and have matched technological developments in remote sensing systems to such an extent that they now form a field of study in their own right (Swain and Davis, 1978; Lillesand and Kiefer, 1979; Moik, 1980; Estes *et al.*, 1983). Although much can be accomplished through simple visual interpretation of Landsat black-and-white and colour photographic products at different scales, the full potential of the satellite data to provide useful information can be realized only after computer processing. The advantages of analysing original computer compatible tape (CCT) data in an interactive computer system with display facilities include avoidance of data loss and degradation associated with transference of imagery to film formats, easier removal and correction of image distortions, considerable interpretation and analytical flexibility, and reproducible results. Recent developments in microprocessor technology have also resulted in dramatic reductions in the cost and operation of image processing systems, which are now readily accessible to engineering organizations either through direct purchase or by hire at regional or national centres such as the National Remote Sensing Centre, RAE, Farnborough, UK.

A full discussion of the wide range of image processing and interpretation techniques available to the engineering interpreter is beyond the scope of this chapter, and for more information reference should be made to Chapter 4 on digital image processing of remote sensing data, and to current literature whose continuous publication is indicative of the rapid advances being made in this highly active field of research. A brief outline of some of the simpler techniques and principles of computer analysis are given below with the intention of reviewing their practical use for regional engineering planning studies.

7.4.1 Techniques and applications

The three main areas of image processing and interpretation can be summarized under the following headings.

Image restoration is concerned with the correction of defects, distortion, degradations and noise induced in the imaging process. Atmospheric, radiometric and geometric corrections are normally applied, the geometric correction usually being adjusted to a cartographic grid. Over very large areas these and other data processing methods are deployed in the production of digital mosaics.

Image enhancement alters the visual presentation of the image to improve quality and assist interpretation of pictorial information by contrast stretching, edge enhancement, density slicing, spatial and directional filtering and pseudo-colouring.

Information extraction involves image transforms and utilizing the arithmetical and statistical functions of the computer to identify areas of equal spectral response by band ratios, hybrid ratios, differencing, principal-components analysis, multispectral classification and change detection.

Ideally, on becoming familiar with this range of interpretation techniques and image processing options, the engineering interpreter should be in a position to select the most appropriate methods for acquiring a specific type of information in a recognizable environment or set of conditions. Unfortunately, the information required by planning engineers is diverse and the problems associated with geographic variability can affect the utility of a particular technique between different regions. It is consequently very difficult to recommend a rationale which will practically aid the interpreter in selecting when to use a particular technique or method for acquiring different types of engineering and planning information.

Although general principles can be determined, such as the superiority of the infrared wavelength bands for drainage analysis and the green wavelength band for tropical coast sea-depth studies, the most significant factor to affect the relevance or potential success of a particular analytical technique, as in manual interpretation, will be the experience of the interpreter. Selection of the methods likely to produce the best results however, can be greatly assisted by an appreciation of the spectral characteristics of the study features within the region of interest (Lillesand and Kiefer, 1979; Landgrebe, 1981). Significantly, to date some of the most successful advances in the development and application of image processing and interpretation methods based on spectral analysis have been achieved in geological studies (Goetz et al., 1975; Rowan et al., 1976) where a strong commercial impetus has been provided in oil and mineral exploration programmes.

In addition to acquiring physical terrain and drainage data, the engineer involved in interpreting Landsat imagery for regional planning studies will need to implement analytical procedures for acquiring maximum information on land utilization. The selection of appropriate interpretation techniques to discriminate vegetation is therefore important both as a means of identifying land cover and for detecting relevant terrain features of engineering interest such as materials and subsurface water, associated with particular types or conditions of plant communities (Myers et al., 1983; Tucker, 1978). As the spectral pattern elements on Landsat imagery are largely determined by differences in reflectance properties of plant, soil and rock surfaces, techniques based on identifying areas of equal response have similarly been emphasized for computer-aided mapping of natural resource and cultural features in regional planning studies.

Although utilization of image processing and interpretation techniques will vary according to the nature of the specific project, in general, the engineering interpreter can be expected to develop a strategy whereby, after using the computer to produce the best possible image for visual interpretation, through implementation of restoration and enhancement routines, a programme of feature extraction is initiated in order to undertake detailed investigation, measurement or mapping of specific engineering interests, as for example in selecting potential sites for location of construction materials, relevant to the regional planning study. On most image processing systems the following routines are now usually available as standard packages, which can be called upon to assist in the interpretation and acquisition of relevant information from Landsat data.

7.4.1.1 Colour enhancement. The objective of image enhancement is to aid the human analyst in the extraction and interpretation of pictorial information by optimally displaying the features of greatest interest. Before the widespread use of computer-based image processors, the simplest enhancement techniques involved the use of colour additive viewers (as described in Chapter 2) incorporating projector systems which allowed several images to be simultaneously viewed on a screen. Each black-and-white image could thus be filtered, brightened and scaled independently so that the hue, brightness and saturation of the resulting false-colour composite image could be adjusted to suit a particular need. These procedures, however, may now be accomplished far more effectively, and with greater speed and accuracy, using digital CCT data in an interactive computer processing facility. In regional engineering planning studies, colour composite images may be enhanced to evaluate the distribution of particular land use classes, soil types or construction materials, areas of poor drainage and low bearing capacity, geomorphological units exhibiting particular engineering problems, landslides and unstable ground, or any other aspect of the terrain which is likely to affect proposed construction or planned development. Similarly, enhancement may be used to delineate cultural features such as urban area boundaries. The only disadvantage to using colour enhancement procedures lies in their subjectivity, as there are no simple rules to produce a single best image and opinions may differ as to quality and best product for a specific aspect of study.

7.4.1.2 Contrast stretching and density slicing. Contrast stretching is primarily concerned with producing an image that optimally uses the full dynamic range of the data and display facility. Undertaken photographically, a series of pictures with various exposures is produced on high contrast paper. Each product will exhibit various tonal values, represented within a distinct band of equal density, being stretched across the entire density range of the photographic paper, so that the relative contrast between subtly different features should be more apparent. In the more commonly used computer image processing systems, the grey-level distribution created by pixel intensity values is electronically adjusted to obtain the best imagery for visual display.

In density slicing, film densities, or pixels with similar intensity levels after combination and coding, are measured or subdivided into distinct, ordered, and often uniformly coloured, categories in order to detect and delineate subtle variations in the image tone (see Plate 7). Optimum contrast stretching is usually achieved in computer processing by initially referring to a histogram display which illustrates the grey-level distribution in the image, which is the number of pixels lying within specific grey intensity intervals. The contrast stretch involving pixel-by-pixel change in grey intensity level is then often matched to a newly defined function such as uniform, Gaussian or linear output distributions. After obtaining optimum contrast within each spectral band for the particular study in hand, the images are then also able to be combined and colour enhanced to facilitate visual interpretation.

Contrast stretching provides one of the most effective analytical techniques available to the engineering planner, enabling useful detail to be discriminated in areas appearing uniformly too dark or light for interpretation on the original imagery. This interpretation aid is particularly useful for geological studies and materials investigations (Siegel and Gillespie, 1980) especially in semi-arid and desert areas where lack of vegetation and strong reflectance produce high brightness levels and often a consistent light tone over much of the recorded imagery. Virtually all regional features of engineering and planning significance interpreted from Landsat imagery can be enhanced through adjustment to contrast, although the technique is most effective for distinguishing subtle spectral differences which would normally be obscured in the original grey-level distribution. Subtle variations in rock and soil types, vegetation cover and land use are thus often discriminated by these means.

The often dramatic effects achieved through contrast stretching are illustrated in Figure 4.7 which compares an original Landsat scene and a contrast stretched version together with their respective histograms for grey-level distribution. As this analytical technique can be quickly implemented and often proves successful, it is usually one of the foremost to be applied in a comprehensive interpretation programme.

7.4.1.3 *Filtering.* Digital filtering is accomplished either in the spatial or frequency transform domain by convolving an image with a suitably chosen array (Schreiber, 1978; Moik, 1980) with the object of improving sharpness and visibility of detail in both light and dark areas. Particular examples are, smoothing, where boundaries are regularized, and which is equivalent to low-pass filtering, and edge enhancement high-pass filtering, which is a means of highlighting the boundaries between specific phenomena with similar radiance levels. Two images which illustrate the effect of smoothing and edge enhancement are Figures 4.8(c) and (d). In all filtering routines, the interpreter has to be aware of the trade-off between image sharpness and noise, and adjust the degree of implementation of the method to the study in hand. Problems of loss of resolution may be overcome by using non-linear operations such as the mode filter, which removes small variations in brightness and creates relatively large regions of completely uniform character with almost no loss in boundary resolutions (Coleman and Andrews, 1979).

Apart from improving image quality through removal of noise, striping, or other defects, filtering (and especially edge enhancement techniques), will usually be used by the engineering interpreter only to acquire specific detailed information, as for example, in the discrimination of geological units,

Plate 1 Airborne MSS image of part of Heathrow Airport, near London, obtained using a Daedalus 1268 scanner. The image consists of bands 2, 4 and 5 processed to form a simulated true colour composite. Note the high resolution of the image when compared to that obtained from the Landsat satellite (Plate 4). (Reproduced by kind permission of Hunting Geology and Geophysics Ltd.)

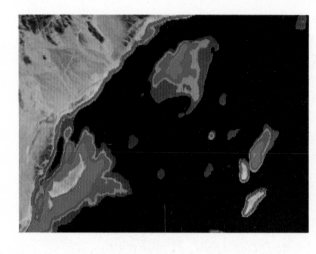

Plate 2 Landsat 3 MSS false colour composite of the northern region of the Red Sea. (Reproduced by kind permission of the National Remote Sensing Centre, RAE.)

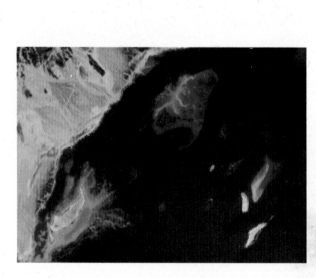

Plate 3 Density sliced image of Plate 2 illustrating variations in water depth. Compare with bathymetric chart shown in Figure 3.12. (Reproduced by kind permission of the National Remote Sensing Centre, RAE.)

Plate 4 Landsat MSS and TM false colour composite images of Heathrow Airport, near London. Note improved resolution of the TM imagery. (Left) Landsat MSS (May 1979, bands 4, 5 and 7). (Right) Landsat 4 TM (February 1983, bands 2, 3 and 4). (Reproduced by kind permission of the National Remote Sensing Centre, RAE.)

Plate 5 MOMS false colour composite image of part of the Bolivian highlands. The image was obtained from the space shuttle Challenger on 18 July 1983. (Reproduced by kind permission of MBB/ERNO and DFVLR.)

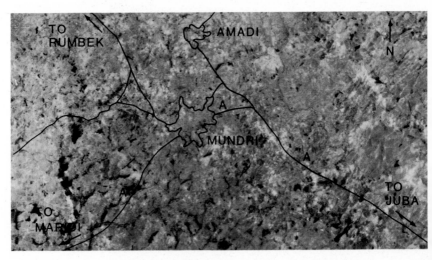

Plate 6 Landsat 3 MSS false colour composite of part of the southern Sudan.

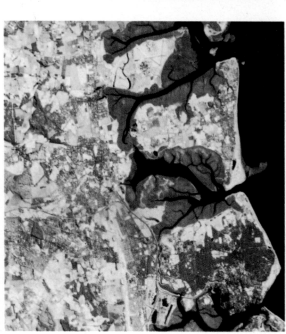

Plate 7 Landsat 4 TM scene of Portsmouth, UK. (Left) Contrast stretched band 4 image. (Right) Density slice of image on left. (Reproduced by kind permission of National Remote Sensing Centre, RAE.)

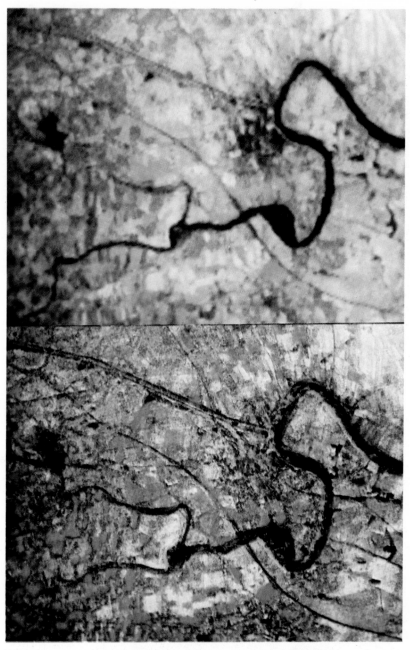

Plate 8 Landsat 3 MSS and RBV images of part of East Anglia. (Top) Landsat 3 MSS false colour composite. (Bottom) Landsat 3 MSS with RBV superimposed. Note improvement in spatial resolution. (Reproduced by kind permission of National Remote Sensing Centre, RAE.)

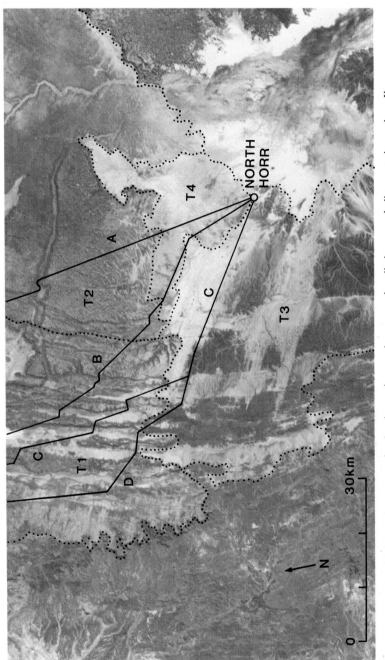

Plate 9 Landsat 3 MSS false colour composite showing major terrain types and preliminary road alignments in northern Kenya.

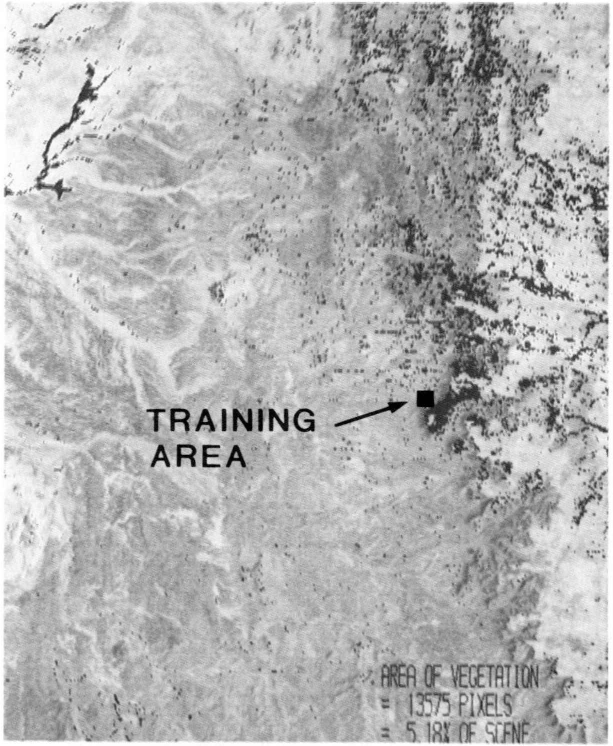

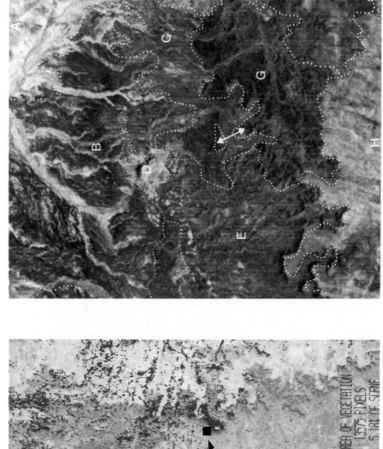

Plate 10 Classification of part of Plate 9. Training area is shown in black, with the resultant classification shown in purple.

Plate 11 Landsat 3 MSS false colour composite of Lake Turkana region of northern Kenya, showing terrain classification.

AREA OF VEGETATION
= 13575 PIXELS
= 5.18% OF SCENE

TRAINING
AREA

Plate 12 Landsat 3 MSS composite image showing channels of Narayani River (Nepal) after three monsoons. See text for description.

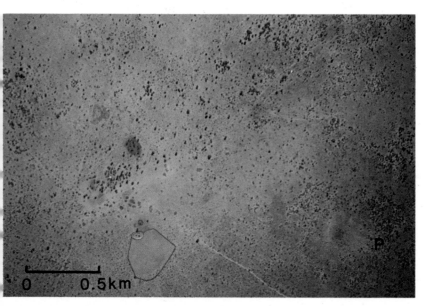

Plate 13 True colour aerial photograph of part of Botswana showing grey sands and a small pan (P).

Plate 14 Landsat 3 MSS false colour composite image of part of central Botswana.

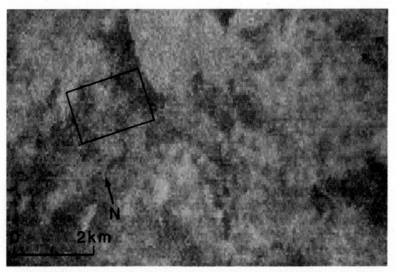

Plate 15 Landsat 3 MSS image of central Botswana. Principal components 1, 2 and 3. Grey sands shown in blue. Outline indicates area of aerial photograph in Plate 13.

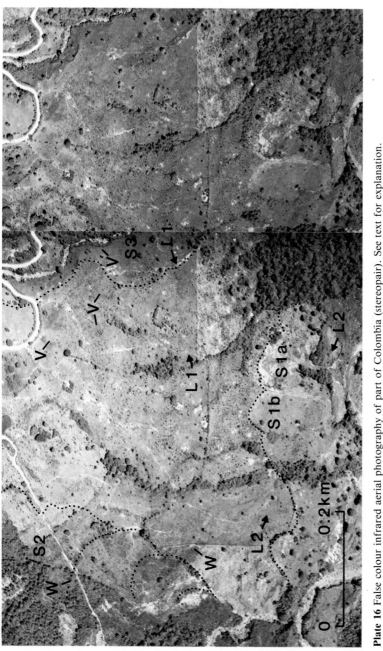

Plate 16 False colour infrared aerial photography of part of Colombia (stereopair). See text for explanation.

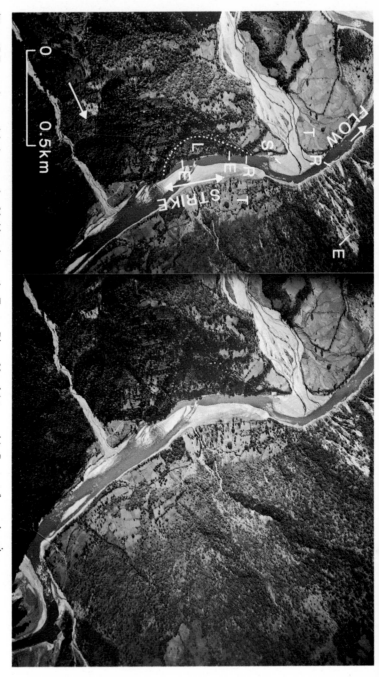

Plate 17 True colour aerial photograph of bridge site on the Tamar River, Nepal (stereopair). See text for explanation.

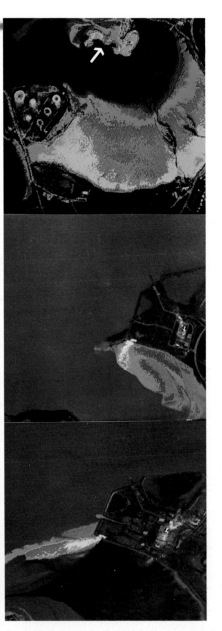

THERMAL DISCHARGE MONITORING

LOW

FLOOD

EBB

Plate 18 Thermal discharge monitoring: digital colour imagery of a power station outfall. Arrow indicates discharge plume.

Plate 19 Delineation of water bodies. (Top) False colour infrared aerial photograph. (Bottom) True colour aerial photograph.

Plate 20 False colour infrared aerial photograph illustrating the extent of flooding.

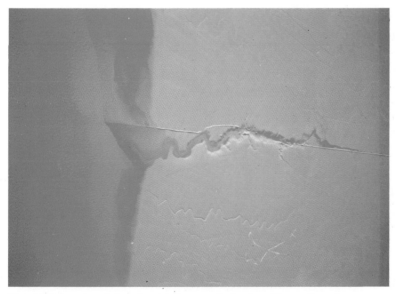

Plate 21 False colour infrared aerial photograph showing effluent disposal.

Plate 22 Airborne thermal infrared linescan images illustrating thermal inertia variations. (Left) Daytime, (Right) Nighttime image.

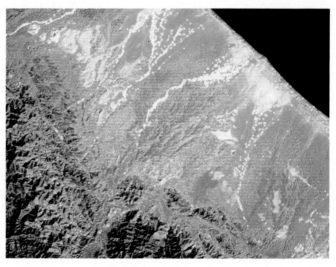

Plate 23 Landsat 3 MSS classification for groundwater detection.

lineaments and fold structures. These methods have also proved successful in the analysis of drainage networks, as often the morphometric character of stream direction and pattern can be related to hidden geological structure. Other applications include the enhancement of road, rail and canal alignments, field and soil type boundaries, land-use interfaces, water-body limits, urban area infrastructure and settlement patterns.

7.4.1.4 Destriping, digital mosaicing and enlargement. If the outputs from the six detectors associated with each spectral band on the Landsat scanner are not radiometrically corrected, then the resulting image will appear striped. This is overcome by using a procedure that equalizes the means and variances of the radiance levels associated with each detector. Similar processing methods may also be deployed to overcome radiometric and geometric problems associated with mosaicing selected image scenes recorded at different times. Significant advances have recently been made in the reproduction of compatible imagery (both MSS and RBV) for the construction of digital mosaics covering large areas of the earth's surface and in the creation of map-projected Landsat databases (Zobrist *et al.*, 1983).

Landsat mosaics are invaluable to the planning engineer for providing a broad overview of natural resources, and displaying the interrelationships of the physical and cultural environments throughout one or more regions. They also prove most useful for purposes of base mapping, geographical studies, planning, multiple resource applications, engineering investigations of large-scale geological and other ground features, and regional studies involving development, land evaluation, planning and geotechnical classifications of terrain (Overseas Unit, 1982; Beaumont, 1978).

To enlarge the pixel size, and produce imagery up to scales of 1 : 50 000 or larger from Landsat CCT data, a procedure involving resampling, based on different statistical analyses (such as nearest neighbour, cubic convolution, linear or Hanning interpolation) selected in accordance with the study, can be implemented. Usually, to achieve the best hard copy results, a combination of digital processing and photographic enlargement techniques is used. Digital enlargement, now often instantaneously available through a zoom facility on modern image processors, is one of the most valuable and frequently deployed techniques utilized by engineering interpreters wishing to acquire maximum detailed information and undertake larger-scale thematic mapping within regional planning studies.

7.4.1.5 Geometric transformations. Correction of geometric distortions requires, besides earth curvature, rotation and satellite attitude error adjustments, the selection of ground control feature points that can be readily identified on both the Landsat imagery and a map of the same area at an appropriate scale. After locating sufficient points, a least-squares fit is performed to determine the transformation between image and map coordinates. This then forms the basis to transform the image into the local map coordinate system using one of the resampling techniques referred to above.

Geometric transformations are of most use to engineering planners in enabling imagery to be combined from different sensors (Moik, 1980). RBV imagery from Landsat 3 has a significantly better spatial resolution than that from the MSS system, but by bringing the two data sets into register, it is possible to combine their spectral and spatial properties. The value of undertaking such a transformation is illustrated in Plate 8. Similarly, the Landsat MSS spectral data may be complemented by radar imagery which is superior for showing relief and detailed variations of surface form. In the future, the potential of such methods for regional planning purposes will be greatly increased by the availability of data with improved spectral and spatial characteristics from Landsat TM, SPOT, ERS-1, MOS, J ERS-1 and other satellites. Combinations of satellite imagery and photography, together with high-altitude, small-scale aerial photography are also likely to become more prevalent as further earth surveillance programmes are implemented.

Other advantages of using geometric transformations mainly relate to the deployment of multi-temporal analyses in planning and engineering monitoring studies, whereby images acquired from different seasons or years may be compared by transforming the various scenes into a common projection, which for most purposes is usefully served by the National Grid. The ability to relate different data sets and systematically monitor spatial changes also emphasizes the potential value of this technique for establishing regional planning and management geographic information database systems.

7.4.1.6 *Digital image ratioing.* Image ratioing involves dividing the reflectance values of each pixel by a value in some other wavelength band. The various possible quotients of the division produce an array of numerical values to which grey tones are assigned, so that a picture can be constructed based on the ratio values rather than on the individual bands themselves (Figure 4.8). In working up values for various combinations of bands, it is possible to produce several different black-and-white pictures that can then be projected through colour filters to give band ratio colour composites. The most common combinations in colour are bands 4/5, 5/6 and 6/7, displayed as blue, green and red, respectively.

Ratioed images suppress changes in brightness caused by albedo and topographic relief so that, using this method, subtle spectral variations are enhanced and one type of material will appear the same regardless of local slope angle. Ratioing may concurrently increase atmospheric effects, or random and coherent noise which is usually removed before enhancement. The technique is most likely to be used by the planning engineer in specific geological or geotechnical investigations, such as tunnel site selection (Vincent et al., 1973; Krinsley, 1977), or in the location, recognition and interpretation of vegetation in land cover and surface indicator studies. Band ratio composites can be extremely sensitive to, and emphasize, small spectral differences produced by changes in rock lithology (Goetz *et al.*, 1975; Rowan *et al.*, 1976), plant varieties, extent, density and vigour, and soil types. It is thus a most useful tool for specific aspects of study in regional mapping programmes.

7.4.1.7 *Principal components analysis.* Principal components is a standard statistical technique applied to analyse variance of the Landsat spectral data based on linear combinations in each of the four multispectral bands. Each of the combinations is uncorrelated and ranked according to information content when measured by the percentage of total scene variance. As there is normally a high correlation between the individual spectral bands associated with a multispectral image scene, principal components (eigen vector) analysis involves the selection of a new set of orthogonal (or principal) axes such that the newly formed spectral bands are uncorrelated. Consequently, the technique can be used to improve the discrimination between similar types of ground cover and is especially useful for engineering soil, land use and geological studies.

The value of using this interpretation technique for improving the acquisition of useful information in arid areas on regional geology, soils, drainage and associated geotechnical aspects of the terrain is illustrated in Figure 4.11, and specifically in the location of potential sites for engineering construction materials, such as calcretes, in Plate 15. Principal components analysis is most likely to be used by the engineering interpreter to assist in mapping features of interest in detail, but due to the relative complexity of the analytical procedure, will often remain the final option after other techniques prove unsuccessful. In making fullest use of the spectral data available, the potential of this analytical method has probably not been fully realized for engineering applications of Landsat imagery. This is likely to change in the near future, however, as research progresses and the engineering interpreter has to evaluate and utilize the additional spectral bands of imagery which will be available from the Thematic Mapper and SPOT satellites.

7.4.1.8 *Image classification.* A significant advantage of using interactive image processing facilities for the interpretation of multispectral Landsat imagery lies in the capability available to the planning engineer for training the computer to automatically identify classes of ground cover on the basis of their spectral characteristics. As soon as a feature of interest is identified on the interactive display, various algorithms can be deployed, based on statistical sampling (e.g. maximum likelihood, or parallelpiped (box) classification methods) and clustering techniques, which enable the computer to automatically classify and display those features with the same spectral characteristics, in addition to calculating the ground area which they occupy within the image scene (Lillesand and Kiefer, 1979; Tom and Miller, 1984).

The three basic steps in a typical spectral pattern or 'signature' recognition

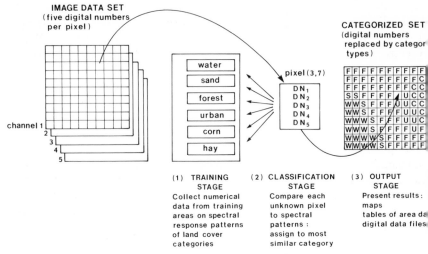

Figure 7.1   Typical spectral pattern recognition process. (After Lillesand and Kiefer, 1979).

procedure in computer associated image interpretation are shown in Figure 7.1. Supervised classification, where the analyst trains the computer through the compilation of an interpretation key or signature-set analogous to the spectral attributes for each feature of interest, can be most successfully used to prepare regional thematic maps of land use, soil types etc. for field checking in a very short space of time. Unsupervised methods, however, where statistical clustering techniques are used to classify natural spectral groupings, have had little application to date for regional engineering studies, their use being restricted to large-area ecology and agricultural crop inventory programmes.

Image classification techniques are particularly useful for the engineering planner required to prepare regional inventories and undertake studies based on thematic mapping surveys of natural resources. Similarly, multi-temporal analyses and environmental change detection are often based on deploying image classification routines for interpreting Landsat imagery. The ability of these procedures to discriminate uniform spectral patterns can also be important where Landsat data is utilized for engineering terrain evaluation and land classification investigations.

A very good illustration of a successful implementation of this technique has been in the mapping of land cover categories and specific crop acreages from Landsat imagery within an irrigation engineering, and water withdrawal analysis project in the Portland region, USA (Johnson *et al.*, 1981). In this study, water requirements for irrigated crops were determined by combining the Landsat classified image crop acreage estimates with historic crop water requirement statistics. Similarly, using sequential Landsat data, it was possible to identify areas of irrigation expansion, measure the rate of irrigation growth, and determine the cover types converted to irrigation. Besides determining requirements for water and energy, the project was also able to demonstrate the feasibility of integrating classified Landsat and other remote sensing imagery with data from a geobased information system to determine the potential of the land for future irrigation development (Johnson et al., 1980).

As most planning studies often concern to varying degrees the classification of both physical and cultural information, whose presentation is usually required in map form, computer-assisted image interpretation programmes involving spectral classification methods are highly regarded and most frequently deployed by those concerned with regional planning and development. The advantages of using image classification techniques for mapping land use, urban areas, settlement distribution and other relevant features of interest are also likely to increase in the future as a wider range of spectral data becomes available from new satellites, and the implementation and regular update of regional geographic information data base systems becomes more widespread.

7.4.2 Future developments

Reference has already been made in Chapter 3 to the TM and SPOT satellite development programmes which will ensure in the near future continuous availability of data with improved spectral and spatial characteristics. As has been mentioned, the TM employs a pixel size or ground resolution of 30 m in six bands, selected primarily for vegetation monitoring; this allows classification of areas as small as 2.5 to 4 ha (6 to 10 acres), whilst in the thermal infrared band, a resolution (pixel size) of 120 m is used. The SPOT satellite system is discussed in detail in section 3.2.3.3, Chapter 3. Apart from improvements in ground resolution (10–20 m), the other major advantage which this system will offer is the ability to obtain information on relief and relative elevations. This development is very significant with respect to future beneficial use of satellite imagery for engineering studies, as to date the inability to determine height information has been the greatest limitation affecting the deployment of Landsat data by engineers.

Although the availability of multispectral satellite imagery has been ensured in the near future with the TM and SPOT systems, and different programmes are being planned and implemented by the European Space Agency, Japan, India and other countries, most of these developments are experimental in nature and to date no commitment has been made to a commercially operational service. It is for these reasons that many developing countries have felt reluctant to invest in ground stations and associated processing facilities as there can be no guarantees that there will be an uninterrupted flow of data from successive future satellites, in addition to which must be considered the difficult questions of cost and political control. In this respect it is significant that no commitments have been made to an earth satellite sensing programme in the USA beyond the TM series and that current government attitudes are favouring private sector developments to overcome associated problems of cost and operational management (Lillesand, 1983; Voûte, 1984).

Even though the future direction and nature of global surveillance programmes are currently difficult to predict due to the uncertainties surrounding required international cooperation and different national political objectives, the development of satellite remote sensing will undoubtedly continue and provide a valuable source of information to engineers and planners. The value placed on Landsat data and other types of satellite imagery by the user community has recently been emphasized by the establishment of pressure groups such as the Geosat Committee which, through research programmes (Henderson *et al.*, 1983), surveys and related activities hopes to identify requirements and thereby influence appropriate decision-making agencies on future satellite sensing systems and surveillance programmes. It is significant, however, that the strongest influences are coming from the geological and agricultural sectors where substantial commercial impetus has provided the basis for making fullest possible use of the available data.

Considerations of cost are likely to be the most important in determining future developments in the availability and improvement of satellite imagery. It is interesting from an economic viewpoint that the Landsat 5 TM satellite is designed for retrieval and replacement by the Space Shuttle and possibly this may provide the means to launch and maintain operational satellites much more cheaply. If satellite imagery becomes too expensive to the user, a much greater emphasis is likely to be placed on high-altitude aircraft aerial photography and remote sensing operational programmes. The role of space photography should also not be forgotten, as recently demonstrated by the success of a Russian manned satellite in using this method to quickly select the route of the new Siberian gas pipeline.

Improvements in the spectral sensitivity and spatial resolution of satellite imagery come at the cost of substantial increases in the volume of data to be processed, however, and require equal development in computing capacity and interpretation techniques. Continuous improvement to spatial resolution may not always be cost effective (Hyde and Vesper 1981, 1984) as is evident from Figure 7.2. Fortunately, the development of microprocessors and low-cost memories has dramatically lowered the cost of digital image-processing, and now powerful mini- and microcomputers provide ever better price/performance ratios for engineers to undertake interactive image processing and interpretation (Kiefer and Gunther, 1983). Other interesting recent trends include the development of custom-built image-processing integrated circuits which increase speed of operation but decrease flexibility, and the integration of image processing with geographic information system techniques. The latter development is likely to become increasingly important for those engineers and planners who become involved in regional management and database planning systems.

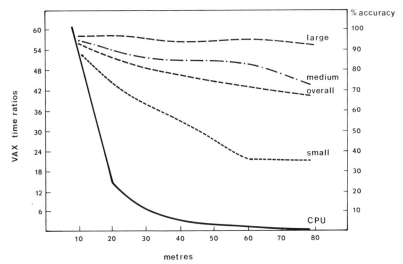

Figure 7.2   Cost $v.$ resolution. Comparisons of machine processing times for overall, small, medium and large parcels are presented. The optimum range is reached somewhere between 20 m and 40 m resolution (Hyde and Vesper, 1984).

Finally, in reviewing the future development of image processing and interpretation techniques it is evident that there will be a general increase in the level of algorithm sophistication, especially in the types of input features (e.g. textural, contextual etc.) and the methods by which they are used. The spatial context in images will become a more important aspect in computer interpretation (Landgrebe, 1981) and also the use of texture to improve accuracy in discriminating and classifying features (Shih and Schowengerdt, 1983), although this is likely to substantially increase computational requirements. Another contemporary trend in image interpretation is the move from numerical decision-theory models to the more complex aspects of advanced pattern recognition and models in artificial intelligence. However, for the immediate future, it is sufficient for engineers making use of satellite and remote sensing imagery to know that research has increased our awareness of the inherent complexity of the human interpretation process. A better understanding of this process now provides a substantial basis for further refinement of computer-assisted techniques and overall improvement in interpretation accuracy and efficiency.

7.5   Landsat data and engineering planning in practice

In reviewing the engineering applications of Landsat satellite imagery in regional planning studies, it is obvious that the greatest benefits are likely to be achieved in overseas countries where existing sources of information are inadequate. Engineers will probably also make more use of Landsat data overseas as the value of satellite imagery can be severely limited in temperate climates where cloud cover is often predominant for large parts of the year. It is for these reasons that the case studies chosen in this section to illustrate the varied uses of Landsat data in regional engineering planning practice have been taken from projects executed in developing countries. Although the greatest cost benefits of utilizing satellite imagery will be attained in these situations, the value of Landsat data must not be ignored for planning activities in industrialized countries where there is a growing need to monitor environmental features, pollution and land use changes and to establish regional geographic information database systems for management purposes.

The following case studies have been selected with the intention of demonstrating the very wide scope and range of application for the processing and interpretation of Landsat data in current engineering planning practice.

7.5.1 Feeder road planning, People's Republic of Benin

Development of the national transport system is important in Benin for improving rural access in order to open up new areas, stimulate production, encourage tourism, and assist marketing in most regions. As improved transport could become a powerful lever for agricultural, industrial and commercial development, a rural access roads programme has been initiated with World Bank funding to provide better communications and facilitate the expansion of agriculture in the most undeveloped parts of the country.

In order to plan the rural access roads in Atacora Province, and ensure that the levels of economic activity could grow in association with better overall efficiency in transport and marketing, information needed to be provided on the current distribution of subsistence farming and the likelihood of it being extended under population pressure to neighbouring regions. New areas also had to be identified where the land was possibly capable of sustaining agricultural development on either a subsistence or more capital-intensive project basis. Similarly, evaluation of important woodland and wildlife resources was required for the region, so that appropriate access could be planned for purposes of timber extraction, management or conservation, and tourist development in association with the Pendjari National Reserve which is gazetted over an extensive area in the north of the Province.

Although the absence of information on the physical properties of the terrain and of up-to-date topographic maps initially posed many problems in studying the natural resources of the Province, the availability of multidate regional data from the Landsat series of satellites enabled an interpretation programme to be implemented, whereby, using bulk processed products, sufficient information was determined on which to base a preliminary assessment as to where rural access roads were most likely to be needed. As costs had to be minimized at this phase of the project, standard photographic products were utilized for simple manual interpretation based on a routine analysis of the black-and-white and colour tone pattern elements recorded on the bands 5 and 7 and colour composite imagery respectively. After interpreting different seasonal imagery in conjunction with a background review of existing sources of information, a multidisciplinary team was able to use these simple methods to prepare a series of transparent thematic map overlays at a scale of 1:250 000 for the whole area of over 30 000 km² at a low cost and within an office period of eight weeks.

The thematic overlays, which accompanied an up-to-date Landsat photo-mosaic base map, were able to show (a) surface drainage, watersheds and all other relevant hydrological features; (b) regional geology including lithology and structure and identification of those areas exhibiting the greatest potential for groundwater location and development; (c) vegetation, including plant community distribution and structure relevant to livestock and rangeland development; (d) current land use, with designation of areas under cultivation, and land capability including an indication of those areas where the greatest potential exists for expanding agriculture and forestry; (e) regional distri-bution of soil types and their significance in relation to geotechnical considerations for road design and location of sources of appropriate materials for low-cost, rural access road construction; and (f) existing roads and settlements, in addition to selected routes for access roads required to open up those areas chosen as being most suitable for agricultural development.

In addition to the overlays, a detailed report was also submitted with the study, which included recommendations for the subsequent phases to be followed in order to implement the total investment of 757 km of rural access roads proposed for Atacora Province. Provisional alignments for the feeder roads were located, after closely studying the land use and capability, drainage, geology and groundwater, engineering soils and construction materials map overlays, on the basis of achieving, wherever possible, a compromise between the following criteria: (a) shortest possible route between settlements, (b) minimum requirements for drainage crossings and thus the possibility of structures, (c) minimum frequency of steep gradients, (d) avoidance of low-lying areas likely to provide poor foundations and to be subject to flooding, and (e) nearest distance to possible sources of construc-tion materials to minimize haulage.

On completion of the preliminary study, more detailed investigations were undertaken using an interactive, digital image processing and film writing system to provide 1:100 000 scale hard copy products from which the different types of homogeneous landscape occurring throughout Atacora Province could be classified. This terrain evaluation, based on interpreting specially processed Landsat data, allowed the compilation of an initial inventory of land systems and their engineering, soils, land use, vegetation, agricultural capability, water development and other significant properties, in order to provide a practical framework for planning and assessing all subsequent development projects and highway engineering activities within the Province. To obtain maximum information from the Landsat CCT data, a whole range of processing, enhancement and feature extraction routines were used with emphasis being placed on geometric correction, contrast stretching, digital mosaicing and enlargement, and principal components analysis for the geomorphological related aspects of study. In applying these techniques it was also possible to utilize the terrain evaluation study as a working basis for establishing a preliminary system of data storage.

Utilizing the Landsat terrain-based planning framework, in conjunction with an analysis of future sequential data available from the Thematic Mapper, SPOT and other satellite surveillance programmes, it should be possible to monitor accurately the relationship between feeder road construction, visible induced benefits, land use changes and impact on rural agricultural development (Beaumont, 1983). Additionally, as the results of the Landsat study of Atacora Province are extrapolated to other neighbouring regions, it is envisaged that use of an established data storage system will prevent wasteful repetition of survey effort, and facilitate the transfer of engineering data and experience in construction and rural development to similar areas throughout West Africa.

7.5.2 Water resources planning, north-east Somalia

Northern Somalia consists predominantly of semi-arid to arid terrain where meagre annual rainfall can for the most part only support rangeland, which forms the basis for the major economic activity of livestock rearing. As the rearing of cattle and other animals is crucial to the livelihood of the nomadic people living in these rural areas, and to the economy of Somalia as a whole, considerable attention continues to be given, through international aid, for improving the rangeland and management practices so that livestock carrying capacity can be significantly increased. Achieving this objective, and expanding the agricultural potential of the rangelands, depends on the development of water resources and improving rural access roads to obtain better efficiency in transport and marketing.

Engineers and agricultural specialists working in northern Somalia face the common problem existing in most Third World countries: available topographic mapping, aerial photography and sources of information on natural resources are inadequate for planning purposes. This problem was largely overcome, however, on a recent project undertaken within the development programme for the region, where the potential of surface and groundwater resources were evaluated in relation to watering sites, flood irrigation and fodder production required to increase the livestock carrying capacity of the land over an area of approximately 200 000 km^2 (see Figure 7.3). Easy access to good quality Landsat data of this region enabled a multidisciplinary team to prepare, after interpreting different seasonal imagery in conjunction with

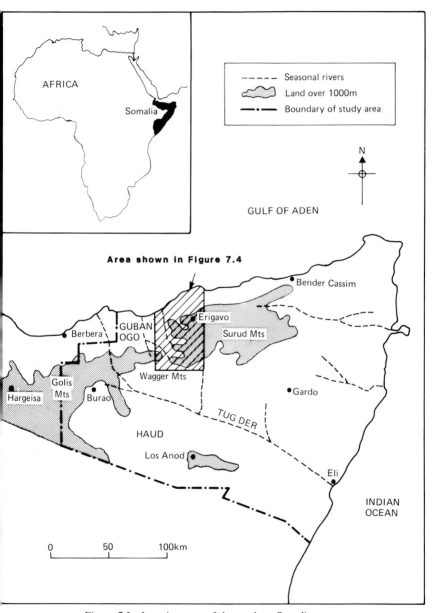

Figure 7.3 Location map of the northern Somalia area.

Figure 7.4   Portion of a Landsat MSS Band 7 image recorded over northern Somalia.

a background review of existing information sources, a series of transparent thematic map overlays for the whole area to show drainage and surface water resources, geology, vegetation types and structure, groundwater potential, and land capability, within a period of three months (Beaumont, 1982a).

As time schedules and budget restraints on the overall project required costs to be minimized, the majority of the mapping programme was accomplished by means of manual interpretation of bulk processed Landsat image products subject to simple photographic processing, enlargement and colour enhancement procedures. In addition to the overlays which accompanied an up-to-date Landsat photomosaic base map for the region at a scale of 1:500 000, a detailed report could also be produced from the study which included recommendations for the subsequent phases to be followed in order to improve the animal carrying capacity of each part of the rangeland in northern Somalia. Figure 7.4 illustrates the clarity of terrain, and especially surface drainage information, recorded on infrared, MSS Band 7 imagery over part of the study area, and Figure 7.5 the level of detail interpreted and mapped from the same imagery as a thematic overlay for each feature of interest. The success of the Landsat study can be judged from the fact that only a few minor adjustments were required to the interpretation maps when they were checked in the ensuing field programme.

In overcoming the problems of inadequate planning data, the cost effectiveness of utilizing Landsat data was clearly emphasized by the interpretation and mapping studies taking just twelve weeks to complete at a fee of only £12 000 in 1979/80. Post-evaluation appraisal of the project results has also demonstrated that they are equivalent to those presented for neighbouring regions of similar size where, using traditional methods, comparable surveys have taken several years to complete and accordingly involved considerably more expense. Information acquired from Landsat data has thus enabled potentially profitable areas to be initially identified for the development of surface and subsurface water supplies necessary for increased fodder production, and as such also provided a sound basis for the planning of an adequate feeder roads and transport infrastructure required to advance this and associated economic development within the region.

7.5.3 *Agricultural development planning, southern Sudan*

Agricultural development in the Southern Region of the Sudan has been severely affected over a long period of time by major prolonged conflict preventing stabilized settlement of the land. Consequently, with stability only returning to the Region in recent times, there has been a continual problem of reinstating subsistence agriculture to sufficiently productive levels to sustain the present and future food requirements of the local population. As food shortages can become critical in prolonged times of drought, priority has been given within financial and technical aid to those districts west of the River Nile,

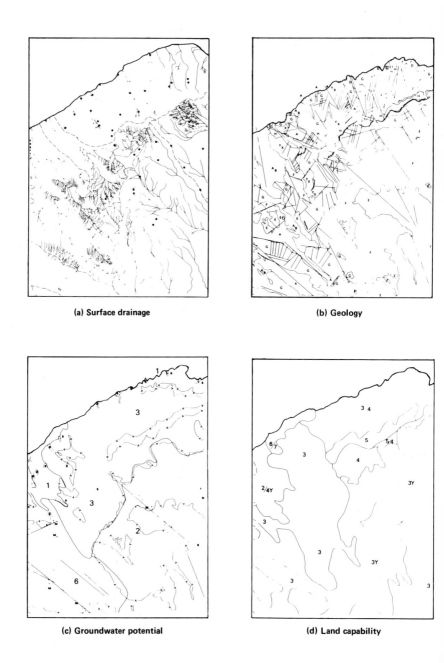

(a) Surface drainage

(b) Geology

(c) Groundwater potential

(d) Land capability

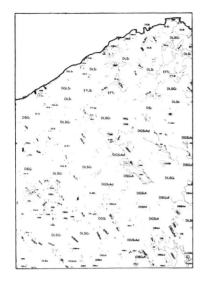

LEAF FUNCTION
D   Deciduous
E   Evergreen

LIFE FORM   Dominant/Secondary
F   Forest
T   Thicket
S   Scrub
L S Low scrub
G   Grassland
M   Seasonal marsh liable to flood
C   Cultivation and grazing

DENSITY
c   Continuous growth
i   Interrupted growth
s   Sparse tufts or groups
b   Barren: largely or entirely absent

SPECIAL FEATURES
A   Arcuate vegetation patterns
A d Dispersed arcuate vegetation patterns

(e) Physiognomic vegetation classification

(a) DRAINAGE OVERLAY

——— Drainage lines
- - - - - Drainage zone with no definite
        channel
●   Permanent surface water
— — — Watershed

(b) GEOLOGY

A Alluvium (recent)
B Boulder beds (quaternary)
C Braided channel nets
D Inter bedded   Shales, Marls, Grits
   Limestones (Miocene)
E Limestone (Kerkar, Middle Eocene)
F Anhydrite (Lower, Middle Eocene)
G Limestone (AuraduLower Eocene)
H Nubian sandstone (Cretaceous)
I Limestones (Jurassic)
J Basal rocks
X Metamorphic rocks
Y Granite rocks

⌐   Fracture
ᴧᴧᴧ Escarpment

(c) GROUND WATER POTENTIAL

Ⓜ   Moisture zones
←   Springs
Ⓢ   Zones of surface water percolation
———   Potential ground water along
        fractures/faults
—v—v—   Potential ground water zones in
        aquifers. Gypsum-free
—Y—   Potential ground water zones in aquifers
        which are probably high in solutes,
        especially gypsum

(d) LAND CAPABILITY

1 Land primarily suited for fodder cultivation under
   natural rainfall (None in area shown)
2 Land primarily suited for fodder cultivation
   with irrigation
3 Land suitable for managed grazing in the wet season
4 Land suitable for managed grazing in the dry season
5 Land suitable for forestry applications
6 Land suitable for managed grazing with limited
   potential for improved pasture
7 Land unsuitable for improvement
Y as suffix indicates that gypsum-resistant species
   will be necessary

Keys to   (a–d)

Figure 7.5   Examples of information interpreted from Landsat imagery. These were originally presented as overlays to the image shown in Figure 7.4.

where most people are known to be concentrated, and the land resources and climate are likely to be more favourable for expansion of agricultural smallholdings and food production.

One of the major programmes within the overall development strategy has been to prepare agricultural development plans for several of these administrative districts and provide assistance to the Regional Ministry of Agriculture and Natural Resources, so that an administrative and operational organization could be established to collect and coordinate relevant data for project identification and planning purposes. The Land Use and Physical Planning Unit was thus established to acquire physical resource data, whilst other units were developed for related aspects of study including economics, agricultural statistics, farm management and extension, agronomic research, road and agricultural engineering and sociology. As the Southern Region, in its entirety, is larger in area than the whole of Kenya, the acquisition of regional planning data posed a formidable problem which was additionally exacerbated by virtual lack of infrastructure in the region, difficulties of logistic support for field operations, and the total absence of adequate mapping, airphoto coverage and other relevant information.

Funding constraints and the schedules for the planning programme ruled out the possibility of full topographic air survey and mapping, whilst the remoteness of the region, coupled with the overwhelming difficulties of organizing vehicles, fuel, spare parts, food and other basic commodities, made the prospect of acquiring data by appropriate traverses and field sampling an unrealistic alternative within the time available. In order to overcome these problems, therefore, it became evident that a remote sensing interpretation study of available Landsat MSS and RBV satellite imagery could provide the only viable method for preparing up-to-date base maps at a 1:250000 scale for each district so that all survey data could be placed in the proper spatial context. Similarly, in the short term, this also provided the means to satisfy the requirement for current land use maps showing where existing agriculture was being undertaken, and where settlements, indicating the highest concentrations of population, were located.

After an intensive period of interpreting multidate standard black-and-white and colour composite 1:250000 scale Landsat image products, supported by minimum ground checking and sampling, a preliminary series of base and land use maps were prepared for each district within a period of six months. This programme also enabled counterpart staff to be trained in the use and interpretation of Landsat data, for which a special manual was prepared and adapted for local needs and conditions (Beaumont, 1982b). The need for a viable source of planning information was further confirmed when existing 1:250000 scale national map sheets, based on the pioneering work of explorers in the early 1900s, were compared with the Landsat imagery. In remote areas the map sheets mainly consisted of empty space, whilst in other areas, the satellite imagery revealed great inaccuracies in positional detail, with some rivers being up to forty miles out of true position. Similarly, village settlements and lines of communication had greatly changed with time, and in some instances, it was also found that there were anomalies on the graticule of geographical co-ordinates drawn on to the map sheets.

The ability quickly to produce base maps from interpreting Landsat imagery and integrating local knowledge so as to show drainage, status of roads (current standard, trafficability by lorry, four-wheel drive or alternative vehicle, and whether access is seasonal or all year round), names and location of settlements and villages, names of rivers, identification of chiefs' villages, dispensaries, hospitals, agricultural extension centres and other related features for each district proved invaluable to all those concerned with the different aspects of agricultural development planning. Similarly, this also proved true for the district maps showing areas under cultivation and different classes of land use, for before the Landsat study programme, very little knowledge existed on exact location of roads, settlements, nature and extent of cultivated areas, gazetted forest and game reserves, and their spatial re-lationship to each other, especially in the remoter areas. This information was urgently required, however, by the planning authorities, as the main strategy within the overall agricultural development plans for each district consisted of focusing attention on and developing extension services in those areas already under smallholder cultivation, and for reasons of practical logistics, which also afforded easy access to existing road communications.

A wide range of information interpreted from the Landsat imagery also proved to be most useful for associated highway and water engineering studies carried out within the planning programme. For example, route alignments could be studied in relation to such factors as bridging and materials requirements, areas susceptible to flooding and poor subgrade conditions in addition to overall transport problems associated with rural access and seasonal transhumance. Similarly, the water resources of each district could be evaluated with respect to supplies for village communities and the potential for both small- or large-scale irrigation schemes. Sequential studies of Landsat data additionally provided information on seasonal flooding which signi-ficantly affects many aspects of agriculture, engineering and socio-economic activities within the region.

The important relationship between communications, settlement and agricultural development, so clearly evident on Landsat imagery of the region, is illustrated in Plate 6 which shows in the Mundri district how ribbon development is expanding along the extent of a new road constructed under German aid between Juba, Mundri and Maridi. A significant trend is also apparent from the imagery in that people are attracted to create new settlements and develop agriculture wherever roads have been newly con-structed or upgraded. The most obvious example can be discerned in Plate 6 where the settlement area of Mundri has greatly expanded at the expense of the old provincial centre of Amadi, to the north, due primarily to the recent construction of the good-standard gravel road.

As many of the selected districts extended into the swampy grasslands on the margin of the Sudd, where the grazing of livestock is a dominant factor in the local economy and social practices of the population, an important requirement also existed for information on rangeland, vegetation and patterns of grazing in relation to flooding and water availability in these areas. In this respect, the repetitive nature and monitoring capability of Landsat satellite data similarly provided one of the best and most cost-effective means of acquiring essential data on the seasonal changes which affect these areas and their significance with respect to district and overall regional development planning (Vass, 1983). These types of studies using sequential Landsat data have also greatly contributed to environmental impact investigations being undertaken in the Sudd region associated with the development and construction of the Jonglei Canal which has been designed to increase the volume of water flow down the River Nile. It is envisaged that in the near future similar use will be made of Landsat data with respect to the engineering developments now taking place for oil and gas development within the region. There can be no doubt that Landsat satellite imagery will also prove especially useful in the selection of the alignment and associated engineering studies required to locate the new pipeline planned to transport the region's oil over a distance of 1500 km to a new refinery and possible export terminal at Port Sudan.

7.5.3 Highway maintenance planning, Niger

The planning and implementation of highway maintenance is becoming increasingly important in developing countries where the simultaneous requirements to keep up standards of existing infrastructure and continue new developments pose severe strains on the availability and allocation of scarce financial and technical resources. One approach to overcoming these problems is to increase efficiency through improved practice in planning and methods of management which, in turn, are initially dependent on acquisition of reliable information. Landsat satellite imagery can play a significant role in providing relevant data for highway maintenance both for purposes of inventory (e.g. roads, drainage structures, sources of construction material) and the identification of physical and socio-economic features which will influence the road network and possibly the measures required to keep it in good repair. This has recently been demonstrated on road studies undertaken for the Ministry of Public Works and Town Planning in the Republic of Niger.

The paved road between the provincial centre of Goure and N'guigmi on the old shoreline of Lake Chad in the south-east of the Republic of Niger, after falling into disrepair, has been the subject of recent maintenance and rehabilitation studies. In undertaking a design review with respect to overall maintenance, and possible realignment for the rehabilitation of the failed sections of the road, Landsat satellite imagery was interpreted, in conjunction with ground surveys, to acquire relevant geotechnical information on the physical characteristics of the terrain traversed by the present and proposed alternative sections of the 420 km route. This was necessitated in part by the poor map coverage of the region, and the need to acquire hydrological data and identify additional sources of construction materials within a six-week study programme.

Before the alignments on the ground were inspected, useful background studies to familiarize the engineers with the different types of terrain occurring in the region were accomplished by interpreting the Landsat imagery with reference to the maps and volumes produced from the Land Resources Study of North-East Nigeria carried out by the Land Resources Division of the Overseas Development Administration (Bawden et al., 1972). In this respect it proved significant that the land systems mapped for north-east Nigeria could readily be identified on the Landsat imagery and extrapolated across the international border to the neighbouring region traversed by the Goure–N'guigmi road alignment in the Republic of Niger. Relevant information on landforms, soils, geology, hydrology, land use and other relevant features, summarized for each facet of the different land systems, could thus be related by means of the Landsat imagery to different sections of the route for purposes of maintenance appraisal, geotechnics and design review.

As anticipated from the preparatory investigations, most of the road from Goure to N'guigmi running without earthworks through areas of pre-dominantly fixed sand dunes was found to be in sufficiently good condition to require resurfacing only. About 90 km of the route, however, had totally disintegrated and required complete reconstruction. Significantly, this section was identified from the Landsat imagery as coinciding with Land System Vf4, (see Figure 7.6) the alluvial flood plain of the Komadougou Yobe River, which extends up to 20 km north of the existing course of the river. Although readily apparent on the Landsat images, the widespread nature and boundaries of the flood plain could not easily be appreciated either on available maps, airphotos or even on the ground, due to the large scale of the terrain system and the relatively uniform landscapes characteristic of the region. The reasons for road failure in the 90 km section of the route were thus easy to predict and confirm in the field, for the disintegration of the pavement correlated perfectly with the extent of the alluvial flood plain land system where the predominant subgrade material is a silty or very silty fine sand (containing 10–14% silt) which replaces the normal fine, single-sized, dune sand subgrade material containing little silt (0–10%). This more silty material which, with a higher water table, retains moisture for longer periods than the dune sand, is less permeable and exhibits a loss of strength when its moisture content is increased. The strength of the dune sands, however, is much less sensitive to changes in moisture content.

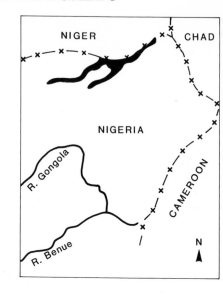

Facet	(i)	(ii)	(iii)	(v)	(iv)	(vi)
Landform	Recent alluvial plain	Point bars	Swales	Drainage lines	Spill plains	Back swa
Soil	Weakly developed soils	Weakly developed soils	Vertisols/ hydromorphic soils	Hydromorphic soils	Halomorphic soils/ vertisols	As (iii)
Vegetation wooded	N. alluvial complex	*Leptadenia* spp	N. alluvial complex	As facet (i)	As facet (i)	As (i)
Vegetation grassland	Alluvial complex	*Aristida* spp	*Schoenefeldia/ Panicum* spp.	Alluvial complex	*Schoenefeldia Panicum* spp.	As (v)
Land use	Scattered cultivation Dry season grazing	Sparse cultivation Grazing	Dry season grazing	Dry season grazing	Dry season grazing	Dry seas graz

3 m
↑
altitude

Figure 7.6   Land System Vf 4: the Yobe flood plain. (After Bawden *et al.*, 1972)

Identification of the flood plain land system and its associated silty soils is facilitated on the Landsat imagery by the distinctive pattern of land use produced by the settlement and agricultural exploitation of these areas of better water retention.

As detailed ground surveys further revealed that the road pavement in the failed section was on the same level or below the surrounding ground on a silty sand subgrade with no drainage works, the process of disintegration could easily be understood. After periods of heavy rain, run-off water collecting in the lower-lying areas penetrates the side ground and gradually wets up the subgrade beneath the pavement. Loss of strength due to increased moisture content results in failure of the road base and cracking of the surface under traffic. During further flooding of the road, water penetrates the cracks and accelerates the base failure. Consequently, to reinstate the failed section of the alignment, reconstruction has been recommended whereby the road will be raised on a 1.5 m high embankment with provision for adequate drainage structures, the siting of which has been guided by interpretation of the Landsat imagery in conjunction with ground surveys.

In conclusion to the design review and maintenance studies, it was determined from interpretation of Landsat data and field investigations that the probability of road failure due to the water table rising above ground level and the incidence of flooding from the Komadougou Yobe River could be discounted. Consequently, on the basis of this information, recommendations could be put forward as to the most suitable alignment for the section of road requiring rehabilitation and the most cost effective design options for subsequently involving minimum maintenance. As these investigations had to be undertaken within a very short period of time, the contribution of information acquired from Landsat data proved invaluable with respect to obtaining an understanding of the physical causes of pavement failure on the road and the engineering options required to overcome repetition of similar problems in the future.

7.6 Conclusions

In this chapter an outline has been given of the applications of Landsat satellite imagery in regional planning and the various interpretation techniques available to acquire information relevant to engineering investigations associated with these studies. The value of Landsat imagery as a source of regional planning information has also been illustrated by reference to actual projects where it is considered that the use of such data significantly contributed to improved practice. In emphasizing that the greatest cost benefits of utilizing satellite imagery are likely to be achieved by engineers in overseas countries with limited sources of relevant information, attention must also be drawn to the main limitation of cloud cover which can adversely affect the deployment of Landsat data in temperate and equatorial climates.

Although it is unlikely that MSS type sensors will be developed that can acquire data through clouds, Landsat imagery should still prove to be useful when recorded in these climatic zones, especially if deployed in tandem with orbiting radar systems, such as the SIR-A recently operated from the Space Shuttle flights, which have a greater ground resolution and all-weather, day and night capability.

Continuing improvements in the spectral sensitivity and spatial resolution of Landsat data, coupled with increased sophistication in image processing and interpretation techniques to extract relevant information, will require the engineer who is likely to make use of satellite imagery in the future to become increasingly involved with software and computer development. The information content within a current single Landsat MSS scene is large, as to cover a ground area of 336 000 sq. km calls for the processing of more than 30 million numbers before any of the data returned to a ground station can be used in the form of an image. It is also significant that in its present operation the spacecraft has the capability to return more than a million separate items of information to the earth each second and, whenever on the daylight side of the globe, 30 billion bits a day for every day of the year. As the TM system becomes fully operational on Landsat 5, there will also be a substantial, exponential increase in the volume of data to be processed due to the greater 30 m spatial resolution of the system and the three additional spectral bands.

Within the immediate future, engineers and planners, besides making routine use of Landsat MSS and RBV data, are most likely to be preoccupied with evaluating new, improved image products recorded by the TM, SPOT and other satellite systems for specific interests and fields of application. The significant capability of this new technology to acquire information, as outlined above, for regional studies is already acting as a catalyst to induce necessary change in planning practices which have become evident in the recent developments to establish regional engineering and geographic information database systems for management purposes. As engineers become more fully involved in environmental issues, and are called upon to further participate in development studies and coordinated planning, the role of Landsat satellite imagery, and remote sensing in general, to provide an integrated, multidisciplinary framework for the acquisition, evaluation, storage and extrapolation of information will be greatly appreciated and highly valued.

Acknowledgements

Grateful acknowledgement is made to the following who gave permission to use the data presented for the case studies referred to in this chapter: Scott Wilson Kirkpatrick and Partners; Ministère des Travaux Publiques de la Construction et de l'Habitat, Direction des Routes et Ponts, Division des Routes de Desserte Rurales, République Populaire du Benin; Sir William Halcrow and Partners; Ministry of Livestock and Forestry, Government of the Somali Democratic Republic; Booker Agriculture International Limited; Overseas Development

Administration; Land Use and Physical Planning Unit, Southern Regional Ministry of Agriculture and Natural Resources, Government of Sudan; and Ministère des Travaux Publiques et de l'Urbanisme, République du Niger.

References

Aitchison, G. D. and Grant, K. (1968) 'Terrain evaluation for engineering', in *Land Evaluation: Papers of a CSIRO symposium (Canberra)*, ed. Stewart, G. A., Macmillan of Australia, Melbourne, pp. 125–142.

Bawden, M. G., Carroll, D. M. and Tuley, P. (1972) *The Land Resources of North East Nigeria* Overseas Development Administration, Foreign and Commonwealth Office, Land Resource Study No. 9. Land Resources Development Centre, Tolworth, Surrey.

Beaumont, T. E. (1977) *Techniques for the Interpretation of Remote Sensing Imagery for Highway Engineering Purposes*. Department of the Environment, Department of Transport, Transport and Road Research Laboratory Report LR753, Crowthorne, Berks.

Beaumont, T. E. (1978) *Remote Sensing for Transport Planning and Highway Engineering in Developing Countries*. Department of the Environment, Department of Transport, Transport and Road Research Laboratory Report SR433, Crowthorne, Berks.

Beaumont, T. E. (1979a) Remote sensing for the location and mapping of engineering construction materials in developing countries. *Q. Jl. Engng. Geol.* 12(3) 147–158.

Beaumont, T. E. (1979b) Remote sensing survey techniques. *J. Instn. Highway Engrs.* 26(4) 2–12.

Beaumont, T. E. (1980) 'Remote sensing for route location and the mapping of highway construction materials in developing countries', in *Proc. 14th Int. Symp. on Remote Sensing of Environment*, ERIM, Ann Arbor, Michigan, pp. 1429–1441.

Beaumont, T. E. (1982a) 'Land capability studies from Landsat satellite data for rural road planning in North East Somalia', in *Proc. OECD Symposium on Terrain Evaluation and Remote Sensing for Highway Engineering in Developing Countries*, OECD, Paris 1980. Department of the Environment, Department of Transport, Transport and Road Research Laboratory Report SR690, Crowthorne, Berks., pp. 86–95.

Beaumont, T. E. (1982b) *A Manual for the Use of Landsat Satellite Imagery for District Agricultural Development Planning in the Southern Region of the Sudan*. Land Use and Physical Planning Unit, Southern Regional Ministry of Agriculture and Natural Resources, Sudan Government, Juba, 111 pp.

Beaumont, T. E. (1983) 'Satellite data as a basis for planning studies of infrastructure and related rural development in Atacora Province, Benin, West Africa', in *Study of Land Transformation Processes from Space and Ground Observations: Proc. Symposium 10 of COSPAR 24th Plenary Meeting (Ottawa)*, ed Ragan, R. M. and Wolman, G., *Advances in Space Research* 2, Pergamon Press, Oxford, pp. 91–96.

Brink, A. B. A., Mabbutt, J. A., Webster, R. and Beckett, P. H. J. (1966) *Report of the Working Group on Land Classification and Data Storage*. Military Engineering Experimental Establishment Report 940, Christchurch, Hants, 97 pp.

Coleman, G. B. and Andrews, H. C. (1979) Image segmentation by clustering *Proc. IEEE* 67(5) 773–785.

Deutsch, M. and Ruggles, F. H. (1978) Hydrological applications of Landsat imagery used in the study of the 1973 Indus River flood, Pakistan. *American Water Resources Association, Water Resources Bulletin*, 14(2) 261–274.

Deutsch, M., Wiesnet, D. R. and Rango, A. (eds.) (1981) *Satellite Hydrology*. American Water Resources Association, Minneapolis, Minnesota, 727 pp.

Dowling, J. W. and Beaven, P. J. (1969) Terrain evaluation for road engineers in developing countries. *J. Instn. Highway Engrs.* 16(6) 5–22.

Estes, J. E. *et al.* (1983) 'Fundamentals of image analysis: analysis of visible and thermal infrared data', in *Manual of Remote Sensing*, Volume 1, (2nd edn.), ed. Colwell, R. N. and Simonett, D. S. American Society of Photogrammetry, Falls Church, Virginia, pp. 987–1124.

Forster, B. (1983) Some urban measurements from Landsat data. *Photogrammetric Engineering and Remote Sensing* 49(12) 1693–1707.

Goetz, A. F. H. *et al.* (1975) *Applications of ERTS Images and Image Processing to Regional Geologic Problems and Geologic Mapping in Northern Arizona*. California Institute of Technology, Jet Propulsion Laboratory, Technical Report 32–1597, 188 pp.

Glass, C. E. and Slemmons, D. B. (1978) *State-of-the-Art for Assessing Earthquake Hazards in the United States, Report II—Imagery in Earthquake Analysis*. U.S. Army Corps of Engineers, Miscellaneous Paper S-73-1, 32–41.

Graybeal, G. E. *et al.* (1974) 'ERTS-1 data in support of the National Programme of Inspection of Dams', in *Proc. NASA Goddard Space Flight Centre, Symposium on the Earth Resources Technology Satellite-1*, NASA, Washington, D.C., Vol 1, Sec. B, pp. 1023–1039.

Hays, W. W., (ed) (1981) *Facing Geologic and Hydrologic Hazards. Earth Science Considerations*. U.S. Geological Survey Professional Paper 1240-B, 109 pp.

Henderson, F. B. *et al.* (1983) 'Evaluation of future geological remote sensing systems from space: the joint Geosat—NASA/JPL test case programme', in *Proc. Symposium on Remote Sensing and Mineral Exploration: National Case Histories based on activities of IGGP Project 143, 24th Plenary Meeting of COSPAR, 16th May–2nd June 1982*, ed. Carter, W. D., *Advances in Space Research 2*, Pergamon Press, Oxford.

Howarth, P. J. and Wickware, G. M. (1981) Procedures for change detection using Landsat digital data. *Int. J. Remote Sensing* 2(3) 277–291.

Hyde, R. F. and Vesper, N. J. (1981) 'An evaluation of the utility of smaller Landsat ground resolution levels', in *Matching Remote Sensing Technologies and their Applications, Proc. 9th Annual Conference of Remote Sensing Society, (London)*, Remote Sensing Society, University of Reading, pp. 475–484.

Hyde, R. F. and Vesper, N. J. (1984) Some effects of resolution cell size on image quality *NOAA, Landsat Data Users Notes* 29, 9–12.

Jensen, J. R. (1981) Urban change detection mapping using Landsat digital data. *American Cartographer* 8, 127–147.

Jensen, J. R. *et al.* (1983) 'Urban/suburban land use analysis', in *Manual of Remote Sensing*, Vol. 2, (2nd edn.), ed. Colwell, R. N. and Estes, J. E., American Society of Photogrammetry, Falls Church, Virginia, pp. 1571–1666.

Johnson, G. E., Vining, R. F. and Loveland, T. R. (1980) 'Remote sensing applied to irrigation engineering', in *Proc. 1st International Conference on Computing in Civil Engineering (New York)*, American Society of Civil Engineers, pp. 545–560.

Johnson, G. E., Loveland, T. R. and Anderson, W. H. (1981) *The Columbia River and Tributaries Irrigation Withdrawals Analysis Project*. Technicolor Graphic Services, Inc. EROS Data Center, Executive Summary Report CRT-45, 18 pp.

Khorram, S. (1982) 'Development of a remote sensing—aided digital databank for large scale land use planning', in *Proc. 16th Int. Symp. on Remote Sensing of Environment*, ERIM, Ann Arbor, Michigan, 13 pp.

Kiefer, R. W. and Gunther, F. J. (1983) Digital image processing using the Apple II microcomputer. *Photogrammetric Engineering and Remote Sensing*, 49(8) 1167–1174.

Krinsley, D. B. (1977) 'Use of ERTS-1 (Landsat 1) images for engineering geologic applications, North-Central Iran', in *Proc. 1st Annual Wm. T. Pecora Memorial Symposium*, eds. Woll, P. W. and Fischer, W. A., U.S. Geological Survey Professional Paper 1015, 113–121.

Landgrebe, D. A. (1981) Analysis technology for land remote sensing. *Proc. IEEE*, 69(5) 628–642.

Lawrance, C. J. (1977) *The Use of Punched Cards in the Storage and Retrieval of Engineering Information in Ethiopia*. Department of the Environment, Department of Transport, Transport and Road Research Laboratory Report SR248, Crowthorne, Berks.

Lillesand, T. M. and Kiefer, R. W. (1979) *Remote Sensing and Image Interpretation* John Wiley and Sons, New York, 612 pp.

Lillesand, T. M. (1983) Issues surrounding the commercialization of civil remote sensing from space. *Photogrammetric Engineering and Remote Sensing* 49(4) 495–504.

Lo, C. P. and Welch, R. (1977) Chinese urban population estimates. *Annals, Association of American Geographers* 47: 246–253.

Marble, D. F. and Peuquet, D. J. (1983) 'Geographic information systems and remote sensing', in *Manual of Remote Sensing*, Vol. 1 (2nd edn.), ed. Colwell, R. N. and Simonett, D. S., American Society of Photogrammetry, Falls Church, Virginia, pp. 923–958.

Mathur, B. S. (1979) Remote sensing sensors for environmental studies. *Am. Soc. Civ. Engrs. Transportation Engineering Journal* 105(TE4) 439–455.

Mitchell, C. W. (1973) *Terrain Evaluation—An Introduction Handbook to the History, Principles and Methods of Practical Terrain Assessment*. Longman, London, 165 pp.

Moik, J. G. (1980) *Digital Processing of Remotely Sensed Images*. NASA Scientific and Technical Information Branch, NASA SP-431, 330 pp.

Myers, V. I. *et al.* (1983) 'Remote sensing applications in agriculture', in *Manual of Remote Sensing*, Vol. 2 (2nd edn.), ed. Colwell, R. N. and Estes, J. E., American Society of Photogrammetry, Falls Church, Virginia, pp. 2111–2228.

National Academy of Sciences, (1977) *Resource Sensing from Space: Prospects for Developing Countries,* National Academy of Sciences, Washington, D. C., 202 pp.

Ogrosky, C. E. (1975) Population estimates from satellite imagery. *Photogrammetric Engineering and Remote Sensing* 41 (6) 707–712.

Overseas Unit., ed. (1982) 'Terrain evaluation and remote sensing for highway engineering in developing countries', in *Proc. Symp. OECD*, Paris, 12–14 September 1979, Department of the Environment, Department of Transport, Transport and Road Research Laboratory Report SR 690, Crowthorne, Berks. 172 pp.

Pavlin, G. B. and Langston, C. A. (1983) An integrated study of reservoir-induced seismicity and Landsat imagery at Lake Kariba, Africa. *Photogrammetric Engineering and Remote Sensing* 49(4) 513–525.

Richards, P. B. *et al.* (1983) 'Recommended satellite imagery capabilities for disaster management', in *Proceedings of the Meeting of the International Astronautical Federation, Paris, September 1982,* Paper IAF-82-103.

Rowan, L. *et al.* (1976) *Discrimination of Rock Types and Detection of Hydrothermally Altered Areas in South-Central Nevada by the Use of Computer-Enhanced ERTS Images.* U.S. Geological Survey Professional Paper 883, Washington, 35 pp.

Schreiber, W. F. (1978) Image processing for quality improvement *Proc. IEEE*, 66(12) 439–453.

Shih, E. H. H. and Schowengerdt, R. A. (1983) Classification of arid geomorphic surfaces using Landsat spectral and textural features. *Photogrammetric Engineering and Remote Sensing* 49(3) 337–347.

Siegel, B. S. and Gillespie, A. R. (1980) *Remote Sensing in Geology.* John Wiley and Sons, New York, 702 pp.

Swain, P. H. and Davis, S. M. (1978) *Remote Sensing: The Quantitative Approach.* McGraw-Hill, New York, 396 pp.

Todd, W. J., George, A. J. and Bryant, N. A. (1979) Satellite-aided evaluation of population exposure to air pollution. *Environmental Science and Technology* 13.

Toll, D. L., Royal, J. A. and Davis, J. B. (1980) Urban area update procedures using Landsat data. *Proceedings, American Society of Photogrammetry, (Oct.)*, 12 pp. (1980).

Tom, C. H. and Miller, L. D. (1984) An automated land-use mapping comparison of the Bayesian maximum likelihood and linear discriminant analysis algorithms. *Photogrammetric Engineering and Remote Sensing* 50(2) 193–207.

Tucker, C. J. (1978) A comparison of satellite sensor bands for vegetation monitoring. *Photogrammetric Engineering and Remote Sensing* 44(11) 1369–1380.

Turner, A. K. (1978) A decade of experience in computer route selection. *Photogrammetric Engineering and Remote Sensing* 44(12) 1561–1576.

Vass, P. A. (1983) 'A Landsat study of the vegetation and seasonal livestock grazing in the Southern Sudan', in *Remote Sensing for Rangeland Monitoring and Management, Proc. 11th Annual Conference of Remote Sensing Society (Silsoe)*, Remote Sensing Society, University of Reading, 51–68.

Vincent, R., Drake, B. and Jackson, P. (1973) *Tunnel-Site Selection by Remote Sensing Techniques* Environmental Research Institute for Michigan, Report 191701-3-P, ERIM, Ann Arbor, Michigan, 10 pp.

Voûte, C. (1984) Agreement and disagreement on an international satellite monitoring agency. *Remote Sensing Letters, International Journal of Remote Sensing* 5(2) 479–483.

Zobrist, A. L., Bryant, N. A. and McLeod, R. G. (1983) Technology for large digital mosaics of Landsat data. *Photogrammetric Engineering and Remote Sensing* 49(9) 1325–1335.

8 Interpretation of aerial photographs for site investigations

M. C. MATTHEWS

8.1 Introduction

The recent developments in satellite imagery and image processing techniques have provided an invaluable source of data for the reconnaissance and feasibility stages of regional engineering surveys discussed in Chapter 7. The ground resolution provided by the present satellite imaging systems is not suitable, however, for detailed site investigations which are normally carried out at the design stage of a project. The objectives of the design stage investigations are to provide a detailed assessment of ground conditions and the necessary geotechnical parameters on which to base the final design. This stage clearly involves a physical survey of the ground which can only be carried out cost effectively if problem areas can be isolated in the early phases of the investigation. Before the layout of any boreholes, drill holes, trial pits or geophysical surveys can be designed, a thorough desk study is necessary in which all the available background information about the site and surrounding area is carefully studied. Aerial photography should form a fundamental part of this study. Aerial photographs, unlike maps, do not suffer the limitations of subjectivity and scale. They provide a comprehensive yet inexpensive source of data in the form of an instantaneous and definitive picture of the ground. This 'bird's eye' view allows the engineer to draw conclusions of engineering significance such as soil type, drainage conditions, slope instability, location of abandoned mineshafts and workings, mining subsidence, sink-holes, spring-lines, areas of seepage, faults, rock outcrops, sources of construction materials and erosion. Old aerial photographs, when available, can give a history of changes in topography and drainage system, coastal erosion, filling of pits and quarries, removal of trees and the previous uses of the site. The latter is particularly valuable in developed countries where the history of the site may be a critical factor in the design. It should be remembered that aerial photographs, although a valuable source of data, are complementary to maps and other information about the project area and hence should be examined in conjunction with these. The conclusions should be confirmed or revised by site inspection where possible. In undeveloped and developing countries where background data in map or report form may be limited, aerial photographs will be required to provide most if not all the preliminary information.

The interpretation of aerial photographs is not as straightforward as the interpretation of maps since little surface detail is omitted. Much information can be gained from aerial photographs by the non-specialist and hence an engineer should not be deterred from attempting to use them due to lack of experience. It is possible to carry out useful work with aerial photographs after only basic tuition. Expertise in interpretation rapidly comes with practice. The interpretation of any image whether digital or photographic involves two stages; firstly the identification of ground features and secondly the evaluation of their significance. In contrast to the precise and quantitative nature of photogrammetry, interpretation is usually carried out as a qualitative or semi-quantitative exercise. Military intelligence was probably the first application of air-photo interpretation, and World War II gave rise to some major advances in aerial photography. Since then air-photo interpretation has been applied extensively in the fields of geology, geomorphology, agriculture, forestry, archaeology, hydrology, pedology and plant ecology. The geotechnical and engineering geological interpretation of aerial photography is discussed by Burton (1969), Norman (1969), Dumbleton and West (1970), Norman (1970), Norman et al. (1975), Edwards (1976), Rengers and Soeters (1980), Clayton et al. (1982), and Bennett (1983).

It is the aim of this chapter to describe the parameters which affect the interpretation of photography and hence aid the selection of the material best suited for a particular job, and to outline the fundamental principles of image interpretation. These fundamental principles apply both to digital images produced by scanning remote sensing systems and to photographic products.

8.2 Photographic parameters affecting interpretation

Regardless of the skill of the interpreter or the methods of viewing the photographs, the amount of information which can be obtained will depend largely on the photographic image. The parameters which affect the image include:

(i) geometry of image (orientation of camera axis);
(ii) emulsion (type of film) and filter combinations;
(iii) scale of photographs;
(iv) image medium;
(v) time of day of photography;
(vi) season of photography.

All these parameters are relatively constant and easily controlled. The photographic image is also affected by natural factors which are variable and include colour of objects photographed, position of an object with respect to the angle of the sun, and amount of haze in the atmosphere. The constant factors may be varied to suit the application for which the photographs are to be used and hence may be considered as criteria for the selection of existing photography or for commissioning aerial photography.

The major types of aerial photography are defined by the orientation of the camera axis, film and filter combinations, and the amount of overlap between adjacent photographs. These have been defined in Chapter 2 and hence only those factors which affect interpretation will be discussed here.

8.2.1 *Geometry of image*

On the basis of the orientation of the camera axis, aerial photographs have been classified as either vertical or oblique. Both types of photography may be used for site investigations. Vertical photographs are, however, used more extensively because oblique photographs cannot be easily used for photogrammetric measurements and hence existing coverage tends to be very limited. Furthermore the information which can be obtained from oblique photographs, although very useful, is less comprehensive than that which can be gained from vertical photography, for the following reasons:

(i) The change in scale across the photographs can be rapid in the case of high oblique photographs and complex in areas of high relief.

Figure 8.1   Low oblique photograph of the Isle of Sheppey taken using a 35 mm camera mounted in a remotely piloted aircraft. (Reproduced by kind permission of D. Teal.)

(ii) The distortion of shapes on oblique photographs can give the wrong impression of the importance of a ground feature.

(iii) A considerable amount of ground can be hidden from view by hills (dead ground).

(iv) The production of print laydown or mosaic using oblique photographs is difficult and in many cases impossible.

Despite these disadvantages oblique photographs are more easily interpreted particularly by the inexperienced interpreter since they give a more familiar view of the scene than that provided by vertical photographs. The value of oblique photography is often underestimated. Obliques are particularly useful when viewed in conjunction with vertical photographs. The great advantage of oblique photography is that it can be obtained very rapidly and cheaply by using a 35 mm camera mounted in a remotely piloted aircraft as described in Chapter 2. An example of a photograph taken in this manner is shown in Figure 8.1. A number of photographic companies are now offering a model aircraft photography service (see Appendix A).

8.2.2 *Emulsion (type of film) and filter combinations*

The main types of film used in aerial photography include black-and-white panchromatic, infrared true colour, and false colour infrared, details of which are given in Chapter 2. Of these, true colour is the only one that gives a true picture of the ground surface. Objects seen in true colour photographs are made readily identifiable since the eye is capable of separating at least one hundred times more colour combinations than grey levels. Clearly colour photography has a distinct advantage over black-and-white photography and has proved most effective in geological interpretation (Fischer, 1958; Chaves and Schuster, 1964). Colour films however have less definition than the corresponding black-and-white films and furthermore it can often be more difficult for the interpreter to assimilate all the information that is contained on a colour photograph. The result is that subtle textural variations and geometric patterns may be easily missed, whereas they are usually more distinguishable on black-and-white photographs. The choice between using colour or black-and-white photography in site investigation is usually made firstly on the grounds of cost and secondly, where existing aerial photographs are being purchased, on the grounds of availability. The cost of colour film and prints is high and the amount of coverage of the UK is small. For these reasons black-and-white photography is most commonly used for air-photo interpretation. The data obtained from black-and-white photography is normally sufficient for most site investigation applications, although if colour photography is available it should be considered.

Infrared films record reflected radiation in the visible part of the spectrum, but are also sensitive to reflected infrared radiation (up to wavelengths of about 0.9μm), which is invisible to the naked eye. The advantage of false colour infrared photography over black-and-white infrared photography is basically the same as that mentioned earlier for the true colour compared with black-and-white photography. False colour infrared photography is used extensively in forestry, agriculture and vegetation studies. This is because differences in reflectivity between different plants and between healthy and diseased plants are most pronounced in the infrared part of the spectrum.

False colour infrared photography can also be useful for detecting landslip areas and swallow holes (Edwards, 1969; Barr and Hensey, 1974) and made-up ground (Beaver and Wood, 1973). An example of the use of infrared photography for landslip studies is given in Chapter 9.

Water totally absorbs infrared radiation, making false colour infrared photography most useful for studying drainage. Springs and seepages can be easily located using this film. Objects which reflect primarily blue energy appear as black images on both colour and black-and-white infrared photographs, since blue energy is normally filtered out. Free-standing unpolluted water therefore appears as a black image on an infrared photograph. Polluted water is highlighted by false colour infrared photography.

Despite the advantages of true colour and false colour infrared photography they are little used in site investigations. This is mainly due to the high cost of these types of aerial photography. The remotely piloted system described in Chapter 2, however, does offer the opportunity to obtain relatively cheap colour and false colour photography of small areas. With respect to obtaining existing colour or false colour photography the high costs have generally limited the amount of coverage.

Although little used, black-and-white infrared photography costs less than the colour equivalent. In common with all infrared films it has the advantage of being capable of penetrating haze and producing high tonal contrasts. It does however suffer the disadvantage that the ground details in areas of shadow which would normally be visible on panchromatic and true colour films are sometimes lost. This is because light of short wavelengths is eliminated and often areas in shadow are largely illuminated by reflected and scattered light of short wavelength, and hence appear very dark. The elimination of short-wavelength light also means that the resolution of infrared film is reduced, thus reducing the amount of information that may be obtained, particularly from small-scale photographs. It is for these reasons that black-and-white infrared film is little used in conventional aerial photography.

The various advantages of all the types of films mentioned above may be combined using multi-spectral photography as described in Chapter 2. This utilizes film and filter combinations to provide pictures of the ground taken simultaneously in a number of predefined spectral bands. Within each spectral band certain ground features will be enhanced while others are suppressed Thus an examination and comparison of the images may enable features that are normally subdued in conventional photographs to be more easily identified. Furthermore by projecting the images through the appropriate filters in a colour additive viewer as described in Chapter 2, they can be combined to form true colour and false colour composite photographs. Multi-spectral photography has been used with success in the fields of photogeology (Ray and Fischer, 1960; Fischer, 1962) soil mapping (Tanquary and Miles, 1970) and archaeology (Hampton, 1974). Some specific applications of multi-spectral photography in site investigation would include the detection of unstable ground, sinkholes and abandoned mine shafts. Existing multi-spectral photography however is not readily available in the UK and hence it is usually specially commissioned. For large-scale projects particularly in remote, poorly developed regions it is advantageous to commission such photography. This may be carried out at reasonable cost using the system described in section 2.2.3.1 of Chapter 2 and discussed by Heath (1980).

The interpretation of all the types of photography described requires some knowledge of film processing in order to maximize the information gained. This is of greatest importance in the interpretation of true colour, false colour infrared and multi-spectral photography.

8.2.3   Scale

The amount of detail that can be seen on an aerial photograph will depend to a large extent on the scale of the photograph. Unlike a topographic map the scale of vertical aerial photographs varies in relation to the terrain elevation. The contact scale given for an aerial photograph refers to the scale at an average terrain elevation.

The scale of aerial photographs can vary from about 1:1 000 000 to about 1:1 000. Table 8.1 shows the area of ground covered by conventional 230 mm × 230 mm (9 × 9 inches) contact prints made from aerial photographic film. Since the area of ground seen on an aerial photograph is inversely proportional to the scale, by increasing the scale it becomes progressively more difficult to place large features such as major landform or drainage systems into an environmental setting. At the other extreme, local features such as sinkholes and minor landslips become too small to be easily recognized. Clearly the scale of photography depends on the amount of detail required and hence the selection of scale must be a function of the type of project and the type of the investigation. The range of scales and correspond-ing ground coverage suitable for different types of investigation are given in Table 8.1.

8.2.4   Image medium

The most commonly used photographic product is the familiar positive paper print. This may be a contact print or enlargement. The standard format size of aerial survey prints is 230 mm × 230 mm (9 × 9 inches). The size of the contact

Table 8.1. Altitude, scale and coverage for standard aerial survey cameras

Scale of photography	Flying height Focal length 6 in (152 mm)	Focal length 3.5 in (88 mm)	Width of ground cover strip (km)	Area covered by one 230 × 230 mm print (km²)	Suitability
Large-scale					
1:2000	304 m (1000 ft)	176 m (583 ft)	0.46	0.21	Design stage investigations
1:5000	760 m (2500 ft)	440 m (1458 ft)	1.14	1.31	
1:10000	1520 m (5000 ft)	880 m (2917 ft)	2.29	5.23	
				⎱ Area covered by OS 1:2500 map = 6.25 km²	
1:20000	3040 m (10000 ft)	1760 m (5833 ft)	4.57	20.90	
				⎱ Area covered by OS 1:10000 map = 25 km²	
1:30000	4560 m (15000 ft)	2640 m (8750 ft)	6.86	47.03	
1:40000	6080 m (20000 ft)	3520 m (11667 ft)	9.14	83.61	
				⎱ Area covered by OS 1:25000 map = 100 km²	
Small-scale					
1:50000	7600 m (25000 ft)	4400 m (14583 ft)	11.43	130.64	Reconnaissance and feasibility stage investigations for road projects and regional planning
1:80000	12160 m (40000 ft)	7040 m (23334 ft)	18.29	334.45	
1:100000	15200 m (50000 ft)	8800 m (29167 ft)	22.86	522.58	
1:150000	22800 m (75000 ft)	13200 m (43750 ft)	34.50	1190.25	
				⎱ Area covered by OS 1:50000 map = 1600 km²	

print for each image produced from a multi-spectral camera system is between 50–70 mm square. It is not the normal practice to enlarge standard aerial survey photographs since not only are they more expensive but secondary processing tends to reduce the resolution of the original. In some cases, however, it is necessary to enlarge the photographs to a more convenient working scale; this is particularly true of the small-format multi-spectral photographs.

The photographic image often appears sharper when printed with a glossy finish. Often aerial photographs are printed with a non-reflective matt silk finish which tends to reduce image sharpness and tonal contrast. Special photographic paper may be employed to increase the tonal contrast of black-and-white photographs. During a site investigation it is likely that often the photographs will be handled and taken into the field. The prints should therefore be printed on thick paper to increase their durability. An alternative to the opaque paper print is the positive transparency. This may be the initial film product, as is the case with true colour reversal film or infrared Ektachrome (false colour infrared) or it can be produced directly from the negative (diapositives) as is often the case with black-and-white photographs used for photogrammetric purposes. Film transparencies are more difficult to handle and work with than paper prints but in some instances colours can be more true and the image sharper. The positive transparency is more expensive than the paper print.

3.2.5 Time of day of photography

The time of day at which aerial photographs are taken can have a great influence on the appearance of ground features. The controlling factor is the sun's elevation. At low elevations (i.e. during early morning or late evening) long shadows are cast by objects on the ground, which in some cases can aid the recognition of certain surface features. The use of shadow as a recognition element is discussed later.

While shadow can be an aid to interpretation, it can also be a hindrance, particularly in areas of high relief, since important detail may be hidden. It is for this reason that most vertical air photography is taken during late morning or early afternoon when the sun's elevation is at or near maximum, and hence the amount of shadow is minimal. Low sun angle vertical aerial photography is therefore not readily available for most of the UK. Oblique air photography taken during early morning or late afternoon tends to be more common, but existing oblique photography is very limited in terms of areas covered.

3.2.6 Season of photography

The time of year in which aerial photographs are taken can be a critical factor in detecting features of geotechnical interest such as springs, seepages, instability, and made-up ground. Springs and seepages may not be visible on photographs taken during summer when the ground water-table is low. Moisture differences show up best in spring. Variation in soil types or moisture content may be seen directly as soil patterns or indirectly in the form of crop marks or patterns. These variations may be natural or due to disturbance such as trenching for services or the presence of land drains, buried foundations, or archaeological remains. Soil patterns representing such features are best seen during spring or autumn, particularly when the ground is bare.

Crop marks are best seen only in certain types of crop during the summer months, particularly during dry periods. The nature of crop marks will be discussed in detail later.

In general, photographs taken during spring and autumn will normally provide sufficient data for identification of most geotechnical features. Of course the choice of season is limited to a large extent by the availability of existing photography. In the UK periods of good weather which are favourable for obtaining air photography (i.e. minimum cloud and good visibility) amount to less than 500 hours in a year. The summer offers the most settled conditions, however spring and autumn have the highest proportion of days with good visibility and hence photographs taken during these seasons should be readily available.

8.3   Interpretation of aerial photography

The examination of any photograph for whatever purpose involves interpretation. Photographs of an area which is well known to the viewer are clearly more meaningful than photographs of an area which is totally unfamiliar. This fundamental difference in capacity for interpretation is a function of the amount of background knowledge about the area stored in the mind of the interpreter. This has been termed the reference level of the interpreter (Tait, 1970). In practice the successful interpretation of aerial photographs depends upon a basic reference level and the degree to which this can be extended for each site. Interpretation also demands keen powers of observation, imagination and patience.

For site investigations, the basic reference level required by the interpreter is a knowledge of physical and cultural features, their relationship with geology, geomorphology and land use, their engineering significance, and their common form of appearance on aerial photographs. The development of such knowledge clearly requires substantial experience of examining aerial photographs. The starting point is a basic knowledge of geology, geomorphology and geotechnical engineering. Good use can generally be made of black-and-white panchromatic and colour photography at this level without special experience in air-photo interpretation. As the interpreter's experience is increased the basic knowledge mentioned above can be extended to a level where the maximum information may be gained from the images. When interpreting colour, infrared, or multi-spectral photography a knowledge of the science of photography must be added to the basic reference level.

Since every site is different it will be necessary to extend the basic reference level by examination of all the available information concerning the project area such as topographic maps, geological maps, geological memoirs and survey reports and site investigation reports. This will enable the interpreter to concentrate on identifying features of specific interest. It may also help in the interpretation of ground features whose significance is ambiguous. Further familiarization is provided by site inspection.

8.3.1 *Method of viewing aerial photographs*

In the examination of aerial photographs it is important that the interpreter is able to view features in context with their surroundings and also to fully appreciate the topographic relief of the project area. The former is achieved by either selecting photography of a suitable scale or by viewing a print laydown or photomosaic. The latter is achieved by viewing overlapping pairs of photographs (stereopairs) with the aid of a stereoscope (described in Chapter 2). Viewing the photographs in this way gives rise to a three-dimensional image of the ground in which the vertical scales are exaggerated. Provided the interpreter is aware of the degree of vertical exaggeration (which is a function of the amount of overlap), this is an invaluable aid to the recognition and interpretation of topographic features. Aerial photographs wherever possible should be viewed stereoscopically.

Where photographs of different dates but similar scales are available it is possible to examine a stereopair comprising two prints of different dates. This technique allows small differences in the two prints to be easily identified and hence aids the study of site history. Pairs of prints with dissimilar scales may be viewed in a similar manner with the aid of a machine such as the Karl Zeiss Jena Interpretoscope which allows each print to be magnified by a different amount.

8.3.2 *Principles of image interpretation*

Every image must be treated on its own merits and hence there are no rules which define how an image should be interpreted. This makes teaching image interpretation for any purpose difficult without practical examples.

The people in a family snapshot, for example, are recognized largely on the basis of shape, tone, colour, and size. These recognition elements are used subconsciously in this case because the reference level of the interpreter is high. In the case of an image of the ground surface the situation is different in terms of the features to be identified and the reference level of the interpreter. The interpreter, particularly an inexperienced one, will make a more conscious and systematic use of recognition elements. The elements used relate mainly to the characteristics of the image alone. They include tone and colour, shadow, texture, pattern, shape, size and associations between features and their surroundings. In addition to these basic elements certain ground characteristics are employed. These include landforms, vegetation, land use, drainage and erosion, and lineations. The recognition elements and ground characteristics and often intimately related and in most cases they are used in combination to identify and deduce the significance of the features being examined.

In the following description of recognition elements and ground characteristics the emphasis is placed on black-and-white aerial photography. The same basic factors however can be employed in the interpretation of other forms of aerial photography (e.g. true and false colour) as well as digital images produced by scanning systems.

8.3.2.1 *Recognition elements. Tone* refers to the colour or reflective brightness of features shown on the photographic image. Since tone is a fundamental component of texture, pattern and shadow it may be considered the most important recognition element. Differences in reflectivity of surfaces are often associated with difference in surface composition and, in the case of soil and rock in particular, differences in moisture content. In general, on black-and-white photographs dark tones are indicative of dark-coloured materials or wet conditions (e.g. poorly-drained soil) and light tones indicate light-coloured materials or dry conditions.

Figure 8.2 shows an example of features which may be identified on the basis of tone. The picture shows clearly a series of sinuous light-toned features due to the tonal contrast they exhibit with the ground between them. These features represent a former natural drainage system which has been infilled. The material infilling the channels is a fine calcareous sand which is relatively light in colour and free-draining in contrast to the poorly-drained peat and clay which forms the ground between the channels. The peat often appears darker than the clay. In many cases a narrow band of dark tone occurs within the light-toned features. This represents peat which filled the last channel line. The fine sand which marks the former channels is a much better foundation material than the clay and peat. Figure 8.2 shows the preference for building over these infilled channels rather than between them.

In most cases features are identified by tonal contrast and hence aerial photographs with strong tonal contrasts are generally desirable. Prints made from black-and-white panchromatic film are often produced as well-balanced tonal images. Tonal contrasts can be enhanced by using high-contrast film, high-contrast paper, or by specialized image processing techniques such as dodging or digital enhancement. Digital techniques, however, are costly and rarely produce significant benefits. The use of infrared film will give enhanced tonal contrast, but with loss of resolution and loss of detail in areas of shadow.

Shadow as a recognition element depends primarily on the use of shape and tone. The shapes of objects, together with relief, are enhanced by shadow. With vertical aerial photographs shadow permits an effective profile view of certain

Figure 8.2 Infilled channels shown as soil patterns, Fenlands, East Anglia. Date March 1971, scale 1:15000. (Reproduced by kind permission of Soil Survey of England and Wales.)

Figure 8.3   Stag Hill, Guildford, looking E (high sun angle). (Aerofilms.)

Figure 8.4   Stag Hill, Guildford, looking NE (low sun angle). (Reproduced by kind permission of Meridian Airmaps Ltd.)

features. Mounds may be distinguished from depressions, and embankments from cuttings using shadow. One of the most important uses of shadow is in aiding the recognition of subdued topography which may be associated with landslipping or other forms of disturbed ground. These features are best seen on photography taken during early morning or late afternoon when the shadows are long (Norman *et al.*, 1975). Photographs taken near midday during winter may in certain cases provide sufficient shadow to enhance subdued relief. The oblique photographs shown in Figure 8.3 and Figure 8.4 show how shadow can enhance landslip features. It should be remembered however that too much shadow can hinder interpretation by masking important detail.

Texture may be defined as the frequency of tone change within the image. It is produced by an aggregate of unit features too small to be clearly discerned individually, and is a composite of several image characteristics such as tone, shadow, size, shape and pattern. For example, leaves are too small to be recognized individually on most aerial photographs, but the size and shape of many leaves, together with the shadows they produce, combine to give a characteristic texture which allows trees and shrubs to be readily identified. The scale of the photographs is clearly an important factor affecting the recognition of texture. A feature may appear as a texture at one scale and as a pattern at a larger scale since more of the component features can be identified. If the scale becomes too large the feature giving rise to a texture at a smaller scale may not be recognized because the component features cannot be properly viewed in relation to each other or the surrounding ground. A reduction of scale from the optimum will result in the texture becoming indistinct and eventually lost. Photographic texture is therefore a comparative feature within any one general scale of photography.

Texture is most useful in the identification of slope instability. The hummocky ground (often enhanced by shadow), and the impedance of drainage give rise to variations which often result in characteristic textures. Clayton *et al.* (1982) describe a 'turbulent' texture which is commonly associated with landslips that have involved the flow of material down slope (e.g. solifluction lobes and mudflows). An example of this texture may be seen in Figure 8.5. The area shown in this photograph is part of the Southern Chalk Downs of the Isle of Wight, in which Chalk and Upper Greensand strata overlie Gault clay.

Springs and seepages which issue from the base of the Upper Greensand have caused the Gault clay to soften and flow, giving rise to the turbulent texture which is apparent in the northern part of the image. The mud flow at A is easily recognized because of this distinctive texture. The line of springs and seepages (*S*) is made clearly visible by the contrast between the relatively smooth texture of the ground above the line and the turbulent texture below. The texture associated with Gault landslips is not easily recognized in Figure 8.6 which includes the same area at a much smaller scale. The optimum range

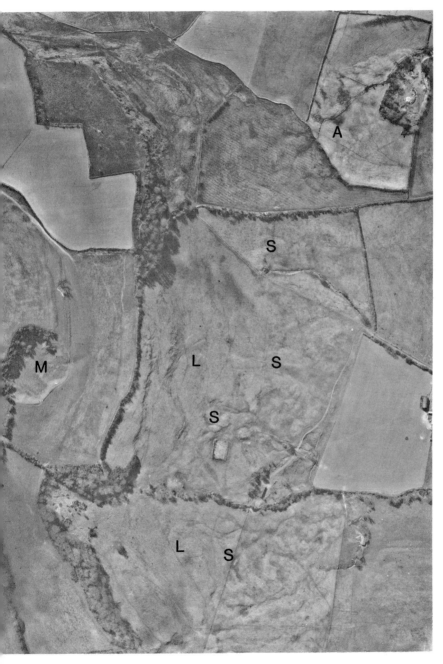

Figure 8.5 St Martin's Down, near Wroxall, Isle of Wight. Date April 1968, Scale 1:7000.
Reproduced by kind permission of the Department of the Environment.

Figure 8.6   Southern Downs between Shanklin and Ventnor, Isle of Wight. Date 1959, Scale 1:20000. (Reproduced by kind permission of Meridian Airmaps Ltd.)

of scales for the recognition of this type of texture is generally between 1:2500 and 1:10 000, but this will be influenced by the scale of landslipping.

The term 'texture' is also used in relation to the density of a drainage network and to describe the degree of dissection of the land surface (topographic texture).

Pattern refers to the orderly spatial arrangement of geologic, topographic, vegetation or man-made features. The most noticeable patterns seen on aerial photographs of the UK are either a 'patchwork' of fields in rural areas, or a network of streets in urban areas. Land use patterns are essentially a ground characteristic and are described later. Variation in near-surface soil types may give rise to soil or crop patterns. The manifestations of such patterns are dependent on the season of photography discussed earlier. Patterns produced by natural drainage are generally related to the geological structure. Man-made drainage measures produce distinctive patterns on aerial photographs, the most common being a herringbone pattern. These features are indicative of poorly-drained ground or slope instability.

In areas not covered by a great thickness of superficial deposits, patterns resulting from particular distributions of gently curved or straight lines may be common and often represent faults, joints and bedding within the bedrock and hence aid interpretation of geological structure. A single lineation may also be regarded as a pattern. This may result from an orderly arrangement of stream segments, trees or depressions. The recognition of patterns depends on the scale of the photography. A reduction in scale can cause a pattern to become a texture.

Figure 8.7 shows a distinctive polygonal pattern associated with fossil ice wedges. These were formed by severe frost action under periglacial conditions during the Pleistocene, and have since become infilled. The area shown in the photograph is in the chalkland north of the Breckland District of East Anglia, UK. In this area the chalk is overlain by a thin mantle of drift. The pattern, known as polygons (or stripes in certain cases), is associated with undulations in the surface of the chalk. The dark tones indicate where the chalk is nearest to the ground surface and the light tones indicate the infilled ice wedges. The pattern seen in Figure 8.7 is produced by differential ripening of crops (Clayton *et al.*, 1982). The soil pattern more commonly produced by these features has the same general appearance but tones are reversed, i.e. areas where the chalk is nearest to the surface appear lighter than the infilled ice wedges. Trench sections excavated in silty clay till for a gas pipeline north of Wolverhampton, West Midlands, UK, were observed to collapse because of sand-infilled ice wedges intersecting them (Morgan, 1971). Had these features been identified on aerial photographs before excavation precautions could have been taken to prevent the trenches collapsing in these sections.

Shape refers to the form of features seen from the air. Man-made features are normally characterized by straight lines or regular curves, and hence are often recognizable by shape alone. Many natural features have distinctive shapes.

Figure 8.7   Crop marks produced by fossil ice wedges (polygons and stripes), near Narborough, Norfolk. Date June 1976, scale 1:3000. (Reproduced by kind permission of Meridian Airmaps Ltd.)

For example, mudflows are generally lobate and sinkholes are commonly circular. With natural features, however, shape is significant only in its broadest definition which involves relief and topographic expression and hence these features may be difficult to identify on the basis of shape alone.

The *size* of objects can often aid identification. It should be pointed out that the size of objects on the photograph must be considered in relation to the scale of the photograph, or in relation to objects of known size to avoid misinterpretation. Vertical exaggeration will make objects appear much higher than they are in reality.

Association or the relation of features to their surroundings or mode of formation can often provide significant clues to interpretation. For example, dark-toned arcuate features associated with a flood plain of a river may be interpreted as infilled oxbow lakes whereas similar features not associated with a floodplain may be interpreted differently. It is therefore important that features be viewed in context with their surroundings. Furthermore the reference level of the interpreter with respect to the project area will provide important associations which not only give the interpreter an indication of what features to look for but also limit the number of likely interpretations of ambiguous features. Considerable use is thus made of associations, both consciously and subconsciously, by the interpreter.

8.3.2.2 *Ground characteristics.* When aerial photographs are viewed stereoscopically, the first feature that is noticed is relief. Using the stereo image various distinctive *landforms,* such as hills, mountains, ridges, scarps, valleys and plains, may be identified, allowing the area covered by the photographs to be broken down into a number of sub-areas. Identifying the landform commonly identifies the natural process that formed it, and often gives an indication of the types of material that can be expected. The use of landforms is of greatest use in reconnaissance and feasibility studies where mapping is at a small scale. In such cases the principles of terrain evaluation are best employed. When investigating sites of limited extent it is likely that the area of study will be within one major landform. The identification of minor landforms such as drumlins, kames and eskers however is significant in such site investigations. In order to understand fully the significance of landforms in relation to the underlying soil or rock, a knowledge of geomorphology is required.

Vegetation in cultivated areas is controlled by various environmental factors, the most important of which are soil type and the availability of water. Hence local differences in soil characteristics, depth and moisture condition can be detected from the resulting differences in the growth of crops or natural vegetation and the ripening of cereals. This produces tonal variations known as crop marks. Crop marks are used extensively by archaelogists to detect disturbed ground associated with ancient settlements and field systems. They occur where there are differences in water retention properties of the soil which in the right conditions affect the growth rate of certain crops. In limestone areas the moisture-retaining nature of soil contained within sinkholes causes the vegetation cover to be greener and hence aids detection of these features (Edwards, 1969). Crop marks are entirely transitory features, being visible only during the summer months when the soil becomes increasingly dry and the best conditions are during a particularly dry period. Aerial photographs taken during the drought of 1976 provide some good examples of crop marks—the photograph shown in Figure 8.7 was taken during this period. The pattern seen in this photograph is an example of cropmarks produced by differential ripening, the cause of which is discussed in section 8.3.2.1. Cropmarks are best seen in barley, sugarbeet and peas between June and August. They may also be seen in grassland, but only during the driest weather. Semi-natural vegetation such as moorland shows the best effect in late autumn when it is dying back and in spring when differences in reflectivity from dead vegetation are greatest (Dumbleton, 1983). The period of time over which these features are visible is usually only several days and hence it is a matter of chance whether they appear on existing photography. Different assemblages of flora may be indicative of different soil types, but it is very difficult to identify plant species from aerial photographs without experience and a knowledge of botany. Different types of vegetation can be identified by interpreters without specialized knowledge on the grounds of tonal differences. Thus, the area covered by the photographs can be broken down into sub-areas based on vegetation. These data may be used in conjunction with other ground characteristics to interpret soil and rock boundaries together with other features of geotechnical interest. Cropmarks and different types of vegetation show up more clearly on false-colour infrared photographs than on con-ventional black-and-white panchromatic photographs.

  Land use may be divided into five broad categories:

 (i) agriculture;
 (ii) urban development;
 (iii) forest;
 (iv) uncultivated (e.g., grassland, moorland and rock slopes);
 (v) materials extraction (quarrying and mining).

In general the most useful categories for interpreting ground conditions are (i), (iii) and (iv). In well-cultivated regions farming patterns can provide useful indicators of ground conditions. Farming in the UK is intensive, particularly in the lowland areas of the country. During the long history of farming in Britain, farmers have adjusted their farm management to take account of the difference in soil type. For example Webster (1965) found that in the Upper Thames Valley the villages and farms tend to stand on the terrace gravels associated with the river. These terrace gravels are also used predominantly for cereal growing, and hence there is little or no woodland on these deposits. Thus in this area woodland is restricted to the less valuable clay soils associated with the Oxford Clay. Alternating grass and arable farming is the main form of land use on the clay and on the flood plain of the river Thames the land is in permanent grass. The fields on the clay and flood plain tend to be smaller than those on the gravel terraces. The size and pattern of fields in cultivated areas provides a useful indicator of ground conditions. Thus an area can be readily subdivided on the basis of land use, and provided the interpreter is aware of the general cultural patterns for the region the significance of these subdivisions in terms of ground conditions may be deduced.

Drainage patterns are easily identified from aerial photographs. The type of drainage pattern and the density of the drainage network (texture), are often indicative of geological structure as well as rock/soil type.

In areas where bedrock is exposed at the ground surface or where the cover of superficial material is very thin the drainage patterns will be strongly influenced by the lithologic character of the rock, and the arrangement and spacing of planes of weakness encountered by the run-off. Stream characteristics are often influenced by the thickness and type of superficial material and hence in areas where the thickness is great the stream patterns are unlikely to be controlled by bedrock structure and type. Under these conditions the drainage reflects differences in soil types.

In areas where resistance to *erosion* is more or less uniform the drainage pattern is commonly dendritic (tree-like). The texture of such patterns is related to the permeability of the underlying materials. Coarse-textured patterns (wide spacing of streams) develop on materials with good internal drainage with little surface run-off. Fine-textured patterns (close spacing of streams) develop on materials with poor internal drainage and high surface run-off. Loess, however, is an exception to this rule since it has good internal drainage but is characterized by fine-textured drainage patterns. The texture is also a function of resistance to erosion of the underlying materials. Coarse textures tend to be associated with resistant materials such as granite, and fine textures with easily erodable materials, such as clay and shales.

It should be mentioned that unless quantitative meaning is given to drainage texture, the term must be used on a comparative basis within any one general scale of photography.

Where geological structures are well developed, characteristic trellis, radial, annular or other drainage systems may develop. In Figure 8.8(a) two drainage patterns can be identified: (i) a dendritic pattern associated with the more or less homogeneous basalt forming the plateau and (ii) a trellised pattern associated with the underlying steeply dipping rocks (Figure 8.8(b)). It will be seen from Figure 8.8(a) that as the streams crossing the plateau approach the edge of this landform they appear to become more controlled by the structure of the basement complex, indicating that they have cut through the basalt. These subtle changes in drainage pattern are common and can be of use, particularly for geological interpretation.

The identification of drainage patterns and changes of pattern is very much

(a)

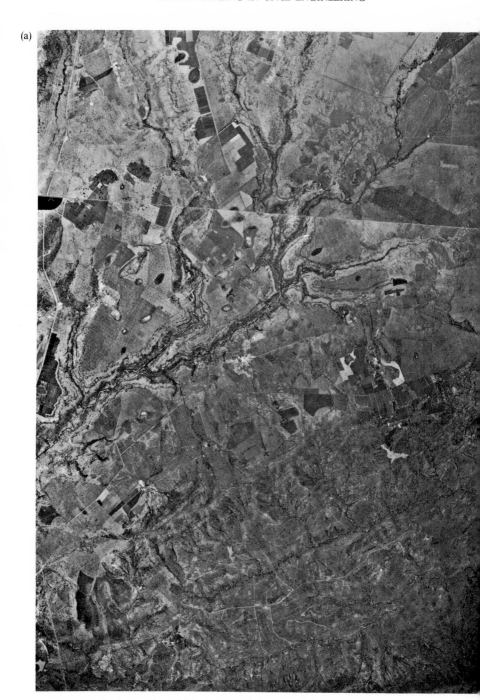

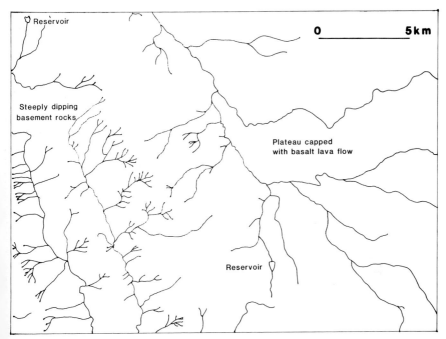

Figure 8.8(a) (left) Dendritic and structurally controlled drainage patterns. (b) (above) Drainage maps of area shown in (a).

dependent upon the scale of photography. With large-scale aerial photographs the area of ground covered will generally not be large enough to show the complete drainage pattern. Small-scale photographs and in particular photo-mosaics will often allow complete drainage systems and watersheds to be identified. In superficial materials and weak rocks and engineering soils, drainage characteristics are closely related to erosional characteristics. The most important erosional characteristics are the shape and transverse sections of gullies, which are controlled largely by the physical properties of the soil. Thus an examination of gully erosion on aerial photographs can provide useful information about soil type. Granular soils commonly develop sharp V-shaped gullies that have short steep gradients.

Cohesive soils are generally indicated by uniform gentle gradient of gullies that extend well back into the upland, and by broadly rounded shallow V-shaped transverse profiles. The loess soils and sandy clay exhibit U-shaped gullies with flat bottoms and low gradients. These ideal gully forms are often modified, particularly where erosion has cut down through layers of soil of different types. Climate can also influence the type of gully formed on a particular soil. For example a clay in an arid region where flash floods may occur will commonly exhibit abnormally steeps slopes, in contrast to the same soil in a temperature climate where the gully slopes are usually softly rounded.

Ray (1960) gives a reasonably comprehensive discussion with illustrations on the use of drainage and erosion in the geological interpretation of aerial photographs, and Norman (1969) identifies some of the drainage and erosion features associated with glacial soils.

Many features, both natural and man-made, appear on aerial photographs as *lineations*. Such features are commonly the linear expression of characteristics such as tone, texture, landforms, drainage and vegetation. In some cases, these characteristics may be disrupted in a linear fashion, thus giving rise to a linear feature. Natural lineations can be used to interpret soil and rock boundaries, together with structural features such as faults and bedrock jointing. Norman (1968) has made an extensive study of the significance of natural lineations in photogeology. Lineations may also be associated with buried features of man-made origin, such as services and infilled trenches.

8.4 General procedure for interpretation

A general procedure for the interpretation of aerial photographs and other imagery involves four stages:

  (i) preliminary examination;
 (ii) detailed examination;
(iii) interpretation;
(iv) compilation.

The preliminary examination stage involves obtaining a general overview of the site and surrounding area, allowing the interpreter to become familiar with the area. Familiar or easily recognized features can be identified at this stage. The basic reference level of the interpreter is extended during this stage by the examination of maps and reports concerning the project area together with the aerial photographs. In order to obtain an overview of the site, it is often necessary to work from the whole to the part. This is best done by making a print laydown or a photo-mosaic. The photographs should also be examined stereoscopically during this stage to observe the topography of the project area. Little distinction is made between the detailed examination stage and the interpretation stage as in practice they are normally carried out simultaneously. The detailed examination stage involves a systematic stereoscopic examination of the photographs. Full use is made of recognition elements and ground characteristics discussed earlier. It is often useful to make separate tracings of certain recognition elements and ground characteristics in the form of overlays. This allows patterns and trends to be identified which are not clearly visible on the photographs due to the abundance of visual information contained therein. The overlays may be viewed together in order to find common features that are likely to be of engineering significance. When studying site history, overlays made from each set of photographs can in certain cases aid in identifying areas where changes have taken place.

In many cases, small features of geotechnical interest are easily missed because they are overshadowed by larger features of less significance. The most efficient method of searching for such features is that of logical search (Tait, 1970) which involves a systematic visual scanning of the photography. The areas of the image in which the features are most likely to occur are singled out and examined first. The remaining area can be systematically scanned. An overlay showing features such as roads, tracks, paths and breaks in field boundaries can be made during this stage. This may be of use for planning access for drilling rigs and site vehicles.

The type of interpretation carried out will depend largely on the type of project, but in general one or more of the following should be included:

(i) *Topography*, e.g. hills, valleys, cliffs, coastline, drumlins, eskers, flood plains, lakes, natural slopes, gullies, depressions (sinkholes, mining subsidence, bomb craters), cuttings, quarry and pit faces, embankments, spoil heaps;

(ii) *Superficial geology*, e.g. soil boundaries, soil variability, moisture condition, soil types (alluvium, peat, clay, sand, gravel), fallen material;

(iii) *Solid geology*, e.g. structure, major joints, faults, dykes, rock types (limestone, resistant rocks, easily eroded rocks, bedded rocks, igneous rocks, metamorphic rocks);

(iv) *Drainage*, e.g. drainage pattern, springs, seepages, likelihood of flooding erosion, major watercourses, streams, disturbed drainage, land drains, soakaways, cess pits, sewer lines, outfalls, wet ground, marshes, bogs, mudflats, ponds, lakes, contaminated ground;

(v) *Localized hazards*, e.g. sinkholes and other solution features, abandoned mine shafts, mining subsidence, land drains, infilled trenches, made ground, buried foundations, contaminated ground, buried services;

(vi) *Site history*, e.g. previous use of site, buildings, structures, made ground, removal of trees and shrubs, buried foundations, waste products, antiquities.

The interpretation of aerial photographs would be of little value if the data were not recorded in some way. The best means of recording and presenting these data is in the form of a map. Thus the final stage of the interpretation process (the compilation stage) is the preparation of a map or sketch map showing features of geotechnical interest. More than one map may be necessary if there is a large amount of detailed information. Ideally maps of this nature produced from aerial photographs should be drawn at a scale not greater than that of the photographs used, hence the need to use large-scale photography for site investigation purposes. Accurate measurements cannot be made from an overlay because of the scale variations and distortions on the photographic image. The features identified on the photographs can be accurately plotted using photogrammetric techniques if these are available.

8.5   Example of air-photo interpretation for geotechnical purposes

The Brenig Dam site, near Denbigh, Clwyd, North Wales

The Brenig reservoir is situated south-west of Denbigh, Clwyd, North Wales, as shown in Figure 8.9. This reservoir together with the adjacent Alwen reservoir (Figure 8.9) provide water for Birkenhead. Investigations for a dam in the Brenig Valley were initiated at the end of the nineteenth century. The site chosen for the dam is shown in Figure 8.10. The main Brenig Valley here is wide, relatively flat-bottomed and generally shallow with a small valley incised on the eastern side. The preliminary subsurface investigations carried out in 1948 indicated the main valley to be a preglacial till-filled valley underlain by shales and gritstones of Silurian age. Subsequent design investigations were carried out during 1969, 1972, and 1973 (Carter, 1983). The main objectives of these investigations were:

(i) to determine the nature of the bedrock and the depth to bedrock across the main valley;

(ii) to determine the geology of the drift deposits at the dam site and locate any weak clay or highly permeable sands and gravels;

(iii) to take undisturbed samples of till and any weaker layers in order to measure their strength and compressibility in the laboratory;

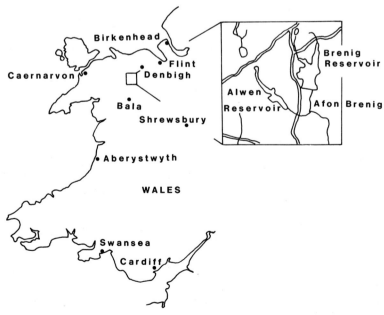

Figure 8.9   Location map.

(iv) to measure the permeability of any sand or gravel layers within the foundations;

(v) to locate suitable construction materials and determine whether there are sufficient quantities to build the dam;

(vi) to determine whether the reservoir basin is sufficiently permeable to allow reservoir impounding to the full height of the proposed top water level.

Figure 8.10   Site of Brenig Dam, near Denbigh, Clwyd, North Wales. (Reproduced by kind permission of the Welsh Water Authority, Dee and Clwyd Division, and Binnie and Partners, Chester.)

Clearly air photography can provide valuable information which could aid in fulfilling objectives (ii), (v), and (vi). The basic interpretation of the black-and-white aerial photographs taken of the dam site is described below. The contact scales of the original photographs* were 1:12 000 and 1:3000. It is unusual to find photography taken at contact scales as large as 1:3000 in areas of high relief such as this due to the obvious difficulties of maintaining a constant altitude. Such large-scale photography was necessary in this case to identify soil boundaries due to the complex heterogeneous nature of glacial deposits.

The main topographic features associated with the project area are best identified by examining the small-scale photography (Figure 8.11) stereo-scopically. These features include three drumlins (A, B, and C in Figure 8.10) and a minor steep sided V-shaped valley (D in Figure 8.10). Drumlins are glacial features composed of till moulded into smooth elongate hills resembl-ing inverted spoons. Normally drumlins have a length to breadth ratio of about 2.5:1 with the long axis more or less parallel to the direction of ice movement at the time of formation (Boulton, 1972; McGown et al., 1974; McGown and Derbyshire, 1977). Another characteristic feature of drumlins is that the end which faced the oncoming ice is generally steeper than the down-ice end. Drumlins A and B in Figure 8.11 are clearly defined on the grounds of topographic relief, shape and association. Association is probably the most important element in recognizing these hills as drumlins since such features are associated only with areas which have been subject to glaciation. The Brenig area is known to have been subject to these conditions during the Pleistocene period. A significant area of seepage is clearly visible on the north-west side of drumlin A and around the southern end of drumlin B (springs and seepages are marked S in Figure 8.10) indicating the presence of permeable material, possibly glacial sands and gravels. Drumlin C is smaller and less well developed than the others. Thirty-five drumlins have been identified from the 1:12 000 scale aerial photographs within the immediate vicinity of the dam site (Carter, 1983). The long axes of these drumlins are shown in Figure 8.12(a). The rosette (Fig. 8.12(b)) indicates a general NE to SW trend. The form of these drumlin A and around the southern end of drumlin B (springs and seepages of soil fabric and the pattern of discontinuities within some glacial deposits (e.g. lodgement till) are closely related to the direction of ice movement. Soil fabric and discontinuities have a strong influence on the geotechnical behaviour of engineering soils (Rowe, 1972), hence the determination of the direction of ice movement is of importance. The scale of photography is important in the identification of these drumlins. At 1:12 000 these features can be easily viewed in context with their surroundings. At large scales the task is made more difficult. For example at 1:3000 drumlin A almost fills the area covered by a 230 × 230 mm contact print. At the other extreme a contact scale

*The illustrations shown here have been reduced.

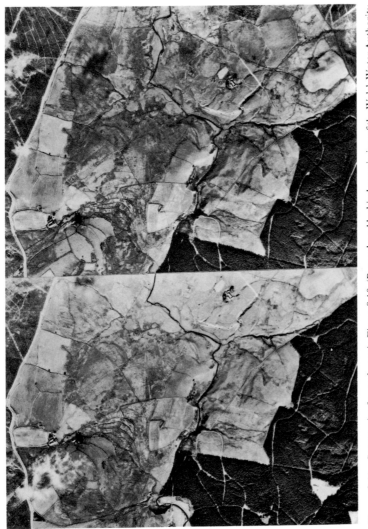

Figure 8.11   Stereopair of area shown in Figure 8.10. (Reproduced by kind permission of the Welsh Water Authority, Dee and Clwyd Division, and Binnie and Partners, Chester.)

Figure 8.12 (a) Long axes of drumlins in the immediate vicinity of the Brenig Dam site. (After Carter, 1983). (b) Frequency rosette of long axes of drumlins within a 13 km radius of the dam site.

of 1:80 000 may result in these features becoming too small to be readily identified, particularly by the inexperienced interpreter.

The eastern side of drumlin A has been oversteepened by the erosive action of the Afon Brenig. Much of this erosion probably occurred during the downwasting of the last glaciers which occupied the Brenig and adjoining valleys. The steep-sided channel thus formed was clearly a critical factor in the choice of the final dam site. Stereoscopic examination of (D) reveals the east

Figure 8.13 Stereopair showing the minor valley occupied by the Afon Brenig. (Reproduced by kind permission of the Welsh Water Authority, Dee and Clwyd Division, and Binnie and Partners, Chester.)

side of the channel to be steeper and less rounded than the western side. Furthermore at E (Figures 8.10, 8.13) there is a feature which probably represents an old landslip scar, since it occurs in a place where the river is most likely to undercut the slopes of the drumlin. A similar but smaller feature is seen to the north of E in Figure 8.10. No similar landslip features exist on the eastern side of the channel. In fact, where landslipping is most likely (at F in Figure 8.10) the slopes appear to be very steep and stable. This suggests that whilst the western side of the channel is clearly formed of till (part of the drumlin) the eastern side is composed of a much stronger material, possibly bedrock. An outcrop of bedrock can be seen at G (Figure 8.10). This outcrop was quarried for construction materials. The existence of bedrock in the east side of the minor valley was confirmed by site inspection (Carter, 1983).

The ground between the drumlins A and C (Figure 8.10) is traversed by a series of drainage ditches. These are clearly identified by pattern and the fact that the spoil has been placed along one side of each ditch in most cases. These ditches and the dark tones suggest poorly-drained ground. Peat probably covers most of the area between the drumlins giving rise to the dark tones. In places small ridges of till rise above the peat and are indicated by lighter tones. The stream on the west side of drumlin C is fed by a series of springs and seepages identified by a marked tonal contrast. These springs and seepages indicate an extensive horizon of permeable material in the west side of the

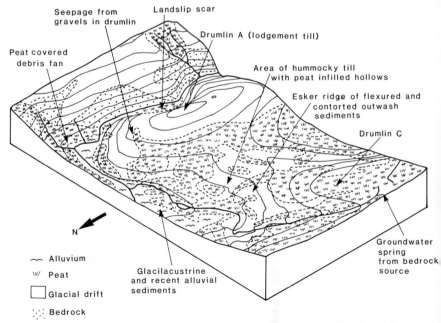

Figure 8.14   Block diagram of the Brenig Dam site showing photo-interpreted landform features and superficial material. (After Carter, 1983.)

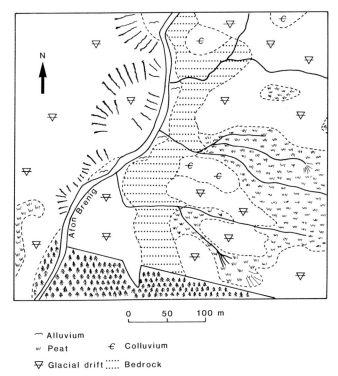

N

0   50   100 m

⌒ Alluvium
ᴠⱼ Peat   ₠ Colluvium
▽ Glacial drift ⠴⠆ Bedrock

Figure 8.15   Air-photo interpretation of the area shown in Figure 8.13. (After Carter, 1983.)

main Brenig Valley. The dark tones associated with the stream probably result
from the presence of peat.

In order to carry out a more detailed examination of ground conditions,
photography taken at a larger scale is necessary. Figure 8.13 shows the minor
valley at a suitable scale for mapping complex soil boundaries and locating
small features which may prove significant. Wet areas probably associated
with peat are clearly seen on these photographs. Careful examination reveals
deep rutting of vehicle tracks at R indicating areas of soft ground. The small
patch of peat at P, and the evidence of minor landslipping at L, cannot be seen
clearly on the smaller-scale photography. The large-scale photography
facilitates a closer examination of the morphology of the sides of the minor
valley and hence allows a more accurate delineation of areas of bedrock, till
and alluvium.

The interpretation described above is typical of what may be achieved from
an examination of the photography with little background knowledge of the
project area. Carter (1983) carried out a detailed air-photo interpretation of
the dam site using the 1:12 000 and 1:3000 black-and-white vertical photography together with coloured oblique photography. Carter's reference level
had been considerably extended through studying all the available infor-

mation about the project area and site inspection. Examples of Carter's interpretation are shown in Figure 8.14 and 8.15. The object of this detailed study was to find the best layout for a subsurface investigation which would establish more thoroughly than earlier investigations the stratigraphy and nature of the materials comprising the foundations of the dam and in particular to locate areas in which permeable materials might exist. The layout of earlier subsurface investigations which had concentrated on the centrelines of the envisaged engineering structures failed to reveal the complex hetero-geneous nature of the glacial deposits. In the later investigations more emphasis was placed on the geology rather than the position of engineering structures, hence the need for a detailed air-photo interpretation. Individual drillholes were laid out on a framework inferred from the geological characteristics of the materials that were expected to be associated with the glacial landform features identified from the air-photo interpretation. The drillholes and test trenches therefore served not only to examine areas considered to be of direct engineering significance, but also to ensure that all the various landform features identified from the aerial photography were investigated in sufficient detail to attempt a reconstruction of the three-dimensional glacial stratigraphy of the dam foundations. Carter found this approach most useful in unravelling the complex nature of the glacial deposits which aided greatly the design of the dam foundations.

8.6 Conclusions

The manner in which aerial photographs are used and the type of information abstracted from them will of course depend on the objectives of the investigation. In most cases topography, soil and rock boundaries, and localized hazards will be of primary importance. In some cases however the objective of the investigation may be to locate particular features, such as sinkholes, to establish a detailed site history in which case more emphasis may be placed on the careful selection of the most relevant photography. In all cases, provided the ground is not permanently obscured by trees or cloud, aerial photography will provide a cost-effective tool for aiding the desk study and later phases of site investigations. The cost-effectiveness stems from the fact that photographic products are relatively inexpensive and that they may be used effectively by persons at all levels of expertise or experience in image interpretation.

References

Barr, D. J. and Hensey, M. D. (1974) Industrial site study with remote sensing. *Photogrammetric Engineering* 36, 1115–1171.
Beaver, R. and Wood J. (1973) Aerial infrared locates solid ground over mine. *Civil Engineering* (A.S.C.E.) March, 161–164.
Bennett, J. (1983) Site Investigation: Part 1. *Construction News Magazine* 9(4).

Boulton, G. S. (1972) Modern Arctic glaciers as depositional models for former ice sheets. *J. Geol. Soc.* 128, 361–393.

Burton, A. N. (1969) Air photograph interpretation in site investigation for roads. *Roads and Road Constr.* 47(555) 72–76.

Carter, T. G. (1983) The site investigation and engineering characterization of glacial and glacilacustrine materials. Ph.D. Thesis, University of Surrey.

Chaves, J. R. and Schuster, R. L. (1964) Use of aerial colour photography in materials surveys. *Highway Research Record* No. 63, pp. 1–9.

Clayton, C. R. I., Simons, N. E. and Matthews, M. C. (1982) *Site Investigation*. Granada Publ. Ltd., London, 424 pp.

Dumbleton, M. J. (1983) *Air Photographs for Investigating Natural Changes, Past Use and Present Condition of Engineering Sites*. Dept. of the Environment, Dept. of Transport, TRRL Report 1085, Transport and Road Research Laboratory, Crowthorne, Berks.

Dumbleton, M. J. and West, G. (1970) *Air-photograph Interpretation for Road Engineers in Britain*. Dept. of the Environment, Dept. of Transport, TRRL Report LR369, Transport and Road Research Laboratory, Crowthorne, Berks.

Edwards, R. J. S. (1969) 'Some aspects of photo interpretation in problem analysis for highways', in *Proc. Symp. on Air-photo Interpretation for Civil Engineering Projects*, Woolwich (Thames Polytechnic).

Edwards, R. J. G. (1976) Aerial photography in engineering geology. *Ground Engineering* 9(3) 19–22, 25.

Fischer, W. A. (1958) Colour aerial photography in photogeologic interpretation. *Photogrammetric Engineering* 24, 545–49.

Fischer, W. A. (1962) Colour aerial photography in geologic investigations. *Photogrammetric Engineering* 28(1), 133–139.

Hampton, J. N. (1974) An experiment in multispectral air photography for archaeological research. *Photogrammetric Record* 8(43), 37–64.

Heath, W. (1980) *Inexpensive Aerial Photography for Highway Engineering and Traffic Studies*. Dept. of the Environment, Dept. of Transport, TRRL Report SR632, Transport and Road Research Laboratory, Crowthorne, Berks.

McGown, A. and Derbyshire, E. (1977) Genetic influences on the properties of fills. *Q. J. Eng. Geol.* 10, 389–410.

McGown, A., Saldivar-Sali, A., and Radwan, A. M. (1974) Fissure patterns and slope failures in till at Hurlford, Ayrshire. *Q. J. Eng. Geol.* 7, 1–26.

Morgan, A. V. (1971) Engineering problems caused by fossil permafrost features in the English Midlands. *Q. J. Eng. Geol.* 4(3) 111–114.

Norman, J. W. (1968) Photogeology of linear features in areas covered with superficial deposits. *Trans. Inst. Min. Met.* 77B, 60–77.

Norman, J. W. (1969) Photo-interpretation of boulder clay areas as an aid to engineering geological studies. *Q. J. Eng. Geol.* 2, 149–57.

Norman, J. W. (1970) The photogeological detection of unstable ground. *J. Inst. Highway Engnrs.* 17(2), 19–22.

Norman, J. W., Leibowitz, T. H. and Fookes, P. G. (1975) Factors affecting the detection of slope instability with air photographs in an area near Sevenoaks, Kent. *Q. J. Eng. Geol.* 8(3), 159–76.

Ray, R. G. (1960) *Aerial Photographs in Geologic Interpretation and Mapping*. U.S. Geological Survey Professional Paper 373, USGS, Washington, D.C.

Ray, R. G. and Fischer, W. A. (1960) Quantitative photogeology—a geologic research tool. *Photogrammetric Engineering* 26, 146–47.

Rengers, N. and Soeters, R. (1980) Regional engineering geological mapping form aerial photographs. *Bull. Int. Assoc. Eng. Geol.* 21, 103–111.

Rowe, P. W. (1972) The relevance of soil fabric to site investigation practice: 12th Rankine Lecture. *Géotechnique* 22(2), 195–300.

Tait, D. A. (1970) Photo-interpretation and topographic mapping. *Photogrammetric Record* 6(35), 466–479.

Tanguay, M. G. and Miles, R. D. (1970) Multispectral data interpretation for engineering soils mapping. *Highway Research Record* 319, 58–77.

Webster, R. (1965) Physiography and soils in the Upper Thames Valley. *Photo-interpretation* 65(63), 15–21.

9 Remote sensing for highway engineering projects in developing countries

C. J. LAWRANCE and P. J. BEAVEN

9.1 Introduction

Aerial photography and remote sensing systems, originally developed in industrialized countries, are finding extensive application in countries of tropical latitudes for mapping and monitoring in agriculture, industry and urban development. Highway engineering is among these applications, since an essential prerequisite of a nation's development is a good road network.

Considerable scope exists for the application of remote sensing to highway engineering in developing countries, for a number of reasons. First, a road alignment, although narrow in itself, can only be selected after an appraisal has been made of a very large area of land. Secondly, terrain characteristics (slope, geology, surface materials and water conditions) have a considerable influence on the location and design of roads, and in developing countries there is much greater scope than in Europe for adjusting an alignment to take advantage of the most suitable terrain. For economic reasons it is often important to minimize construction costs by adopting an alignment that closely follows the profile of the ground, and to use construction materials that occur near the road line. Thirdly, terrain surface patterns in sub-tropical latitudes lend themselves to remote sensing interpretation by virtue of reduced vegetation cover in the dry season and relatively little disturbance by man.

Other reasons for using remote sensing to interpret ground conditions are concerned with expediency. Maps and documentary information are often very generalized, or may be unavailable, and rarely give a comprehensive picture of terrain conditions in areas that may themselves be remote and inaccessible, where field work is very expensive and time consuming. Remote sensing images can be used to co-ordinate sporadic, incomplete data and to plan an appropriate data collection programme.

Remote sensing contributes most significantly to highway engineering during the reconnaissance and feasibility stages of route planning, when general information is to be analysed about large areas of terrain, rather than specific information about a small area, as would be required, for example, for the final alignment. Several remote sensing techniques are available for application to the many aspects of highway engineering survey, and in general low-resolution small-scale images are appropriate for reconnaissance surveys, while high-resolution large-scale images would normally be reserved for the detailed stages. However, there are no rules restricting a type, or scale, of imagery to any stage of investigation: if an image shows a feature of interest clearly, then its use for interpretation is justified.

Aerial photographs, despite their lack of glamour as a 'new' remote sensing system, remain the most important form of imagery for highway engineering studies in developing countries, by virtue of their detail, extensive coverage, versatility in use for large- or small-scale surveys, and relatively low purchase cost. Aerial photography has been used extensively in developing countries to produce contoured topographic maps, and local survey departments can often provide copies for interpretation. What is often overlooked is that a large amount of overseas photography is held in libraries in the UK, following mapping projects carried out by the former Directorate of Overseas Surveys and the RAF. Further details relating to the availability of aerial photography in overseas territories can be found in Appendix A.

In practice the use of imagery depends on what can be obtained and how much it costs. If aerial photography is available, it should be used from the outset, in conjunction with other forms of imagery, to give as wide an information base as possible. Where photography does not exist, or permission to use it is not obtainable, satellite imagery and Landsat, in particular, may provide the only source of remote sensing imagery. The scale of Landsat is ideal for reconnaissance surveys, and can be appropriate for preliminary interpretation as part of more detailed surveys. Just as the use of aerial photography broadens the perspective of ground-based investigations, the wider view of satellite interpretation can depict large-scale features which may be easily missed in the examination of individual stereoscopic photographs.

At reconnaissance and feasibility levels of survey, individual geotechnical aspects of road construction are subordinate to the main aim, which is to identify a route corridor. This chapter begins with uses of remote sensing and terrain analysis applied to these stages of survey, to illustrate a general procedure. At more detailed stages the appropriateness of a technique is strongly related to site conditions and the type of information required, and therefore later sections describe specific problems covering a variety of topics, without reference to stage of survey. Applications include (a) surveys of geology, soils, materials and hydrological conditions; (b) location of river crossing points, a very important aspect of route location because of their 'nodal' nature; and (c) inspection, monitoring and maintenance of events and changes that take place over time, requiring comparison of imagery taken at more than one date.

9.2   Reconnaissance study

The purpose of a reconnaissance or pre-feasibility study is to examine the entire area lying between the end points of a road and to identify route corridors within it. From a geotechnical point of view a reconnaissance survey would establish the relief and geology of an area, the main soil types, climatic and hydrological conditions, and hazardous areas. Maps can be used to compile some of this information, but they contain little about minor surface features that often affect road design. Aerial photographs are ideal but are not always available, especially if the project is planned from a UK base. Landsat images provide a reasonable amount of terrain detail and are easily obtainable.

9.2.1   *Route corridors in northern Kenya*

An interpretation of Landsat imagery was carried out to provide a geotechnical background for road alignments in northern Kenya, in support of a reconnaissance survey by a firm of UK consultants for the Ethiopia–Kenya Regional Development Programme, a project involving the integrated development of the Omo-Turkana sub-basin. The interpretation outlined a number of possible route corridors to connect North Horr with Banya Fort in the extreme north of Kenya near Lake Turkana. Plate 9 is a digital Landsat image of the North Horr area, showing the first 50–60 km of the suggested routes. Information about this area is extremely sparse.

Information on geology, hydrology and materials was inferred from a land system map of an adjacent area (Scott *et al.*, 1971). Relief information was derived from a 1:250 000 topographic map, but no aerial photographs were available to the interpreter. Although this information is highly generalized, it does indicate the main kinds of terrain that exist, and gives details of minor relief, surface materials, and hydrological conditions that would otherwise be visible only in aerial photographs.

The area between North Horr and Banya Fort is arid, receiving less than 250 mm of rain per year. Vegetation is supported permanently only around springs or perennial streams. The rocks are almost all volcanic lavas of basaltic type, with some ashes and agglomerates; the dry climate has left some of the lava surfaces in an almost unweathered state. The area has been strongly faulted by activity associated with the formation of the Rift Valley into north-south ridges with west-facing escarpments and gently tilted back slopes. The fault troughs are now filled with alluvial and wind-blown materials. The lavas near the lake have been severely dissected by erosion into complex relief with steep slopes and narrow stream channels.

The country to the north of North Horr can be divided into four different terrain types, or land systems (see Chapter 5). These can be denoted Linear Ridges, Lava Field, Cuestas, and Plain (Plate 9, T_1–T_4). The Linear Ridges comprise an ancient lava surface, strongly faulted into ridges 1–4 km wide separated by troughs of equal width. The Lava Field consists of an unfaulted lava flow whose surface still bears the original flow pattern. On the ground the surface would consist of a highly complex micro-relief of lava ridges and debris-filled hollows, with no organized surface drainage pattern. Towards the north the plateau is cut by a very distinct gorge with steep sides and a flat floor, whose origin is not known but is perhaps related to regional faulting.

The Cuestas terrain is similar to the Linear Ridges, except that the plateaux, dipping gently to the east, are much broader (10 km), with inter-ridge troughs of similar width. Although the topography is aligned north to south, there is a distinct east-west arrangement of independent drainage channels and associated fan deposits, running down the dip slopes into the troughs. Overlaid upon this faulted landscape to the west of North Horr is a covering of windblown sand with a WNW orientation. Small groups of shifting dunes are just visible in the image. The last terrain, the Plains, is of uncertain topography but appears to consist of a gently sloping plain, dissected by many small drainage channels and a few major watercourses.

Although the relief in these terrains is not high, many of the slopes are extremely steep and the micro-relief is often complex. Local relief would be expected to have a considerable influence on the location of a road alignment, but relief in Landsat imagery can only be inferred from shadows because the imagery is not stereoscopic. Four road alignments are now described in more detail.

Route A traverses the Plains terrain for some 15 km, and no problems are expected. There is one major stream crossing, probably prone to flash flooding during rain. Construction materials are probably absent. The route continues into the Lava Field, across a very rugged and rocky surface that may be extremely difficult to negotiate. A more detailed inspection of the surface would be necessary to indicate whether or not it is feasible to build a road on the lava surface. The gorge at km 36 should not be a serious obstacle, despite its large size, apart from negotiating its steep sides. The uniformly dark tone of the floor and lack of evidence of fluvial activity suggests that the gorge never carries any appreciable volume of water.

Route B The route traverses the Plains landscape for 20 km, then crosses a corner of the Lava Field before passing into the faulted country of the Linear Ridges. The route attempts to minimize the contorted micro-relief, but is forced to follow a north-westerly alignment across at least six fault escarpments. The total length through difficult terrain (on this image) is 48 km.

Route C goes westwards across the Cuesta terrain for some 35 km, on thin sandy deposits over smooth lava surfaces. Apart from loose sand (some of which may be prone to drifting) and bouldery lava plains, no severe problems exist. The route then turns north through the Linear Ridges, keeping to inter-ridge hollows and crossing ridges at narrow (low) points. Troughs may be liable to flood during rainy periods but there is no direct evidence of this.

Route D follows the same alignment as route C, remaining on the Cuesta landscape for 44 km before striking across the Linear Ridges at a point where relief appears to be minimal. The route also takes advantage of an area in the north-west where permanent water appears to exist (shown by red strips of vegetation in trough floors), and where a thin cover of wind-blown sand covers the rocks, perhaps reducing the microrelief.

Further information could be interpreted from this Landsat image by displaying small extracts at a larger scale individually colour-enhanced to give maximum tonal discrimination (see Plate 9). The illustration shows the extremely broken nature of the terrain surrounding Lake Turkana, west of the plateau marking the edge of the Linear Ridges. The terrain can be subdivided into areas of consistent surface pattern, related to drainage network, rock colour and morphology. The terrains in this extract are described below: the routes from North Horr do not cross the escarpment at this point, but they encounter similar terrain further north in their descent to the Lake.

(A) Plain. Low relief, with broad river channels and a multitude of small tributary channels. Some of the larger channels contain vegetation (red). Landsat imagery taken at several seasons would indicate whether the vegetation is permanent (maintained by spring water) or temporary, following recent rain. Dark-coloured interfluves suggest that away from river channels the ground is less prone to surface wash, probably similar to terrain (B) but of lower relief.

(B) Dissected plain, that may be of alluvial origin, or represent a weathered lava surface. The dark colour suggests consolidated, weathered material of volcanic origin. The presence of many minor channels, sinuous and braided, suggests very gentle slopes.

(C) Higher terrace or lava surface. Perhaps similar to (B). Separated from (B) by moderate slopes, as shown by many short, parallel stream courses.

(D) Isolated hills, high and steep-sided. Their light colour and occurrence in groups suggests that they may be inselbergs of ancient metamorphic (granitic) rocks of the Basement Complex, protruding through the lava flows. They are surrounded by a pale aureole of weathered material that could contain quartzitic gravels suitable for road construction.

(E) Highly dissected country of low relief, hinted at in the image by a mass of channel fragments and tiny shadows. These features are near the limit of resolution of the satellite sensor, i.e. one to a few hundred metres across.

(F) Dissected lava plateau, with remnant plateaux separated by areas of hilly and broken terrain.

(G) Dissected lava plateau, similar to (F), but streams have cut down and considerably increased the relief, removing the plateau tops. This landscape is similar to several land systems on the western side of Lake Turkana, and would be extremely difficult to traverse by road.

(H) High Plateau. The western margin of the Linear Ridges in Plate 9 forms a plateau with an abrupt edge. The plateau appears almost level, but interpretation of stream flow is made difficult by a thin cover of wind-blown sand, indicated by WNW striations, that partially obscure the surface water pattern.

Feasibility Study

1 Terrain evaluation on the East-West Highway, Nepal

1968 the British Government undertook to construct a 120 km section of East-West Highway in Nepal. The East-West Highway, the only tinuous all-weather road running across the country, traverses the Terai, almost level alluvial plain lying between the foothills of the Himalayas to north, and the Ganges floodplain to the south. Advice was sought on the sibility of reducing the estimated cost of the road by modifying the design suit terrain conditions. The most important factors influencing the align-t were the numerous rivers that cross the road line, the location of con-ction materials in an area of predominantly soft sediments and alluvia, and avoidance of paddy land, which occurs along all the major river valleys. he availability of aerial photographs at 1:12 000 scale and an air-photo saic at 1:150 000 meant that a considerable amount of preliminary work ld be accomplished before field work commenced. Geological information the area was very scanty but the little that was known could be readily tified and amplified from the appearance of landforms in the air-photo saic. Subgrades, river crossings, and possible sources of road construction erial were analysed in aerial photographs to guide field work and to apolate field observations. Examination of the aerial photographs led to siderable modifications of the route.

he road line from Butwal to Narayanghat traverses three major terrain es (Figure 9.1).

1.1 Western section (44 km). In the western section the road passes over a ad alluvial plain, consisting of fine soils. Hard rock outcrops are absent. aerial photographs show a clear separation between wet paddy land and htly elevated ground where forest remains (Figure 9.2), although it was not ays possible to keep the alignment on these drier sites. Partially cleared st indicates areas of easier access, which was of considerable assistance in field. It was noted that river channels widen and meander more as they flow y from the hills. Bridge sites were selected at narrow points where the nnel and banks are stable. It could also be seen that coarse materials in the r bed were concentrated in stretches nearer the hills, where the flow is cked upon levelling out on the plain.

1.2 Dauney Hills. The central section of the road (16 km) crosses the

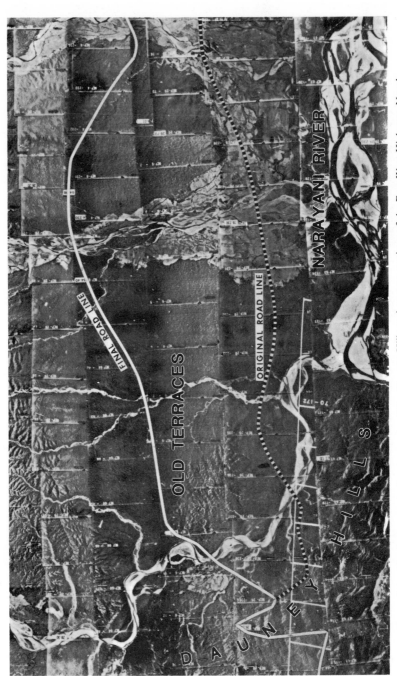

Figure 9.1 Air photo mosaic showing parts of the Dauney Hills and eastern sections of the East-West Highway, Nepal.

Figure 9.2 Air photo mosaic showing a bridge site on the western section of the East-West Highway, Nepal.

Dauney Hills, a spur of Siwalik deposits rising to about 600 m, that extends southwards from the Himalayan foothills (Figures 9.1 and 9.3). The hills form the western end of a synclinal fold basin, now drained by the Narayani River. The Siwalik beds consist of micaceous sandstones and mudstones of Cenozoic age, dipping to the north or north-east at angles between 20 and 90 degrees. It

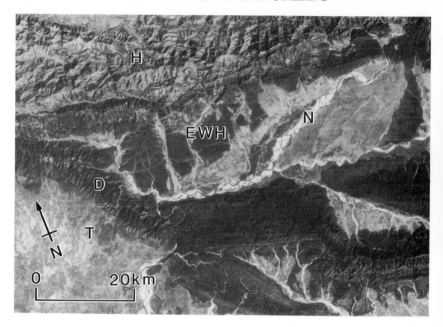

Figure 9.3   Part of a Landsat satellite image of central Nepal (Band 5, red). H = Himalayan foothills, T = Terai, D = Dauney Hills, N = Narayani River, EWH = East-West Highway.

was reported that the beds are highly folded, but air-photo analysis showed that they are not so much folded as strongly tilted, and that the lithology of individual beds is fairly consistent. It was noted that south-facing slopes are steeper, less well forested, and more prone to landsliding than north facing slopes.

9.3.1.3. *Eastern section.* The synclinal fold basin through which the eastern section of the road runs contains several contrasting landforms. The Narayani River is one of the largest in Nepal, with extensive paddy cultivation on its floodplain and along the course of smaller streams flowing in from the north. The tributaries cut through ancient terraces which were deduced to have filled the basin before being partially eroded away by the present river system. The terraces were considered to offer firm subgrades and abundant supplies of gravel for road construction: field work confirmed this interpretation. The tributary streams flowing from the hills into the Narayani have wide, flat valley floors and braided streams which presented problems in locating bridge sites. The aerial photographs were used to select crossing points where the stream and banks appear to be stable. (The narrowest streams and dry braided channels are not visible in Landsat images, Figure 9.3).

As a result of the interpretation and subsequent field survey the original road line was substantially relocated to take more account of terrain conditions. In the Western sector several bridges were re-sited to cross at more stable river positions, although the move sometimes placed the road further south, away from potential gravel sources. The Dauney Hills section was relocated along one of only two routes that were considered feasible, climbing and descending quickly to minimize the length of road. Two major active landslides were avoided, but the predicted instability of the slopes has given rise to sliding and erosion in cuttings, which have since had to be maintained after each rainy season.

In the Eastern sector the alignment was moved about 6 km to the north, away from the paddy lands bordering the Narayani River and on to the dry terraces, where materials could be found for road construction, and where bridge crossings are more stable. Over the 55 km sector, the length of road located on paddy land was reduced from 33 km to 10 km. To compare the relative merits of the two alignments in this section rough estimates of quantities and costs were made. When grossed up, the estimates showed a reduction of some 30 per cent in favour of the more northerly alignment. The road was opened to traffic on this line in 1975.

9.4 Surveys for specific purposes: soils, materials and water conditions

Part of the process of appraising a route corridor during feasibility or more detailed stages of survey involves investigations of specific aspects of terrain. In fact surveys are sometimes carried out without reference to a road line, such as a materials inventory. Published examples of the use of remote sensing are scarce: Davies and Eades (1982) discuss the location of construction materials in Australia, and Hunt (1979) design aspects in Libya. The examples that follow illustrate a range of engineering problems and the use of different remote sensing techniques to solve them.

9.4.1   Construction materials: laterite and subgrades in Uganda

Figure 9.4 is a stereoscopic pair of aerial photographs from southern Uganda, showing part of the Masaka Land System (Ollier et al., 1969, and see Chapter 5). The landscape is developed on Precambrian gneisses and schists that have been deeply weathered, uplifted and eroded. It consists of a dissected old land surface, preserved as flat hill tops, with gentle lower slopes and broad valleys. (The slopes in the aerial photograph are considerably steepened due to stereoscopic exaggeration.) The valley pattern reflects the underlying joint structure in the rocks. The Masaka Land System extends round much of the northern shore of Lake Victoria (Figure 9.5), and the photographs have been annotated to show its component land facets.

The ancient land surface that now forms the flat hill tops (Land Facet 1) was heavily laterized. The laterite, being hard, is often a source of excellent road construction material. It is readily recognized by its three-dimensional shape, elevation, and distinctive air-photo tone. It contrasts with the lower hill slopes

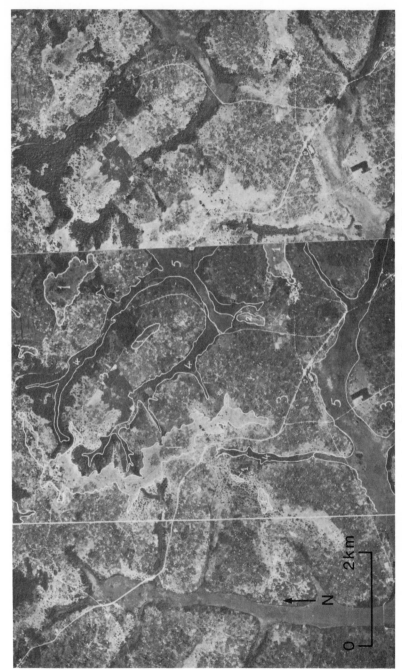

Figure 9.4   Air photo of Masaka Land System, Uganda (stereopair). See text for key.

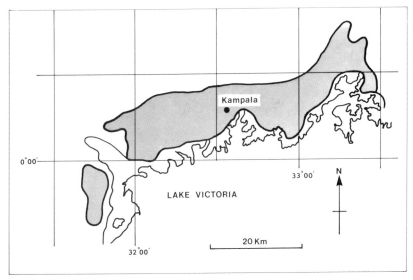

Figure 9.5 Masaka, Uganda, land system location map.

because the thin, stony soils support only grassland and a few small trees. The intensively-cultivated slopes (Land Facet 3) indicate deeply-weathered, freely-draining soils that form a good subgrade but offer no possibility of finding road construction material. Occasionally, quartzitic rocks outcrop as ridges (Land Facet 2) that are also potential sources of construction material. Minor valley floors (Land Facet 4) have soils similar to the hill slopes but the local growth of forest suggests a greater accumulation of water, especially during the rainy season. The main valley floors (Land Facet 5) have been filled with alluvium and now support papyrus swamp. Papyrus has a distinctive smooth texture in aerial photographs, and indicates the presence of a permanently high ground water-table. Road crossings require an embankment and a method of sub-embankment drainage.

These relatively simple observations summarize the potential for road construction in an area 9 km square, and could be made in less than one hour by one who is familiar with residual savanna terrain. With the aid of a Land System map the same interpretation could be extrapolated over the entire 6400 square kilometres of the Masaka Land System.

9.4.2 Construction materials: calcrete surveys in Botswana

The central Kalahari region of Botswana is covered by a thick mantle of wind-blown sand. At the time of deposition the sand was worked into dunes typical of the desert environment in which they were laid down, but since then the climate has become semi-arid, and the dunes are now almost completely levelled by erosion, and vegetated with sparse grass and low scrub. There are practically no rock outcrops in the region, although calcrete, a calcareous material that forms pedogenically in the Kalahari sand, is locally abundant. Calcrete is the main source of road construction material in the Kalahari, but it is extremely difficult to find by field methods alone due to the flatness of the terrain. However, calcrete is known to occur in association with a range of landforms, and an investigation has been made into the use of remote sensing to map these (Lawrance and Toole, 1984).

Calcrete is principally associated with pans and depressions in the sand surface, but also with grey sands. Grey sands are leached sands, occurring in patches up to a few hundred metres across, their neutral pale grey colour forming a strong contrast with the normal reddish brown of Kalahari sand. They often overlie calcrete at one or two metres depth, and in areas where pans are scarce, they may be the only source of calcrete.

Black-and-white aerial photographs have been used to map calcrete bearing landforms, but they fail to depict grey sands because grey and red sand tones appear the same. The colour difference shows up well in true colour aerial photographs (Plate 13), but few if any exist in Botswana and the cost of flying colour photography over very large areas would be prohibitive. The Landsat imagery detects the colour change in the sands, but they do not show up clearly in conventional false colour images because vegetation and grass burning patterns obscure the sand colour (Plate 14).

Digital images are far superior in depicting these low-contrast features because of the strong colour enhancement processes that can be applied. Normal colour stretching of an otherwise untreated image (see Chapter 4) causes grey sands to stand out from the background, although grass-burning patterns still dominate the picture and tend to confuse interpretation. Ways of suppressing them have been sought by further processing. The technique of principal components analysis was found to be particularly effective in achieving this, while also enhancing grey sands. Principal component analysis generates four new bands of data from the original Landsat data, in such a way as to maximize differences between the bands. The effect is to place most of the useful data in the first band (first principal component). The other bands contain progressively less information, the fourth component consisting almost entirely of 'noise' (Figure 4.11). In this instance, the process causes the burning patterns to be placed in the first principal component, and the grey sands, with very little other information, in the second. A false colour composite of the first three principal components is shown in Plate 15. A comparison can be made between this image and a colour aerial photograph (Plate 13). Despite the relative coarseness of the Landsat image a close correlation between the two patterns is obvious.

It was found that digital Landsat imagery is able to depict grey sands in sparsely vegetated parts of a study area sufficiently well to render colour photography unnecessary. Existing black-and-white photography can be used

) map small depressions and pans that are not visible in Landsat imagery.
'ogether these two systems are able to map the range of calcrete-bearing
ndforms in much of southern Botswana, an area of some $350\,000\,km^2$.

4.3   Unstable hill slopes: soil moisture surveys in Colombia

1 young mountain areas of the world slope instability is an ever-present
azard. But landslides, far from being isolated events, can generally be related
) a pattern of instability affecting slopes of the same type within a region. As
ell as a large areal extent, unstable slopes often have a history of movement
tending back over many thousands of years. An unstable area usually
)ntains ancient slides that have ceased movement, potentially unstable slopes
1at could be activated by changes in the environment or disturbance due to
ighway construction, and slopes that are currently moving. Water is nearly
ways instrumental in causing slope failure, and an appreciation of water
istribution on a slope is necessary for the prediction of instability. Although
1b-surface water cannot be seen in remote sensing images, its effect on
?getation is visible. The following example, from Colombia, demonstrates the
resence of potentially unstable slopes from the appearance of vegetation in
lse colour infrared aerial photographs.

False colour infrared aerial photographs record green, red, and reflected
?ar infrared light, and the film depicts these wavelengths respectively in
)lours of blue, green and red. Differences in infrared reflectance from
?getation show up more clearly in false colour infrared photographs than do
iriations in green in natural colour photographs. The amount of infrared
ght reflected from the leaves of a plant is related to the plant's growth vigour,
1ich in turn is related to the amount of water available to the plant. Thus,
?althy vegetation reflects far more infrared than green light, giving bright red
: pink tones in infrared false colour aerial photographs. Less vigorous
?getation appears in orange or brown hues, and dormant vegetation,
though still green to the human eye, is depicted as blue.

The false colour infrared aerial photograph in Plate 16 shows part of a
ountainside which has been unstable in the past, and which now shows both
:tive and potential landslide areas. The grass vegetation with which most of
1e slope is covered shows signs of water stress, indicated by the overall bluish
greenish colour, i.e. growth activity is low. However, there are many patches
pink vegetation (V) where the grasses are actively growing, which suggest an
:cumulation of water near the surface. These patches occur either in hollows,
on the slope itself where springs occur. The shape and arrangement of wet
)llows indicates that they lie at the head of old slip masses. Water (W) lying in
e hollows continues to seep into the hillside: if the equilibrium of the toe area
ould be disturbed, these masses would probably move again. L1 and L2 are

linear features, possibly faults, that are formed by wet areas occurring on a line. They are zones of weakness, as can be seen by increased sliding at the right-hand end of $L1$, on the minor valley side.

Landsliding is far more active on the lower parts of the mountainside, where streams have steepened the slope. Zones of sliding are annotated $S1$, $S2$ and $S3$. $S1a$ and $S1b$ are individual landslide bowls. $S1a$ has been reactivated, possibly by undercutting at the foot of the slope, at the point where lineation $L2$ meets the surface, creating a weakness. The bowl has been largely emptied of its slide debris, and erosion has removed much of the soil in the head, giving white tones in the photographs. $S1b$ is a slide bowl that still contains its original mass of debris, but would, if disturbed at the base, erode in the same manner as $S1a$. $S2$ is a slide zone associated with a minor stream on the left hand side: it contains several arc-shaped slide scars, as well as ponds (W) and damp hollows. Erosion is removing soil and vegetation from parts of the slope. $S3$ is a slide zone associated with a minor stream on the right hand side. Although there is little sign of movement at present, landslide head escarpments and wet patches are common, and scour of the toe zone by the minor stream could reactivate the slope. The road at the top of the photograph passes through this slide zone.

9.4.4 River crossings: bridge site surveys in Nepal

Small-format aerial photography may be very useful in circumstances where a full-scale survey cannot be justified. Cameras of 5-inch, 70 mm or even 35 mm format are light in weight and can be carried in a light aircraft, hired locally. Costs of hiring and flying an aircraft can be £100 to £300 per hour or less, and are usually based only on time spent in the air. A light aircraft can fly at short notice between spells of bad weather, or in areas which may be dangerous or inaccessible to larger aircraft. Photography can be flown at a scale most suitable to the purpose of the survey, using appropriate film and at specified times if necessary. The Transport and Road Research Laboratory has constructed a small-format camera system that can be fitted to a variety of light aircraft (Heath, 1980) consisting of a 5-inch camera with a 125 mm lens, and four 70 mm Hasselblad cameras for multispectral photography (see Figures 2.6 and 2.7). The camera is not calibrated for photogrammetric mapping purposes, but the photographs are excellent for stereoscopic viewing and interpretation.

The Tamar River, in eastern Nepal, is 150 m wide and flows through hills rising 1000 m on either side (Plate 17). During the monsoon the channel is full, undercutting the banks and causing persistent instability. Crossing points are few on such a river, and even the best potential bridge sites are not without some risk to a bridge structure. Small-format aerial photographs of the Tamar bridge site on the Dharan-Dhankuta road were flown at 1:20 000 scale in 1975. The photographs were used in a geotechnical study of the river course to assess foundation conditions and possible hazards. Some of the points of inter-pretation are described below.

The bridge is located at one of the few places on the river where alluvial terraces are situated on opposite banks. The terraces (*T*) are distinguishable from the metamorphic rocks of the region by their flat surfaces and paddy fields. The terraces are made up of loose granular material, but they lie upon a rock base that protects them from scour by the river. These rocks can be seen jutting into the stream (*R*). The orientation of the outcrop shows the strike to be east-west (dip is steeply to the north). Beneath the terrace where the southern bridge abutment is to be built, at the junction between the terrace material and the underlying bedrock, several springs emerge (*S*). The main force of the river is directed towards the outside of each bend, giving rise to erosion and sliding (*E*) (the terraces occur on the inside of river bends where erosion is less active). In the distant past a large landslide (*L*) occurred just upstream of the proposed bridge site: field work has shown this slide still to be active.

The bridge itself is situated on terraces that are at the same level on each side of the river. There is no evidence of instability on the northern bank. The southern bank is subject to undercutting by the river but is not seriously affected. The river bed was considered to be stable, because rapids in the stream seemed to indicate the presence of a rock bar at depth, corroborated to some extent by other rapids both up and downstream, lying in the direction of strike. This implies that the same rock bar has created three sets of rapids. A possible threat to the bridge in the future could be the continued activity of the landslide upstream of the southern abutment (*L*).

Photography of the bridge site was repeated in 1981 when the road had been completed but the bridge itself not built (Figure 9.6). The bridge, being in excess of 150 m in length, has two piers, whose foundations are visible in Figure 9.6, both of which are submerged during the season of high flow and are subject to vigorous scour. The photograph demonstrates the very difficult nature of the terrain, and how the selection of a bridge site may depend as much upon topography and geotechnical conditions in the terrain surround-ing the crossing point as upon conditions at the site itself. The photograph also illustrates a strategy adopted in the design of the Dharan-Dhankuta road, which was to use reasonably stable areas of hillside for climbing in a series of loops, heavily protected by anti-erosion and drainage structures. It was considered better to invest in these rather than to gain height slowly and unavoidably cross highly unstable hillslopes, some of which would inevitably fail.

9.4.5 *River hydraulics: flood damage in Nepal*

The East-West Highway in Nepal is crossed by a large number of streams that flow southwards from the Himalayan foothills (Figure 9.3). Violent thunder-

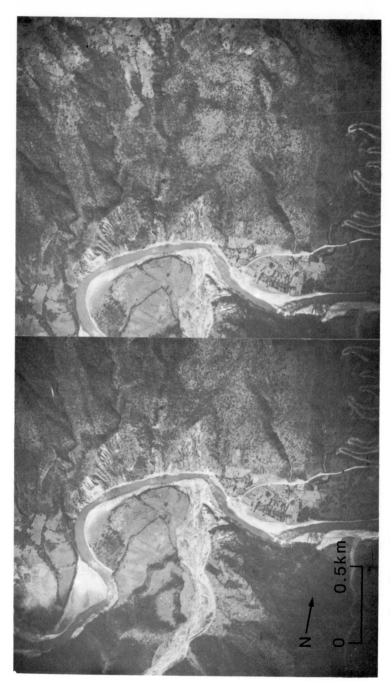

Figure 9.6   Aerial photographs of Tamar bridge site, Nepal, showing bridge foundations under construction (stereopair).

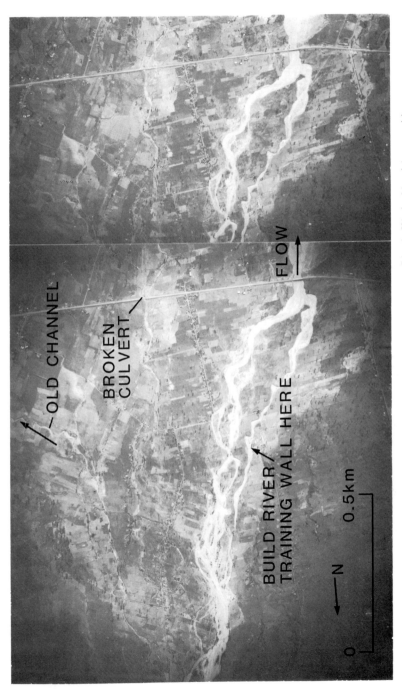

Figure 9.7 Aerial photographs of crossing of East-West highway over Bhaula Khola, Nepal (stereopair).

storms in the hills cause the streams to rise rapidly, and sometimes to change their course where they emerge on to the plain. New channels opened up during periods of flooding represent a change in flow pattern that can adversely affect drainage structures on a road. Following a heavy storm in 1981, two culverts on the East-West Highway were washed away, and two river training walls severely damaged. Events such as these raise questions for engineering: (a) was the structure adequately designed and constructed for expected storm conditions; (b) was the damage caused by a change in river course, and will the river continue to flow in this way; and (c) what additional training or remedial works are required to prevent damage in future?

During an investigation of the four sites in the field it was decided that aerial photography should be flown, to see the failures in the context of their surroundings. A small camera system and light aircraft were used to take photographs of the stream courses for a length of about 5 km upstream from the affected structures. True colour photography at 1:12 000 scale of all four river courses was obtained in under 2 hours. An interpretation of conditions at one site, a culvert on the Bhaula Khola (river), is described here.

In earlier centuries the Bhaula Khola flowed south-eastwards from the hills. Traces of old channels are visible in the aerial photographs (Figure 9.7). The present course is to the south, but during the 1981 storm the river reverted to a south-easterly channel and passed through a twin box culvert, which became overloaded and was washed away. The air photos show the point of overspill, where the river turns abruptly southwards. Evidence at the breach in the road suggests that the culvert was adequately large, even though it may have flowed full for some time, because the embankment on either side has remained intact. Failure was attributed to scour that occurred on the culvert outlet, leading to undermining and collapse of the structure. It was recommended that the culvert be replaced as before, but with increased protection works on the downstream side.

Aerial photographs have also thrown light on the long-term flow pattern of this river, which is difficult to predict in the absence of historical flow data and longitudinal profiles of the channels. A comparison between aerial photography taken in 1964 and the present showed that the overall course of the river had not changed in the intervening 18 years, but that formerly the river was very much more restricted in width and the number of channels than today (Figure 9.8). The 1964 photographs show that most of the area was occupied by forest, although by 1973, before the completion of the road, this had already been cleared, as shown by Landsat imagery dating from this time. The removal of trees from the plains and foothills is seen as a possible cause of increased runoff and sediment load borne by the river. This has resulted in the raising of the river bed and a decrease in lateral stability, causing the channels to broaden and proliferate, and enabling the river to change its course during periods of high flow.

The TRRL aerial photographs indicate an increasing risk that transgres-

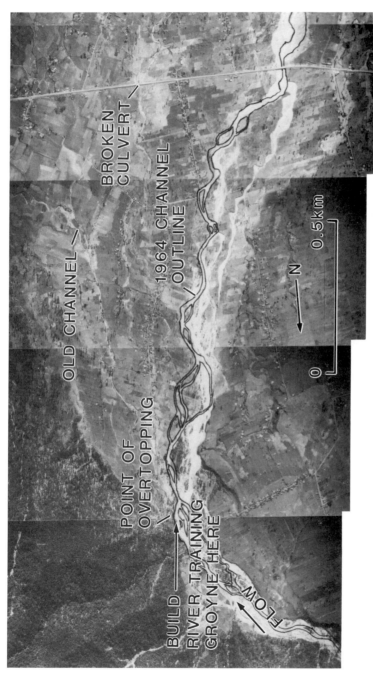

Figure 9.8   Air photo mosaic of Bhaula Khola, Nepal.

sions of water from the main channel will occur. Upstream of the bridge several sites have been noted where there is practically no bank and the river has come dangerously close to overtopping (Figure 9.7). It has been recommended that a river training groyne be constructed at the point of overspill to deflect the river back into its main course, and that the river banks should be raised at strategic points to prevent water escaping into new channels.

At a cost of some £300 (flying time and film) an aerial record was taken of four river courses that were posing a threat to the East-West Highway. The photographs give an overall impression of the stream courses, which is difficult to obtain on the ground, and were invaluable in elucidating the basic causes of failure. They also assisted in the selection of sites for river training measures, and in estimating the future behaviour of the streams. The photographs were interpreted in the UK, where it was possible to seek additional advice and give careful consideration to various proposals for remedial works. The photographs now form an historical record of the river courses in 1981 with which to compare future flow patterns, and to assess the effectiveness of repairs.

9.5 Remote sensing for inspection, maintenance and monitoring

9.5.1 *Terrestrial photogrammetry and ground-based photography*

Remote sensing is normally associated with views of the earth from above, but it can also be used for site investigation at ground level where appropriate. Sites which are too steep or too small to be conveniently viewed from the air lend themselves to study on the ground, albeit at a distance. Sites may be unsafe or inaccessible for inspection at first hand, or they may be too large to be recorded comprehensively by field work. Road cuttings, landslides, structures and buildings are examples. Although theoretically any remote sensing technique can be used on the ground, up to now photography has proved to be of most value in civil engineering applications. As with aerial photographs, the image can be measured photogrammetrically, to yield quantitative data, or interpreted for geotechnical information, or both.

Terrestrial photogrammetric surveys are used to make measurements of the relative positions of objects on site. The technique has advantages over conventional surveying methods if site access or time available to complete the survey is limited, or when changes need to be monitored over a long period of time (Heath *et al.*, 1978). Photogrammetric surveys are carried out by accurately positioning a small number of control points within the area of interest by conventional survey methods, and then taking two or more overlapping stereoscopic photographs of the site with an optically-calibrated photogrammetric camera. Coordinates are taken from the photographs by measuring parallax displacements in a plotter or stereocomparator, and drawing contour plans or elevations if required. Heighting accuracy is within 0.05% of the viewing distance over the entire field, and overall costs can be substantially lower than surveying by conventional means, largely due to the reduction of time spent in the field.

A site record can be limited to a simple stereoscopic pair of ground photographs if no measurement of the image is required. A survey of cuttings on the East-West Highway of Nepal (see above) noted many faces where loose blocks and suspended masses of debris were in danger of falling on to the road. Stereoscopic photography (Figure 9.9) proved very useful in illustrating the orientation of planes of weakness, and for indicating those masses or blocks which should be removed. Stereoscopic photographs can be taken by hand with a 35 mm camera, by taking a picture of the scene, then moving a little to the left or right and taking another. The ratio between the photographic base (distance between the viewpoints) and the distance from the object should be about 1:30 to achieve a satisfactory sterescopic model, but this ratio is not important. Reducing the ratio to, say, 1:20 increases the stereoscopic effect, making small differences in relief easier to see. The ratio can be varied with experience to give the most effective picture under prevailing site conditions. Photographs can be taken over a period of time to record changes in the landscape such as progressive erosion of river banks or the development of a landslide. Sequential photography may be particularly relevant during the post-construction maintenance period of a road project.

Figure 9.9 Stereoscopic photographs of a road cutting. Total height is about 15 m. F = massive sandstone bed, J = joints causing rockfall in sandstone/siltstone series, F—F = fault, B = loose block 1 m³ in size, D = debris.

9.5.2 *Detecting seasonal changes of river course using Landsat imagery*

A bridge depends upon stability of the river course for its safety, but the flow history of most rivers in subtropical regions is not recorded, and analysis of flow pattern at potential bridge sites is based mainly on hydraulic evidence collected at or near the site. Many rivers are subject to seasonal flow, and the amount of water in them varies considerably according to seasonal flux, changes in run-off factor, and the effects of localized heavy precipitation. These variations can cause rivers to change course from year to year, and in the absence of data on former flow patterns, these changes can be unpredictable and potentially catastrophic.

Landsat satellite images provide a source of historical flow data on the world's rivers dating back to 1972. Most scenes have been recorded at least two or three times during this period, sufficient to indicate the main variations that are likely to occur. A study has been made of the course of the Narayani River in Nepal to demonstrate the use of Landsat imagery for this purpose.

The river systems of Nepal rise in the Himalayas and flow southwards towards the Ganges. Upon leaving the mountains they flow over a broad alluvial plain where their course is no longer confined, and every year their channel patterns change. The Narayani is one of the three largest rivers in Nepal, and in recent geological time has built up an immense alluvial fan some 150 km across at the foot of the mountains. Its overall course is now permanent but within the meander belt fresh channels are opened up every season.

Three Landsat images were obtained of the Narayani River, taken in January 1973, February 1976 and October 1976. The rainy season lasts from June to September, therefore these images depict the dry season state for three seasons. The method used to compare the three dates was to overlay the images and use colour coding to differentiate the channel systems. A first attempt was made with photographic Landsat products, and while reasonably successful, suffered from the fact that distortions resulting from changes of satellite attitude prevented the images from superimposing perfectly.

A second attempt was made using digitized photographic images, processed at the National Remote Sensing Centre at Farnborough. An infrared band (Band 7) alone was used, to maximize the contrast of water against the background. Using one image as a reference, the other two were rectified to precisely fit the first. Next, the river channels were isolated from their background by density slicing, and stored as separate images of rivers in red, green and blue (one colour for each date) on a black background. The third stage was to overlay the three coloured river channels onto a monochrome background image. The result is shown in Plate 12. Red, green and blue colours show channels that are filled with water on only one of the three dates: yellow, cyan and magenta colours represent channels filled at two dates (i.e. two of the primary colours are added), and white represents sections of the river that flowed at all three dates. Note that at one section the river channels converge to produce a narrow band where the river always flows: such a site could be a potential bridging point which is unlikey to be bypassed. A number of spurious coloured pixels, not connected with the river system or meander belt, were included with the rivers by the density slicing process. Although these detract from the pictorial effect to some extent they do not hinder interpretation of the river channels. If desired, they could be removed by smoothing or masking processes to 'clean up' the picture.

9.5.3 Traffic surveys

Conventional traffic surveys are based on data collected at fixed points in the road system or from individual vehicles in the traffic stream. Very early in the development of such surveys it was realized that aerial photography provides an alternative source of data with the advantage of recording either a limited area instantaneously or recording a larger area over such a small time span that it can be treated as one record. Over the years there has been development in the recording techniques. Initially full-sized aerial cameras were used, but the advantages of small-format cameras, ranging from 70 mm to 16 mm, have been explored, and video cameras also produce data which can be analysed. The conventional platform is a light aircraft, but helicopters have become more common, particularly for urban studies. Fixed platforms, ranging from aerial balloons to existing buildings or extending masts, may be used to study small sites.

The choice of recording apparatus and platform will be determined by the requirements of the survey, which in turn will dictate the resolution and scale required in the image. Aerial surveys have been used to measure traffic volumes and density and vehicle headways; to identify traffic queue locations, their length and duration; to carry out parking surveys; and to study movement of traffic through a junction. The techniques used in this last type of study can be extended to a larger scale origin and destination survey with a simple classification of vehicle types.

Having identified the purpose of the survey it is then possible to determine whether the analysis of the image is to count vehicles, identify them or measure them in relation to ground coordinates. A suitable scale can be chosen such that enough detail can be seen in the image to identify the required features. Local factors may affect this choice, such as ground contrast, weather conditions, subject colour and angle of the sun above the horizon. To give some guidance on the limits of scale, Table 9.1 shows the likely resolution of a car which can be obtained with various scales and types of film used under normal conditions. Having decided upon the scale of the recording it is then possible to choose the platform taking into account whether the requirement is a single set of images or a sequence of the area over a period of time.

In practice there is considerable experience available regarding procurement of imagery, the limitation in the UK being the weather which may mean

Table 9.1   Assessment of the resolution characteristics of various films and image scales for traffic surveys

Scale	Film	Remarks
1:5000	All	Possible to distinguish enough detail to recognize make of car.
1:10 000	Colour positive	As above.
1:15 000	All	Vehicles clear and defined, make not recognizable.
1:20 000	Black and white	Probable limit of resolution for vehicles.
1:30 000	Colour positive	Approaches limit of vehicle resolution.
1:45 000	Colour positive	Some high contrast vehicles can be seen but only as indistinct patches.
1:45 000	High resolution	Vehicles as clear as colour positive at 1:30 000.
1:60 000	Any film	Very few vehicles could be located even by a trained photo-interpreter.

it is difficult to obtain data at the required time and date. However the techniques to analyse such data for traffic surveys are still being developed and this is the main area of research and development. At present the use of coordinate readers operated by semi-skilled personnel is the most effective way of providing computer input. Digitizing of images is possible but expensive, and the automatic analysis of such images would require more complex and therefore more expensive computer programs. Using commercial computer rates, Mountain and Garner (1981) found that photographic traffic surveys were not economic when compared with ground survey techniques but were competitive when using in-house computing facilities. Coupled with the difficulties due to weather, this explains why remote sensing is still a minor source of traffic survey data despite over 50 years' experience. However the advantages of aerial photography are recognized, in particular the ability to provide a complete record over a large area. This is of great advantage when considering new studies where it is not always possible to predict where the traffic should be monitored. The ability to reappraise an error, or to check suspected errors, has a value which is difficult to quantify.

9.6   Recommendations for use of remote sensing in highway surveys

The application of geotechnical survey techniques to highway engineering covers a great diversity of operations and involves many kinds of environmental conditions. The foregoing examples illustrate some of the ways in which remote sensing and terrain classification methods can be incorporated into engineering surveys, although the precise ways in which they are employed depends upon the circumstances of the survey and the types of imagery available. To emphasize the sequential nature of terrain evaluation procedures and how they are matched to survey requirements, a list of the main engineering activities and appropriate terrain evaluation techniques is summarized in Table 9.2.

It is important to use a scale of imagery appropriate to the level of detail of a

Project stage	Activity	Remote sensing techniques		
		Landsat MSS, TM and RBV	Existing black-and-white air photography	Specialized RS techniques
Regional planning phase Aim—to identify main sources of information and to put project into context with respect to the terrain	Collect together all relevant published material relating to the project to assess requirements for mapping and interpretation during survey stages	Purchase Landsat MSS, TM imagery in a form suitable for the requirements of the project. Select images from several dates or seasons if necessary. Make false colour composite images at 1:500 000–1:250 000. Purchase Landsat RBV imagery if available, 1:250 000–1:100 000	Make enquiries in Europe or of host government to purchase air photography and air photo mosaics	Find out if specialized air photography or other form of RS coverage has been made for some previous project in the area
Reconnaisance Aim—to identify possible alternative routes and define strategy for construction programme	Define project in terms of size, political and physical constraints, and geotechnical complexity Examine possible routes on maps and satellite images, and air photo mosaics if available. Undertake broad terrain classification for collation of regional information Visit site to check interpretations; report on findings and plan next stage	Examine MSS and TM photo products in conjunction with maps. Scale as above. Interpret influence of major terrain features on road alignment, e.g. changing course of major rivers; catchment area of major river system; extent of flooding of low-lying areas; possible sources of water for construction; possible sources of construction materials (e.g. alluvial terraces and fans); pattern of regional instability; extent of erosion; spread of deforestation; assessment of land acquisition/site clearance problems	Air photo mosaics at approx 1:100 000 used in conjunction with Landsat material.	

(Contd.

Table 9.2 (Contd.)

Project stage	Activity	Remote sensing techniques		
		Landsat MSS, TM and RBV	Existing black-and-white air photography	Specialized RS techniques
Feasibility Aim—to appraise route corridors and select best route	Make detailed interpretation of conditions on all routes, and if necessary make a more detailed terrain classification of the area. Interpret foundation conditions, earthworks (borrow and spoil areas), drainage, materials sources (gravels), major bridge sites, hazard zones Carry out site investigation of alternative routes noting key physical and geotechnical features. Cost comparisons. Selected laboratory and field testing. Recommend best route and prepare report	Use MSS, TM and RBV as base map if no more detailed mapping is available. Supplement air photo interpretation with colour information from MSS	Use air photos for all detailed interpretations and terrain classification study. Scale 1:20 000–1:60 000 as available. 1. Foundation condition survey 2. Calculate catchment areas and location of culverts 3. Identify spoil areas, also possibly borrow areas. Minimise erosion risk 4. Identify possible sources of construction material 5. Location of all possible bridge sites 6. Identify major hazard areas, (poorly drained soils, spring lines, unstable areas, erosion in river courses)	Commission specialized air photography (possibly small format) at a scale appropriate to size of task and degree of ground complexity (approx 1:10 000 to 1:30 000). Examine Landsat computer-compatible tapes in interactive processor (scales 1:20 000–1:100 000)

Design Aim—detailed study of selected route to engineering design standards	Comprehensive site investigation of selected route, with full sampling and testing programme. Prepare final design documents	Use air photography to support all field survey activities	
Construction, and post-construction maintenance period Aim—build road and carry out repairs prior to handing-over	Road construction activities	Use aerial photography to locate access roads for construction traffic, in difficult terrain	Large-scale air photography may be used to monitor changes taking place at important sites as construction proceeds. May also be used to record damage done by landsliding, erosion or flooding in preparation for design of rehabilitation measures

survey, beginning with small scales to cover large areas in a general way, and moving to larger scales as the investigation proceeds towards the selection of a final alignment. Until relatively recently aerial photographs taken for mapping purposes were practically the only form of imagery available, but these are now supplemented by Landsat satellite imagery as a small-scale mapping tool. Aerial photography remains the most important form of remote sensing imagery for both general terrain studies and investigations of specific sites. The use of stereoscopic pairs of photographs provides a plan view of the landscape in unrivalled detail. Low-cost non-metric cameras fitted to light aircraft can provide high-quality imagery for interpretation, and the film type and scale can be selected for the subject under study.

Interpretation of any form of imagery involves two stages: recognition of patterns on the image and correlating these patterns with conditions on the ground. Constraints of time and lack of background information can be offset by the use of landform mapping as a rapid but practicable means of identifying reasonably homogenous terrain units upon which to base a sampling programme. An advantage of landform mapping to the engineer is that it represents changes in the terrain that are caused by a diversity of natural factors, including geology, water conditions and processes of erosion, which have an important influence on road construction. Experience has shown that the subdivision of terrain into land systems and smaller units is an effective way of organizing an interpretation exercise, and correlating between known and unknown areas. It has also been found that Landsat imagery provides a good base for creating a coarse terrain breakdown in preparation for more detailed analysis using aerial photography.

References

Davies, A. L. and Eades, G. W. (1982) The application of terrain evaluation to the location of construction materials for highways in Queensland, Australia. In *Proc. OECD Symposium on Terrain Evaluation and Remote Sensing for Highway Engineering in Developing Countries*, Report SR690, Transport and Road Research Laboratory, Crowthorne, Berks.

Heath, W., Parsley, L. L. and Dowling, J. W. F. (1978) *Terrestrial Photogrammetric Surveys of Unstable Terrain in Colombia.* Dept. of the Environment, Dept. of Transport, Report LR816, Transport and Road Research Laboratory, Crowthorne, Berks.

Heath, W. (1980) *Inexpensive Aerial Photography for Highway Engineering and Traffic Studies.* Dept. of the Environment, Dept. of Transport, Supplementary Report SR632, Transport and Road Research Laboratory, Crowthorne, Berks.

Hunt, T. (1979) Geotechnical aspects of road design in Libya. *Ground Engineering* 12(7) 15–19.

Lawrance, C. J. and Toole, T. (1984) *The Location, Selection and Use of Calcrete for Bituminous Road Construction in Botswana.* Department of the Environment, Department of Transport, Report LR1122, Transport and Road Research Laboratory, Crowthorne, Berks.

Mountain, L. J. and Garner, J. B. (1981) Semi-automatic analysis of small format photography for traffic control studies of complex intersections. *Photogrammetric Record* 10, 331–42.

Ollier, C. D., Lawrance, C. J., Webster, R. W., Beckett, P. H. T. (1969) *Land Systems of Uganda.* Military Engineering Experimental Establishment. MEXE Report 959, Christchurch, Harts.

Scott, R. M., Lawrance, C. J., Webster, R., Beckett, P. H. T. (1971) *Atlas of the Land Systems of Western Kenya.* Military Engineering Experimental Establishment, Christchurch, Harts.

10 Environmental engineering applications of thermal infrared imagery

P. A. MASON and ELAINE M. AMOS

10.1 Introduction

Airborne thermal infrared sensing is that branch of remote sensing concerned with measuring the radiant temperatures of earth surface features using sensors operated from an aircraft. The equipment used is a thermal infrared linescanner which essentially consists of an optical system to focus thermal radiation received from the ground on to sensitive thermal detectors; the output from this is recorded on magnetic tape for later playback and production of imagery. Further details, relating to the physical characteristics of thermal scanning systems together with a discussion of the geometrical features of this type of imagery may be found in Chapter 3. The use for a thermal infrared linescanner covers a wide range of applications including energy conservation in buildings and thermal mapping of plumes from power stations, together with some applications in geology.

10.2 Survey planning

Various times of day can be utilized for a thermal survey depending upon the type of classfication required. The planning has to take into consideration the various cooling and warming effects of differing materials, the weather conditions, flight clearances, etc. The importance of diurnal temperature variation is shown in Figure 10.1. The ability of rocks and soils of differing composition to heat up and store thermal radiation produces a variation in condition that must be assessed. The temperature curve for water is quite small compared to that for soils and rocks. Convective currents within a water body result in a relatively uniform temperature at the surface of that water body. The thermal signatures of any water bodies are a reliable index to the time of image acquisition. If water bodies have a warm signature relative to terrain the

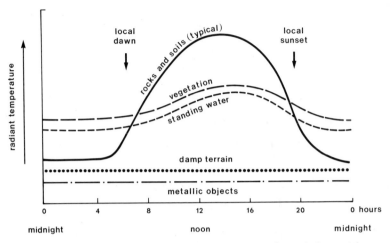

Figure 10.1   Diurnal variations in radiant temperature for typical materials.

image was acquired at night. Relatively cool water bodies indicate daytime imagery. Damp ground is cooler than dry ground, both day and night, because of the cooling effect as absorbed water is evaporated.

Green deciduous vegetation has a warm signature on night imagery. During the day transpiration of water vapour lowers the leaf temperature, causing vegetation to have a cool signature relative to the surrounding soil. Dry vegetation, such as crop stubble, appears warm on night-time imagery in contrast to bare soil which is cool. The dry vegetation insulates the ground to retain the heat.

Around the periods of dawn and sunset, the thermal curves for water and soil meet at the 'cross-over' point when there is little difference in radiant temperatures. Thermal contrasts are low at this time and it is most unusual to acquire imagery during the 'cross over' period.

The extremes and rates of temperature variation of a material are determined by the following.

(a) thermal conductivity—a measure of the rate at which heat passes through a material;
(b) thermal capacity—the ability of a material to store heat;
(c) thermal inertia—the response to temperature changes.

10.2.1 Factors affecting the imagery

10.2.1.1 Solar gain.
During the daytime direct sunlight differentially heats objects according to their thermal characteristics. This can be an advantage in looking for specific differences in tonal signature from differing materials. However, there is the problem of shadowing by trees, buildings and other

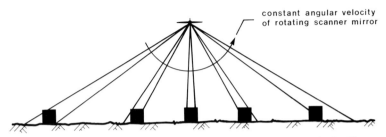

Figure 10.2 Effect of 'look angle'. Only buildings at the nadir are viewed vertically. Those at the edge have a compressed view of the walls in addition to the roof.

objects, which causes thermal shading, and orientation which leads to differential heating patterns on slopes, etc.

10.2.1.2 *Air temperature*. The stability and variation in the temperature range throughout the expected survey period can have a significant bearing upon the interpretation. This is particularly important for the examination of building heat loss where the maximum difference between internal and external temperatures is required. For this application, the air temperature is required to be below $+6\,°C$.

10.2.1.3 *Wind*. Wind speeds are required to be below 15 knots and preferably around 5 knots. There are two reasons for this: firstly, low wind speed reduces the amount of buffeting the aircraft receives; secondly, high winds result in strong wind shadows and differential cooling and an increase in the convective rather than radiative temperature loss.

10.2.1.4 *Look angle*. The scanner scans the ground perpendicular to the line of flight and as such only the area directly beneath the scanner is viewed vertically (Figure 10.2). Away from the nadir the scanner 'looks' at an angle to the ground surface, and for buildings a compressed view of the walls is achieved.

10.2.1.5 *Survey timing*. The mission planning is an important factor in terms of the type of results required. For example, the scanning of hot water from a power station must be completed during the period of power generation. Effects of tides and currents, for example, also have to be taken into account.

10.3 Image interpretation—applications

Thermal infrared imaging systems were originally developed for military applications but since the mid-1960s the techniques have been applied for numerous terrain investigations, principally in the fields of geology and ground-water investigations and in civil engineering for waste tip surveys, thermal discharges from power stations, pipeline detection and hydraulic leakage from dams. Thermal infrared linescan has also been used extensively in the survey of building heat loss for energy conservation purposes.

A selection of applications for which airborne thermal infrared imagery has been used in recent years is described in the following sections.

10.3.1 *Energy conservation*

One of the major tasks facing energy managers is the task of identifying, locating and assessing the relative severity of energy wastage on site, and determining a list for priority action. Infrared imagery has been used during the past four years to determine the relative importance of all sources of energy loss from a wide variety of building types and a wide market sector such as large and small industrial sites, hospitals, universities, local authorities and Ministry of Defence establishments. An example of a thermal infrared image of an industrial site is shown in Figure 10.3. The image was taken at 2054 hours in the evening of the 31st October 1979 from an altitude of approximately 730 m. The black-body reference temperatures in the scanner were set at $+0.5\,°C$ (low) and $+24.1\,°C$ (high) in a 'dummy' preview run over the site. The data were recorded on magnetic tape on board the aircraft and replayed to produce a hard copy image which was subsequently printed (as discussed in section 3.2.1.1).

Desk interpretation identified areas of potential interest on the site with respect to heat loss—these were priority areas to visit at the time of the site inspection. The principal features identified and confirmed by the site visit were the following.

(i) The lack of adequate insulation on an underground steam pipe running the length of the site. This pipe had also suffered a fracture which is shown on the imagery as a bright extended area along the length of the pipe. The reinsulation and repair of the pipe made substantial energy savings.

(ii) The majority of the buildings on site have adequately insulated roofs, shown by the dark grey tone on the imagery. However numerous problems are caused by high heat loss from rooflights and roof vents. The rooflights show as bright white linear patterns or regular dot patterns on the roofs. The roof vents are shown as irregular flaring spots, and as black spots where the vents have aluminium cowlings and are not emitting very hot air. Obviously roof vents cannot be eliminated when heat generating processes occur in the factory, but consideration could be given to heat recovery systems.

The interpretation of the imagery must be undertaken with care, and consideration must be given to the individual factors that affect each client i.e. financial constraints and energy management programmes. Whilst black-and-white and colour coded imagery can be used to determine the relative

Figure 10.3   A black-and-white thermal infrared linescan image of a typical industrial site taken in late 1979. The temperature range is from $+0.5°C$ (black) to $24.1°C$ (white). Various features relevant in an energy conservation programme are clearly shown on the image, notably the inadequate insulation on the underground pipe running vertically through the image. A bright blob on this line between the lower pair of the buildings indicates a fracture of the pipe. On the buildings themselves most of the roofs are adequately insulated, as shown by their dark signatures but rooflights (bright white linear bands) are obviously a problem.

temperature differences, this will not necessarily give the relative importance. For example, a small high-temperature ventilator will appear hotter than a cooler roof surface. However, the mass of the roof surface may well make it appear more important. The imagery only indicates the source of heat loss and not the cause; thus an apparently high temperature of a roof may be caused by poor insulation, uncontrolled temperatures or hot process operations, and this can influence the priority of a building in an energy conservation plan.

It is therefore important to realize that with the interpretation of thermal imagery there is always a need for site staff knowledge and data input. Experience of a large number of heat loss surveys has shown that airborne thermal infrared linescan surveys for building heat loss have the following major advantages:

(a) The very good temperature and spatial resolution of the linescanner enables the slightest variation within individual buildings or pipe runs to be established. Typically a variation in temperature across a roof may be caused by one of several factors; firstly, a change in roof construction, say from asbestos to glass; secondly, insulation defects caused by missing panels or water damage; thirdly, a variation in the internal temperature. The importance of the imagery is that it can give an excellent pattern and location of the variation. Establishing this pattern by any other method would be very time-consuming and in some cases impossible.

(b) The linescanner can detect steam and hot product lines to a depth of approximately 1 m. The identification of inadequate insulation and leaks from underground pipe distribution systems is very expensive. The importance of the thermal imagery in this respect is in guiding maintenance crews to defective areas.

(c) Large and complex sites consisting of a number of buildings of mixed age, construction and use can be surveyed very quickly to give an actual performance level at any one moment in time. Similarly where one client has several dispersed sites, an objective assessment of which site requires priority attention is given.

(d) Unnecessary areas of heat loss are detected, such as buildings which are unused or infrequently staffed and heated 24 hours per day, or excessive loss through doors and steam lines which perhaps lead to unused buildings but have not yet been blanked off.

(e) As a monitoring role the survey provides an assessment of the effectiveness and satisfactory levels of insulation of roofs. A good example of this is in council housing. Not only can the imagery be used to assess the relative effectiveness of different forms of insulation, but it can also be used to monitor on a house-by-house basis whether that insulation has been satisfactorily installed.

(f) Public relations may not be the prime reason for surveying an area but it can certainly provide a very useful lever to energy management. The imagery can generate interest at senior management level in a presentation of what is essentially an 'invisible' loss in a tangible form. This can be important in generating funds for energy conservation. At lower management and shopfloor levels it can be used to generate real interest in conservation by demonstrating graphically the existing problems.

10.3.2 *Thermal discharge plumes: power station cooling water patterns*

Power stations require large volumes of cooling water for use in steam generation. The water is discharged at a temperature higher than ambient water temperature, and if it is discharged directly into a water body (sea, lake or river) can create environmental problems. Problems can also be created for the power station if the outfall and inlet points are incorrectly located with respect to each other. This is particularly so if the outfall and inlet positions are subject to tidal or wind influences.

By using an airborne thermal infrared linescanner, the whole area affected by an outfall can be monitored in a matter of minutes. Repetitive coverage is easily obtained—this is necessary in a tidal situation, in order that all tidal states are covered by the thermal survey.

The thermal linescan survey may also be combined with conventional aerial photography to monitor water patterns highlighted by dye release. Aerial photography can be used as a planimetric base for plotting the results of the thermal linescan data, if adequate base maps are not available. For a tidal survey, overflights would be timed for high and low water and also at intervals between high and low water, on the flood and ebb tides.

Black-and-white contact scale imagery shows the gross patterns of hot water movement but it is not until the imagery is digitized and colour enhanced that the detailed patterns are revealed. The colour-coded digital imagery is used to produce 'thermal contour maps' (contour interval typically $1\,°C$ or $\frac{1}{2}°C$) which overlie a base map on which the inlet and outlet points are marked. In this way the position of the inlet point relevant to the outlet can be checked and altered if necessary.

Figure 10.4 shows sections of thermal contour maps of a power station cooling water outlet at four tidal states. These thermal contour maps resulted from an overflight at low tidal states of a coastal power station in Ireland. The imagery was acquired during spring 1981 during a calm day in order to ensure that there were no wind effects and to maximize the current and tidal effects. Flying commenced at 0700 hours (just before high tide) and continued at intervals until 1618 hours with activity centred around the half-ebb tide, low tide, and half-flood tide. The black-body reference temperatures were set at $+4\,°C$ and $+16\,°C$, except at the flood tide when the settings were $+2\,°C$ and $+20\,°C$. 'Quick look' imagery was produced to determine site coverage and then the imagery was digitized and colour-coded imagery produced. Examples of this are shown in Plate 18. The change in the position of the plume discharged from the power station can be clearly seen on the digitized thermal imagery. The dispersal in no clear direction is shown at the extreme top of the low tide image, and the pattern of tidal flow at flood tide forces the plume in towards the bay. At ebb tide the plume is drawn out away from the power station. Overlays with $\frac{1}{2}°C$ contour were produced to 1:2 500 scale Ordnance

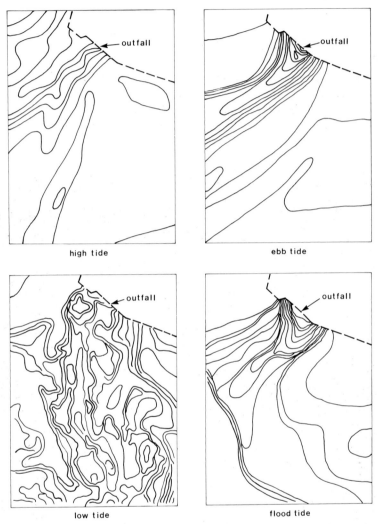

Figure 10.4   Power station cooling water outflow patterns. Examples of thermal contour maps, 1°C contour interval.

Survey plans, for the four tidal states. The whole exercise showed that at no tidal state did the outfall plume impede the intake channel and hence the theoretical design aims were proved.

Further studies were undertaken centred upon the extension of a hot-water discharge pipe into the bay. Using the contour overlays the effects of an extra hot-water outfall were assessed and the optimum location of the pipe determined.

This type of survey is useful for planning purposes, if a second power plant is to be sited close to an existing plant, or if it is suspected that poor efficiency may be due to a high inlet-water temperature.

10.3.3 *Effluent detection*

Thermal infrared linescan can be used to detect effluent discharge into water bodies. This can be monitored either by virtue of temperature differences between the discharge and the water body, or by emissivity differences. The latter is particularly noticeable in the field of oil pollution. Pure water has an emissivity of 0.993 in the 8–14 μm wavelength region. In contrast, water with a thin film of oil has a reduced emissivity of 0.972. This small difference, with

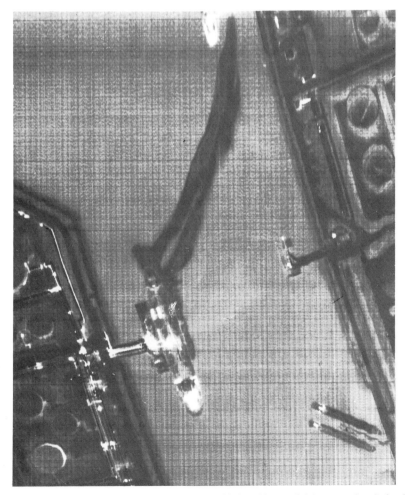

Figure 10.5 This black-and-white analogue thermal infrared image (8-14 μm waveband) clearly shows a tanker discharging oil in a harbour area. The difference in signature between the oil-covered water and the harbour water is due to a difference in emissivity (oil-covered water 0.972, water 0.993 in the 8–14 μm waveband). As the image was taken at night there is an obvious application in the field of oil pollution detection.

suitable calibration of the scanner, is enough to create a noticeable difference on analogue black-and-white imagery.

In the field of oil pollution, the fact that thermal infrared can be flown at night makes it a valuable tool in detecting illegal dumping of oil or washing out of tanks. 'Quick look' paper imagery can be available in real time. This, together with suitable navigation systems, can be the basis for a sophisticated pollution detection procedure.

Figure 10.5 clearly shows a tanker discharging oil in a harbour area. Other sections of the same imagery, flown in 1980, show areas of water which are polluted by oil. The oils shows as darker areas as would be expected due to the lower emissivity in relation to clear water.

Many effluent discharges may be detected by their thermal differences between the discharge and the surrounding water. These discharges are found with monotonous regularity in industrial areas where rivers or water bodies are present. It is of course impossible to discover from the imagery whether the discharges contain noxious elements as well as being thermally pollutive. The great advantage of using thermal infrared is that effluent discharges can be discerned which are not visible either on the ground or by conventional air photography.

Once the effluent locations have been identified by thermal infrared then ground investigations can be initiated to determine the environmental impact.

10.3.4 Waste tip surveys

Waste tips (both coal spoil and household and industrial refuse) are prone to internal combustion and the development of methane gas. The latter particularly applies to household wastetips. Airborne thermal infrared linescan can be used to identify areas of internal combustion and methane gas leaks.

Although areas of internal combustion show clearly on analogue black-and-white imagery, it is usual to utilize digital colour-coded imagery, as temperature levels may then be specified for particular areas of interest. A number of surveys of both coal and waste disposal tips have been undertaken and have successfully identified areas of internal combustion and methane gas leaks. Airborne thermal infrared linescan may also be used to identify moisture seepage areas on tips. Those areas are of importance in studies of stability of the tip. Anomalous accumulations of moisture may well indicate areas of potential instability, which could have disastrous consequences on the tip margins.

Flight timing for these types of surveys is critical. The aim is to record the maximum thermal differences on the tip surface, which means pre-dawn flying before solar radiation warms the ground surface. However, for detecting anomalous accumulations of moisture a midday flight may be indicated. At midday, the difference in thermal signature between water and soil is maximized. There will also be a greater evaporation (and hence cooling of the surface) from damp areas on the tip, which will show as dark patches on the thermal infrared imagery.

Waste tips are increasingly the subject of development plans as the trend towards land reclamation develops. An airborne thermal infrared survey, if conducted as part of the initial planning, can highlight potential problem areas in the field of internal combustion, methane gas leaks and potential areas of instability.

10.3.5 *Geological applications*

The use of thermal infrared imagery has been much investigated in the field of geological applications. Developments are continually being made, both in interpretation techniques and scanner design.

The ground surface temperature continually changes throughout the day in response to solar gain. This is further complicated by differing thermal inertias of materials, differing surface albedos, moisture content and topography, to highlight but a few variables. Various workers have shown that the ideal time for acquisition of thermal infrared data for geological purposes is either pre-dawn or approximately $1\frac{1}{2}$–2 hours after midday. At these times the maximum contrast exists between surface materials (see Figure 10.1). Little or no contrast is apparent between 8–10 a.m. and 5–6 p.m. (points of crossover of thermal inertia curves). Furthermore, post-sunrise imagery is affected by differential heating due to topographic effects. This of course is most severe in areas of pronounced topographic relief. Thermal shadow caused by relief effects may be useful in determining structural geology, as lineaments may be enhanced. Post-sunrise imagery is also complicated by the effects of dew on the surface and variations in the humidity of the air layer close to the ground as the dew is evaporated off. Very little is known at present about these effects.

10.3.5.1 *Thermal inertia mapping.* The determination and mapping of thermal inertia has important applications in geological discrimination. The production of a thermal inertia map of a target area requires the registration of two images flown pre-dawn and post-midday on the same diurnal cycle. It also requires the inclusion of meteorological data and digital topographic data.

Kahle *et al.* (1976) have produced a study of thermal inertia mapping at Pisgah Crater in California. Their thermal model utilized the diurnal temperature range (calculated from calibrated airborne thermal infrared images) taken pre-dawn (5.00 a.m.) and post-midday (2.00 p.m.), albedo, (taken from a visible image 0.4 μm to 0.7 μm) and topography. The magnitude of the diurnal temperature variation was calculated by digitally registering the pre-dawn and post-midday thermal infrared images. Good resolution was achieved by using a 3×3 m sampling grid.

Pisgah Crater is a young cinder cone with basaltic lava flows, situated in the

California Desert. The thermal inertia map was compared with the geological interpretation (produced from thermal infrared imagery). It was found that areas of low thermal inertia correlated with alluvium, aeolian sand and Pisgah Crater cinders. The basaltic lava flows were found to exhibit high thermal inertia. These results were to be expected, as density is one of the major factors influencing thermal inertia. Materials of high density such as basalt, have high thermal inertia. Figure 10.6 shows the almost linear relationship between thermal inertia and density. In terms of radiant surface temperature, basalt and other high thermal-inertia materials have a more uniform surface temperature than materials with a low thermal inertia. In practical terms this means that on a pre-dawn thermal image basalt will have a higher radiant temperature than, for example, volcanic cinders. On a post-midday thermal image the position will be reversed, as solar heat will have raised the surface

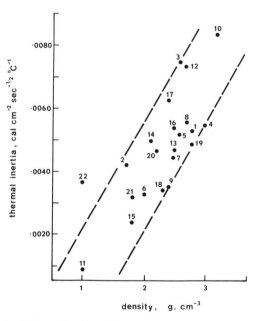

Figure 10.6   Relationship of density and thermal inertia for rocks and water.

1. Basalt	12. Quartzite
2. Moist clay soil	13. Rhyolite
3. Dolomite	14. Sandy gravel
4. Gabbro	15. Sandy soil
5. Granite	16. Sandstone, quartz
6. Gravel	17. Serpentine
7. Limestone	18. Shale
8. Marble	19. Slate
9. Obsidian	20. Syerite
10. Peridotite	21. Tuff, welded
11. Pumice (loose)	22. Water

temperature of the volcanic cinders more quickly than the basalt due to the lower thermal inertia of the cinders.

Kahle *et al.* (1976) found that the values of thermal inertia derived from pre-dawn and post-midday thermal infrared imagery correlated well with laboratory measurements made on similar basalt and cinders to those found at Pisgah Crater. There were several anomalies in Kahle's work mainly due to the absence of a topographic data input in the thermal inertia map. Comparison of the visible image and thermal inertia map shows that north-facing (shaded) slopes or gullies have an apparently higher thermal inertia than the south-facing (sunlit) slopes. A slope that is in shade will achieve a lower surface temperature during the day than a sunlit slope; this will result in smaller change in surface temperature between pre-dawn and post-midday thermal infrared imagery and hence an apparently higher thermal inertia. Thermal inertia models have to be corrected for topographic effects if spurious results are not to be produced.

Thermal inertia information alone does not identify geological units but it can be of use in defining boundaries between materials which have similar albedos but very different thermal properties, such as basalt and cinders.

10.3.5.2 *Thermal infrared mapping of volcanic activity.* Airborne thermal infrared imagery can also be used to map active volcanoes. In 1973, Daedalus Enterprises Inc. acquired imagery of Mauna Loa and Kilauea on Hawaii Island. Studies of this imagery showed that different lava flows could not be distinguished, as little difference in physical properties existed between them, which in turn suggested that little difference in thermal properties existed, a fact which was borne out by the imagery. One feature which did arise from the imagery was a distinction between the dense lava flows which form the scarp slopes bordering the summit caldera, North Pit, South Pit and Lua Hun, and the porous vesicular surface of the lava flows exposed on the flanks of the volcano and in the floor of the summit caldera and pit craters. The thermal imagery also showed an irregular reticulate pattern of very high temperatures on the floor of the summit caldera at both Mauna Loa and Kilauea. This pattern relates to fumes of steam and sulphur dioxide issuing from cracks in the surface of the lava flow. Also observed on the Kilauea imagery were discontinuous arcuate zones of heat. It is though that these may represent the convective flow of heat along umapped fracture zones.

Thermal infrared imagery could be used to monitor an active volcano. Temperature differences observed in the crater area could be indicative of a possible eruption. Pre-dawn thermal infrared imagery was acquired of the Mount St. Helens volcano in Washington State, USA, two days before it erupted in 1980. Temperatures in the area of the crater from which the eruption originated showed a maximum difference of 26 °C over the surrounding rocks.

Similar surveys have also been undertaken in Japan but with the aim of locating suitable areas for test drills for geothermal resources. Repetitive coverage was required for monitoring purposes and therefore all the data were digitized and combined with a digital terrain model of the area, which enabled spurious results due to slope angle and aspect to be eliminated. The conclusion of the study indicated that the refined thermal data (correlated with the digital terrain model) seemed to indicate the deep subsurface geothermal conditions.

Thermal infrared studies of volcanoes and volcanic activity in Italy have also been undertaken. These studies have shown that different-textured deposits can be successfully mapped by using the ratio of two thermal channels (3–5 μm and 8–14 μm).

10.3.5.3 *Sedimentary deposits.* Thermal infrared linescan is equally useful in mapping areas composed of sedimentary rocks.

Sabins (1969) describes the information gleaned from a thermal infrared survey undertaken of an area on the western margin of the Imperial Valley in California, USA. The area is low-relief desert terrain with sparse vegetation. Aeolian sand is present as a surface material in places with the underlying geology composed of Pleistocene siltstones and sandstones. These two rock types have sufficiently different physical, and hence thermal properties to register different signals on a thermal infrared image. In this area the sandstone showed warm on the nighttime thermal image, whereas the siltstone registered a cooler signature.

The significant feature about this study was the identification of an anticlinal structure not previously known and the extension of a fault zone. Aerial photography, both black-and-white panchromatic, black-and-white infrared, true-colour and false colour infrared show little detail as the region has little contrast difference in the visible part of the spectrum. However, the greater differences in thermal properties (against the low differences in visible reflectance) of the rocks and surface materials mean that the thermal infrared imagery was able to highlight structural features which were not otherwise evident.

Similar terrain features have been identified by thermal infrared imagery in the Indo Hills area of California, close to the San Andreas fault. Rocks involved were a poorly cemented conglomerate, which showed warm on the night thermal imagery, and a well-stratified formation of sandstone and siltstone which had a very distinctive pattern of alternate warm and cool bands on the thermal infrared imagery. Geological structures are well shown on the thermal infrared imagery. Plunging anticlines and synclines are identified by their pattern of warm and cool thermal signatures. The San Andreas fault is identified by an alignment of very cool (dark) signatures. This is thought to be due to the barrier effect of the San Andreas fault on groundwater movement. Shortly before the thermal infrared survey took place, a 15 m difference in the level of the water table existed across the fault zone. The higher water table could have resulted in a higher evaporative cooling effect on that side of the fault.

The technique of thermal infrared linescan imagery has also been used in China for the purpose of discrimination between Pleistocene conglomerate and morainic deposits. The conglomerate has a higher thermal capacity than the morainic deposits and hence the two formations can be distinguished on the basis of apparent temperature. The data collected in the 8–14 μm band was digitized and colour-coded to produce a surface temperature map. Existing maps did not show the boundary of the two geological units, as the difference between the units is very difficult to detect on the conventional aerial photography.

Thermal linescan has also been used to detect sinkholes in limestone, especially to identify problem areas in road construction. The scanner essentially detects differences in moisture content—the sinkholes, by virtue of the accumulation of loosely packed materials, have a higher moisture content which leads to a greater amount of evaporative cooling. This in turn results in a cooler signature on the thermal infrared imagery.

Thermal infrared imagery has been used for geological purposes in the UK by a number of commercial organizations and the Institute of Geological Sciences.

10.3.5.4 *Future developments.* All the surveys described above have utilized the 8–14 μm thermal band. Continued development in scanner engineering has given rise to a digital 6-channel thermal infrared scanner. Incoming radiation is separated by a diffraction grating on to 6 HgCdTe (mercury cadmium telluride) detectors covering the range of wave lengths from 8.2 μm to 12.2 μm. The individual channel boundaries were selected from extensive analysis of field and laboratory spectral data. The six channels are 8.2–8.6 μm, 8.6–9.0 μm, 9.0–9.4 μm, 9.4–10.2 μm, 10.2–11.2 μm, and 11.2–12.2 μm.

Investigators at the US Geological Survey and the Jet Propulsion Laboratory have recently published results of work which shows considerable promise in the use of a multispectral thermal infrared scanner for discrimination between and possibly identification of certain rock types. Spectra in the thermal region seems to be affected strongly by the quartz content on the rocks. Although only a limited amount of data has been made available, successful discrimination of rock types has been accomplished using a set of actual data obtained by an airborne thermal infrared multispectral scanner (TIMS).

It is believed that the combination of spectral data from the TIMS scanner with that currently available from airborne multispectral scanners (particularly those with spectral bands related to the Landsat 4 Thematic Mapper bands) will permit the discrimination of silicate rocks, carbonate rocks, and types of altered rocks with only limited ground verification. The successful application of this technique in geologically complex areas with a moderate level of vegetation cover will be a significant advance in geological mapping using remote sensing.

10.3.6 *Soil moisture and agricultural applications*

Thermal infrared linescan is particularly sensitive to moisture content at the surface of the soil. A thermal infrared image of a typical agricultural field will show, as darker patches, those areas of soil which contain higher than average volumes of moisture for that particular soil type. The reason for this is the increased evaporative cooling which is experienced from soil with a high moisture content in contrast to that with a low moisture content.

Airborne infrared linescan can be used in an agricultural application to determine areas of damp soil which need field drainage. The effectiveness of field drainage can also be checked using airborne thermal infrared linescan. If a field drainage system is functioning correctly then the image pattern will consist of evenly-spaced dark lines in the field. This relates to the lines of accumulation of soil moisture along the sub-surface channels. A break or block in one of these channels will result in a spreading of the soil moisture which shows on the image as a large irregular dark patch.

The technique of airborne thermal infrared linescan can also be used to show the environmental impact of man-made structures in soil moisture and drainage. For example if a new road were to be built across a small shallow valley and adequate drainage was not provided, then a moisture build-up would be experienced in the head of the valley. This may possibly have detrimental effects on agricultural crops. The extent of the affected ground could be shown using airborne thermal infrared imagery. An alternative would be to overfly the proposed alignment of the road before construction to determine potential problem areas with respect to soil moisture. Adequate drainage of problem areas could then be planned in conjunction with the road construction.

Airborne thermal surveys can also be used to monitor soil temperature, and indirectly soil air-space and soil surface structure. This is particularly useful on reclaimed soils which tend to be more cohesive in nature. Earthworms are often introduced to work and aerate the soil, thus improving the agricultural capability of the soil. Their progress can be monitored by airborne thermal infrared, as increasing air-space in the soil caused by the earthworms results in a decrease in the soil temperature, which is detected by the linescanner.

The effectiveness of shelter belts can also be determined by airborne thermal linescan surveys. A higher surface temperature results in areas sheltered from wind, as there is a reduced rate of evaporative cooling. Simple measurements can be taken from the analogue black-and-white imagery to determine if the shelter belt is giving its designed protection. Breaks in the shelter belt can be assessed for severity by examining the pattern of surface temperature they produce on a thermal infrared image.

10.3.7 *Ground water and spring detection*

Ground water maintains a relatively constant temperature throughout the year. It is not influenced greatly by local climate conditions, although flow rates will obviously depend on the replenishment rates of the aquifer. Ground water from springs will be cooler than the surface water into which it flows in

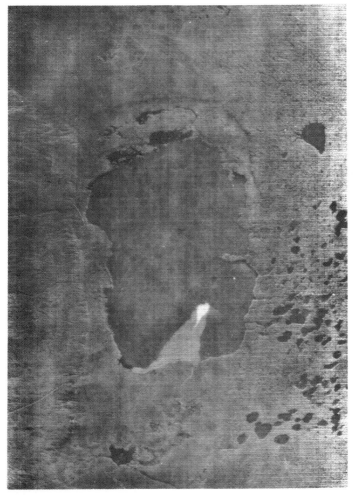

Figure 10.7   Imagery taken pre-dawn in the 8–14 μm waveband clearly shows a spring discharging into a lake. The temperature range was from $-5°C$ to $+6°C$, and as the imagery was flown during the winter months, the spring water is warmer than the lake water into which it is flowing.

summer, and warmer in winter. Although these temperature differences are not great they are sufficient to be detected by an airborne thermal line scanner.

Springs can be detected whether they discharge into water bodies, or as headwaters of streams. These will be seen on analogue black-and-white imagery. Digital colour-coded imagery, which by colour enhancement can highlight temperature differences as small as 0.2 °C (the thermal resolution of the scanner) can locate spring discharges into a flowing river. Figure 10.7 shows a groundwater spring discharging into a small lake. As the survey was flown pre-dawn in winter the ground water is noticeably warmer than the lake water. Black-body temperatures in the scanner were set at − 5 °C (low) and + 6 °C (high). Airborne thermography can also locate freshwater springs along the coast, again by virtue of the temperature difference between the ground water and the surface water. Some idea of the size of flow of the spring can be gained by the length of the 'plume' of colder/warmer water (depending on time of year) from the point of issue of the spring. This applies to springs issuing into land water bodies, rivers and the sea. Once the springs have been located by airborne thermography then areas of groundwater discharge can be mapped and correlated with geological maps. These can then be used for planning purposes. Groundwater studies may be part of a larger geological survey, in which airborne thermal linescan has an important role.

10.3.8 *Forest-fire detection*

These surveys utilize both thermal channels of a dual-channel scanner such as the Daedalus DS1230. The two detectors used are the 3–5 μm InSb (indium antimonide) used to detect the 'hot' spots of the fire, and the 8–14 μm (HgCdTe) is used to generate the 'terrain' image which enables the fire areas to be accurately located.

The technique of forest-fire mapping has been pioneered in Canada. The advantage of using airborne thermal infrared scanning is that the fire front can be detected through smoke (which is always present!) and at night the InSb detector (3–5 μm) is used to trigger a threshold circuit which records an 'event marker' at the edge of the imagery. The HgCdTe (8–14 μm) detector is used normally to generate the terrain image. 'Quick look' imagery is produced on paper in real-time on board the aircraft. The relevant data is then transferred to maps which are then given to the firefighting teams.

10.3.9 *Archaeological sites*

These are detected due to variations in the soil properties. Ancient field patterns have been found which were more readily identified on thermal infrared imagery (8–14 μm, daytime acquisition). Thermal infrared imagery has also been used to survey ancient foundations of buildings where no surface expression of foundations exists.

10.3.10 *Urban climatological studies*

Moderately high-level (approximately 5000 m above ground level) airborne thermal surveys can be used to generate urban microclimate maps. Day- and nighttime imagery is normally flown for comparison. The data are digitized and colour enhanced. Normal presentation is in the form of a mosaic of images, perhaps with a topographical overlay. Striking contrasts are often found between various regions of an urban area, and between the urban area and the surrounding country.

10.3.11 *Pipeline detection*

Buried pipelines across country can be detected by thermal infrared linescan by virtue of the disturbed ground along the alignment of the pipe. The signature will either be warmer or cooler than the surrounding land, depending on the differing rates of moisture retention and evaporative cooling by the disturbed/undisturbed ground.

10.3.12 *Hydraulic leakage from dams*

Water seepage or accumulation can be detected by thermal infrared linescan in two ways; either a bright signature indicating the presence of water at the surface, or a dark signature indicating a high moisture content in the surface material. A severe leak from a dam would show on thermal infrared imagery as a bright linear anomaly issuing from a point source at an anomalous location on the dam. Water accumulation will show as dark area due to the increased evaporative cooling from wet soil.

References

Kahle, A. B., Gillespie, A. R. and Goetz, A. F. H. (1976) Thermal Inertia Mapping—an new geological mapping tool. *Geophysical Research Letters* 3, 26–28.
Sabins, F. G. (1969) Thermal Inertia Mapping and its application to structural mapping in Southern California. *Geol. Soci. Ameri. Bull.* 80, 397–404.

Bibliography

Barratt, E. C. and Curtis, L. F. (1976) *Introduction to Environmental Remote Sensing.* Chapman and Hall, New York, 336 pp.
Curtis, L. F. (1974) 'Remote sensing for environmental planning surveys', in *Environmental Remote Sensing Applications and Achievements*, eds. Barratt E. C. and Curtis L. F., Edward Arnold, London, 309 pp.
Cocking, S. J., Gardner, W. E., Haigh, G. A., Norgett, H. M. J., and Pritchard, S. E. *Estimation of Heat Losses by Aerial Thermography.* Summary Report: AERE—R9543; Technical Report 1—The Survey: AERE—R9898; Technical Report 11—The Visual Imagery: AERE R9899; Technical Report 111—Quantitative Analysis: AERE R9900; HMSO, London.
Daedalus Enterprises Inc. *Daedalus Scanner Applications—Worldwide* 1979/1980/1981.
Ellyett, C. D. and Fleming, A. W. (1974) Thermal infra-red imagery of the Burning Mountain coal fire. *Remote Sensing of Environment*, 79–86.

Haigh, G. A., and Pritchard, S. E. (1981) *Quantitative Analysis of Aerial Infra-Red data for Heat Loss Surveys.* HMSO, London, 109 pp.

Headley, R. B. (1979) *Infra-Red Thermography Requirements Study For Energy Conservation* U.S. Department of Commerce, Washington.

Lillesand, T. M. and Keifer, R. W. (1979) *Remote Sensing And Image Interpretation.* John Wiley, New York, etc., 612 pp.

Madding, R. R. (1979) *Thermographic Instruments and Systems.* University of Wisconsin, 129 pp.

Madding, R. P. (1980) *Thermal Infra-red Sensing Applied to Energy Conservation In Building Envelopes (Thermosense 111).* Society of Photo-Optical Instrumentation Engineers, 216 pp.

Sabins, F. F. (1978) *Remote Sensing Principles and Interpretation,* Freeman, San Francisco, 426 pp.

Various, (1979, 1980) *Thermosense 1 and 11,* American Society of Photogrammetry, Virginia.

11 Remote sensing and water resources engineering

K. BLYTH

11.1 Introduction

The water resources side of hydrology deals with hydrological features which are notoriously variable in both time and space, but frequently engineering projects have severely limited time and funds available for the collection of relevant hydrological data. Archived data generally provides the cheapest source of information, and this should be carefully studied before attempts are made to undertake new measurements. Any shortcomings discovered in the archived data should then be used to aid the design of a more suitable data collection programme.

For small-scale studies, measurements taken with conventional ground-based instruments may provide the most cost-effective solution to the engineer's problem. Ground-based instruments are capable of providing very accurate data over a wide range of time frequencies and may operate in all weather conditions. Their main disadvantage however is that they provide only a point measurement which is unlikely to be representative of the whole. To help offset this, the number of ground measurements can be increased up to a point determined by the available *time* required to install the instruments, the *manpower* required for their installation, operation and data analysis and above all the *cost* of their purchase and operation.

Whilst remote sensing techniques are unlikely to ever match the accuracy of ground-based measurements, they are capable of providing a measure of surface variability which can never be appreciated from the ground. Ground-control measurements such as spectral reflectance (see Figure 11.1) should always accompany the acquisition of remotely sensed data. By incorporating a limited number of ground measurements great savings can be made in the length of time which personnel spend in the field. As many hydrological occurrences are short-lived, the unique ability of remote sensing to 'freeze' information from a very large area until such time as personnel are able to deal with it, can vastly increase the scope and capacity of small work units. It is

Figure 11.1   Measurement of spectral reflectance.

however unlikely that remote sensing alone will provide all the answers to a particular engineering problem, thus from the outset the remote sensing aspect should be carefully integrated into the overall project and should not be expected to stand alone.

It is not possible in this chapter to examine how remote sensing can be applied to the monitoring of all hydrological variables; however, some of the main topics which are likely to be of interest to civil engineers are covered, namely water extent, depth, temperature and quality, and the estimation of groundwater resources and soil moisture.

11.2   Water extent

11.2.1 Open water surfaces

The detection of previously unmapped water bodies, or the measurement of known water body extent, is generally an awkward and time-consuming exercise when attempted at ground level, often due to the difficulty of access

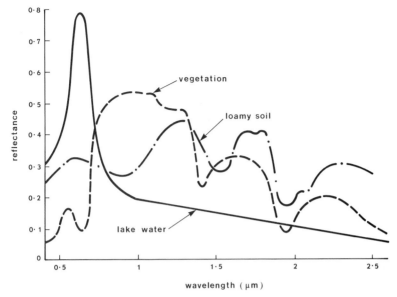

Figure 11.2   Spectral reflectances in the visual and near IR regions of typical earth surfaces. (After Entres, 1974.)

to water bodies and their immediate surroundings. By adopting an aerial viewpoint, water extent is much easier to assess, as shielding by vegetation is usually only effective around the perimeter of large water bodies. Water extent is probably the easiest earth feature for remote sensing systems to delineate due to its high contrast with land features in certain wavelengths, as illustrated by Figure 11.2. In addition, ground verification of water extent is straightforward in that a definite yes/no answer can often be given with fewer grades of qualification than with other variables such as soil moisture, which requires considerable additional explanation of related ground state.

Undoubtedly one of the most effective remote sensing methods of detecting water is through the use of sensors operating in the near-infrared region (approximately $0.75–1.0\,\mu m$). This spectral band is especially useful for differentiating vegetation and water, and can, to a moderate degree, overcome the previously mentioned shielding problem often affected by vegetation of varying density. The reason for this is that water almost totally absorbs near-infrared radiation, whilst healthy vegetation is a strong near-infrared reflector. On false colour infrared film for example, a high contrast exists between the recorded deep blue of water and the bright magenta-red of healthy, green vegetation (Plate 19). On natural colour film, however, vegetation often appears as varying shades of olive whilst water in the shade of trees may be a grey/green colour, making differentiation of the two very difficult. This feature is also illustrated by Plate 19. Water as recorded on true colour film can vary greatly in colour according to its depth and to the colour of any dissolved or suspended solids. With false colour infrared film, although variations do occur, the predominant blue colour of water features is retained, thus allowing more consistent water recognition. Land/water contrast is so strong in the near infrared band that automatic recognition of water is possible using computer-processed multispectral data. Tests carried out at Purdue University using multispectral aircraft data (Hoffer *et al.*, 1972) indicate that water bodies can be correctly recognized 95 times out of 100 using such techniques, and NASA have produced a low-cost program for handling Landsat data which enables bodies of water greater than 6 acres (2.43 ha) to be recognized correctly with better than 95% precision whilst water features greater than 4.0 ha can be recognized with almost 100% precision (NASA News Release, 1977). In theory, the minimum possible width of river which should always be detectable as water is equal to 2 pixel lengths (i.e. on Landsat 374 feet (114 m) across track or 500 feet (152 m) along track). Similarly the theoretical minimum possible area of a water body (pond) that should always be detectable as water would be equivalent to 4 pixels (i.e. on Landsat 4.3 acres (1.74 ha))(Cooper *et al.*, 1975). Although Landsat imagery has been used for monitoring the extent of Playa lakes and wetlands in California (see Carter and Smith, 1974, and Cooper *et al.*, 1975), for such a technique to be of use in Europe for water resource management, much higher ground resolutions would be necessary, this being confirmed by the findings of the World Meteorological Organisation meeting on Satellite Applications in Hydrology (Meier, 1976). Of course it can be argued that satellite monitoring of water extent is not required in Europe, as adequate measures are already taken from the ground. An alternative approach might be to telemeter water-level recorder information from a dense network of instruments to a central point for water management purposes. Real-time data could be obtained to accuracies similar to or better than present satellite data without being dependent on suitable cloud cover conditions (Argos, 1977). The problem of extensive cloud cover over Europe restricts satellite monitoring systems to the use of microwave sensors. Although high-altitude aircraft could supply the required quality of data, their operation is uneconomical for repetitive monitoring of large areas and may be restricted in poor weather conditions.

Where extensive water extent data is required, the method of collection must be carefully matched to the overall requirement, remote sensing methods sometimes, but not always, being the most satisfactory solution. Thermal infrared radiometry may be used to delineate water features, as generally they exhibit a different temperature to the surrounding land, although not always. For best thermal separation of land and water, observations should generally be made before sunrise. Unless thermal information is required in addition to water extent information, thermal infrared techniques would not normally be the first choice for water feature mapping.

11.2.2 *Streams and rivers*

Whilst relatively large water bodies such as lakes and reservoirs can be directly sensed using the aforementioned techniques, for the recognition of stream networks inferential methods may be required due to the small surface area of open water involved. For example, the low resolution of an airborne thermal scanning radiometer may create difficulties in the delineation of small streams, even though a good land/water temperature gradient exists. However, Brown and Holz (1976) found that low-level (750 metres) infrared scanner imagery was capable of resolving streams 1.5 m wide. Side-looking radar on the other hand provides excellent definition of surface topography, from which the location of stream channels can often be inferred, especially in areas of high relief (McCoy, 1961). However, field checks should be undertaken to confirm that streams do exist and that dry valleys are not to be expected. In addition, where streams are large enough to be detected on side-looking radar, they normally appear black due to their low microwave backscattering. The allweather capability of side-looking radar would therefore make it the first choice for such requirements as defining potential reservoir catchment characteristics particularly in mountainous regions possessing a high incidence of cloud.

With small-scale or low-resolution data, such as satellite imagery, the presence of minor streams is often apparent due to the linear enhancement effect of changes in vegetation, topography or human land use on either side of the stream, rather than from the water signal itself. Thus in open moorland areas, such as are found in the Central Pennines for example, the presence of very low-order streams only a few feet wide can be clearly inferred from Landsat MSS images as a result of topographic enhancement in spite of the 80 m ground resolution of the Landsat sensor. Great difficulty may be experienced however in visually identifying quite large rivers in flat terrain, such as the Fenland and Wash areas, where vegetation is similar on both river banks. Where computer processing of digital information is used, the minimum width of a river which should theoretically always be detectable as water is 2 × the sensor pixel size (Cooper *et al.*, 1975).

Satellite imagery may be of great value for delineating stream networks in poorly mapped areas such as the Middle East or parts of the USA, for example see Baker (1973) but it is of little value in the UK where 1:50 000 O.S. maps accurately delineate much smaller streams than are visible from satellite platforms. Although the high-resolution capability of low-level infrared photography may be in theory capable of resolving first-order streams, thus allowing the definition of a complete UK stream network, in practice shading problems are often encountered due to the presence of hedges, trees, buildings etc. Even if the water surface of a complete stream network were visible, the information would be of much greater value for runoff predictions for example, using contributing area models (Blyth and Rodda, 1973) if a positive indication of water movement were also obtainable. Without this knowledge, an over-estimate of the contributing area will result, due to the inclusion of stationary sections of impounded water in the upper reaches of stream channels. Although some measurement of water velocity is possible using remote sensing methods, it is unlikely that velocities below $0.3\,\mathrm{m\,s^{-1}}$ will be practically detectable. For overseas applications, the detection and mapping of spasmodic stream systems (wadis etc.) may be of great importance in water resource studies (IH report, 1976) and also engineering studies, for which purposes the synoptic coverage of satellite data is likely to be the most suitable. In the UK, the detection of unusual surface storm runoff would be of great advantage for structural design purposes and for studies of the effects of changing land-use, and low-cost aerial photography may often be adequate for such requirements.

11.2.3 Flooding

In the United States, Landsat MSS imagery has been successfully used for mapping inundated areas of floodplains of large rivers such as the Mississippi in order to identify priority areas for flood relief aid (Hallberg and Hoyer, 1973). Figure 11.3 illustrates this technique on the River Trent.

Because of the physiological stress placed on the vegetation by waterlogging, its near infrared reflectance may be reduced for extended periods. This may allow successful retrospective mapping of the inundated areas for at least five days after the floodwater recession. Work by Deutsch et al. (1973) suggests that the effect may be apparent in some cases for several weeks after flooding,

Figure 11.3   Landsat MSS ratio (Band 6/Band 7) of the River Trent, illustrating floodwater extent.

but this is more likely to be due to a longterm vegetational change rather than continued plant stressing. Work carried out by the author in the U.K. has shown that flood boundaries over arable and grassland areas are often detectable for at least five days after flood recession, using low altitude false colour infrared photography as the sensing medium from which flood boundaries can be drawn (Blyth and Nash (1980)) (see Plate 20). For vegetated areas it may therefore be feasible to carry out low cost flood monitoring of a whole river system after a flood in order to identify areas requiring flood alleviation attention and other remedial works. Due to the great pressures of housing and industrial expansion on land availability, new building is often established in areas which may be subject to infrequent flooding (Goddard, 1973). Aerially established flood frequency limits would provide a permanent record of past flooding which could be used to great advantage in the siting of new development, and such records are now being used when available.

11.2.4 *Wetlands*

When direct viewing of water surfaces is impaired, as in marsh or other permanent wetland areas, it is often possible to determine the extent of waterlogging by the recognition of marshland plant species. Ground-based ecological studies have shown that in many climatic regions, plant species distribution is highly dependent on the prevailing ground state in the transition zones between water bodies and dry ground (Goodier, 1970). Thus it may be possible to distinguish summer and winter water levels purely by identification of the dominant plant species (Anderson and Wobber, 1972; Klemas *et al.*, 1975; McEwen *et al.*, 1976; Sutcliffe, 1974). If the indicator species is markedly different in colour or texture to its neighbours, then conventional black-and-white, true colour or false colour infrared film may be adequate for its delineation. However, for more positive identification of similar species, multispectral photography or multispectral scanner imagery would normally be used, having previously established the spectral signature of the species of interest from ground radiometric measurements. Microwave sensing systems, especially of the longer wavelengths (around 20 cm), would derive only a small proportion of their ground signal from short marshland vegetation so that an overall low signal would be recorded as a result of the underlying water, thus allowing adequate delineation of its extent (Matthews, 1975).

11.3   Water penetration and depth measurement

11.3.1 *Water penetration for sub-surface mapping*

Before attempting to assess water penetration properties or water depth estimation using remote sensing techniques, the basic reflectance properties of

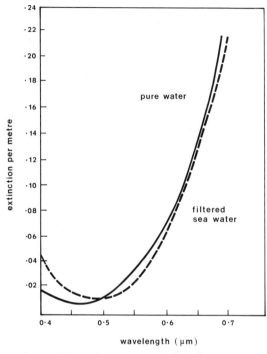

Figure 11.4   Extinction coefficients of pure water and filtered sea water. (After Yentsch, 1960.)

water bodies must be understood. Incoming solar radiation incident on a water surface is partially reflected at the surface, this being largely specular reflectance, but it may be diffuse when the water surface is very rough. The remainder of the radiation entering a bottomless water body is subject to depletion as a result either of absorption and scattering by the pure water molecules, or of scattering, diffraction and reflection by dissolved or suspended particles in the water. In completely clear water, sunlight may penetrate several hundred metres (Fitzgerald, 1974), and so theoretically a small amount of backscattered radiation should also be present from this depth. In practice, signal levels from such depth are too small to be recognizable amongst instrument noise and atmospheric variations, which may be large. As can be seen in Figure 11.4, the maximum transmission of light in distilled water lies near 0.48 μm. Underwater measurements of downwelling light made by Wenderoth and Yost (1975) also indicate that, in relatively clear water, maximum light transmission occurs in the blue/green region of about 0.5 μm (see Figure 11.5) and primarily due to absorption, the transmittance values at longer and shorter wavelengths within the visible spectrum, fall off rapidly. Because of this, it is not surprising to find that tests, using different types of both available and experimental film emulsions, have shown that those most sensitive to radiance in the 0.5 μm region are most suitable for water

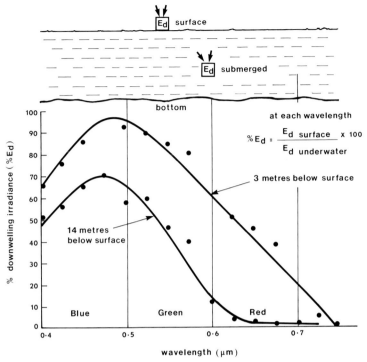

Figure 11.5   Downwelling irradiance in clear ocean water. (After Yost and Wenderoth, 1972.)

penetration purposes and for the detection of ocean bottom detail (Lockwood *et al.*, 1974). Lockwood *et al.* concluded from their tests that the most suitable film for general sub-surface detail mapping was the readily available Ektachrome EF Aerographic with Wratten 3 haze filter, giving a spectral sensitivity of 0.45–0.65 μm. A two-layer film specially devised for water penetration (Specht *et al.*, 1973; Vary, 1969(*a*)) with spectral peaks at 0.48 and 0.55 μm, was capable of similar penetration to the Ektachrome film, but lacked colour contrast. Keller (1975) quotes natural colour film as having a penetration capability of around 25 m in clear waters and compares the suitability of readily-available film emulsions for different types of ocean observation work.

Extensive studies have been undertaken using satellite imagery to map coastal water features and, in the majority of those utilizing Landsat imagery, either the green RBV (return beam vidicon) band of 0.475–0.575 μm was found to be most suitable for mapping underwater features and turbidity variations, or more commonly, when using the MSS data, the green 0.5–0.6 μm band was found superior for water penetration and sediment mapping purposes (Clark *et al.*, 1974). From Landsat MSS imagery, it has been possible in shallow coastal waters to map, within useful accuracies, such variables as seabed

Table 11.1 Typical transmission characteristics of large water bodies. (After Jerlov. 1951.)

Types of ocean water	Wavelength of maximum transmission (in μm)	Per cent transmission per m
Clearest oceans	0.47	98.1
Average oceans	0.475	89.0
Clearest coastal	0.50	88.6
Average coastal	0.55	72.4
Average inshore	0.60	60.8

vegetation (Williams, 1973) sediment types and sand bars (Anderson *et al.*, 1973) and ocean depth up to about 20 m (Polcyn and Lyzenga, 1973).

So far, the discussion has been considering restricted, but still moderately broad-band, techniques of sensing sub-surface water detail. Because of the complexity of factors affecting the transmittance of underwater detail, such as surface roughness, size and colour of suspended particulate matter and bottom type (Fitzgerald, 1974), narrow-band multispectral methods can be more carefully 'tuned' to the prevailing conditions and therefore offer better chances of success than fixed broad-band methods. For example, in clear, deep ocean water, sensing in the blue region is best, whereas for heavily sedimented coastal water, sensing in the green-yellow region would appear to yield better results (see Table 11.1). Yost and Wenderoth (1968) took multispectral photographs of coloured targets both on and below the seawater surface in order to measure the attenuation of the water at different wavelengths. Their measurements indicated that (for coastal water in the Gulf of Mexico) the ability to detect underwater objects was best in the 0.493–0.543 μm band, and also, very importantly, that considerable additional film exposure was necessary to reveal underwater detail compared to the exposure required for surface light conditions. The enhancement of underwater objects and of subtle changes of water colour due to changes in suspended particles (see section 11.4.2) was achieved by using a purely spectral identification technique whereby large variations in scene brightness, as found in coastal waters, were completely removed. Generally, these findings and techniques can be applied to imagery taken from all altitudes, except that atmospheric haze effects increase with increase in altitude, with a resulting loss of contrast below about 0.5 μm. For this reason, a compromise is often necessary between choosing the optimum wavelength for penetration of a water body and its correspondence with a suitable atmospheric 'window' of high transmittance.

11.3.2 *Water depth measurement*

The aerial measurement of water depth can either be absolute, using direct measurement techniques, or it can be inferred by estimating water absorption effects or by the analysis of surface wave patterns. Direct techniques include photogrammetry and laser profiling.

If coastal water is exceptionally clear, it is possible to contour underwater features using conventional aerial photogrammetric techniques (Geary, 1967; Vary 1969(*b*)) by the measurement of parallax in stereopair photographs. The constraints of normal photogrammetry still hold in that at least three reference targets or points of known relative position are required in each photograph, to enable the stereo model to be reconstructed. Surface water conditions must of course be relatively calm and accuracies are likely to be better where the sea-bed is textured, for instance by rocks or vegetation, as opposed to uniform and sandy.

Accurate profiling of water depth can also be accomplished by lidar systems, as discussed in Chapter 3. In this case a pulsed, coherent laser light source is pointed downwards from the sensor platform so as to strike the water surface at right angles. A strong reflected light signal is received from the water surface, followed closely by a weaker reflected signal from the floor of the water body. The depth to which the laser beam can effectively penetrate obviously depends on the water clarity, atmospheric attenuation and laser strength and frequency, but in clear waters, depth measurements down to about 50 m should be feasible from aircraft and to about 20 m from satellites (Naval Office note, 1972). If only a single-frequency laser is available, one operating in the blue-green region will give good water penetration (Hickman and Hogg, 1969), but with tunable lasers, the best wavelength can be chosen to suit the water colour. The calculation of water depth is a function of time of travel of a given pulse of light for the round trip from laser gun to water bed and back to the detector head, minus the round trip time from the sensor to the water surface and back. A measurement of the average index of refraction of the water body is also required, but this value does not change very rapidly. Lidar profilers allow the most accurate aerial measurement of water depth, but only at a point or along a flight line, which offers rather a poor sample. For this reason lidar profilers are best used in conjunction with imaging depth estimation techniques where they provide an accurate depth reference along the centre line of an image, which can then be extrapolated to the whole image frame. In their report *Photometric and Polarimetric Mapping of Water Turbidity and Water Depth*, (1973), the Grumman Aerospace Corporation repeatedly expressed how useful a laser ranging system would have been in providing accurate depth measurements along the centre line of their passive imaging scanner data. Only occasional manual checks of water depth should be required to check the laser performance. Alternatively, the use of a scanning lidar system, such as the Larsen-500 system described in Chapter 3, could also be considered.

The greatest potential for remote water-depth mapping is in lakes, estuaries and shallow coastal waters. In relatively shallow water, the reflected daylight component from the bed of the water body is large and it is the attenuation of this component upon which many inferred water-depth esti-mates rely (see Figure 11.6). Polcyn and Sattinger (1969) realized, however,

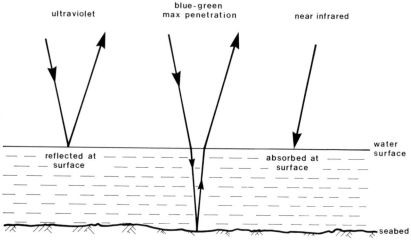

Figure 11.6   Interaction of electromagnetic radiation with a water body (Blyth, 1981.)

that only in areas where bottom type and water clarity are uniform can there be a reliable correlation between recorded signal and depth of water. The use of multispectral scanning methods enables two or more narrow bands of data to be used to sample the spectral signature of each underwater resolution element. Polcyn and Sattinger (1969) devised a method of water depth determination by measuring the differences of attenuation of two such narrow wavebands, brought about by the selective transmission of a given uniform body of water. Because of water's marked differential absorption of, say, red and blue wavelengths, a relatively large difference will exist in the light extinction coefficients of these wavelengths (a function of the depth to which light of a given wavelength will penetrate a pure water column, see Figure 11.4). If the transmissivity of the water body is known and also the ratio of the reflectance of the bottom material for the two chosen wavelengths (established by on-site measurements), then the ratio of the red to blue reflected light will be a function of the water depth. Other variables such as the intensity and angle of illumination, sensor angle, atmospheric effects and sea surface roughness will be constant at any given instant and therefore should not greatly affect the ratio value. In areas of uniform water transmissivity and smooth sandy bottom characteristics, water depth measurements have been made using this method down to 9 m with an accuracy of $\pm 20\%$, but under better lighting conditions, measurements down to about 16 m could be expected (Brown et al., 1971). More recent work by the Grumman Aerospace Corporation (1973) using this technique with a digital photometric mapper has shown that depth increments as small as 0.3 m in 12 m of coastal water can be resolved. Generally, however, accuracies of about 10% at 15 m depths using three spectral bands are normal. Such techniques are best conducted from low altitudes, otherwise differential atmospheric attenuation effects would have to be measured.

Kolipinski and Higer (1969) also used MSS data to recognize water of different depth ranges, but by a much simpler method. They relied on comparisons of multispectral data of unmapped areas, with the spectral signatures of local control points or 'training areas' at known depths and were able reliably to identify depths between 0–1 m, 1–1.5 m and 1.5–5 m. The false detection of tree shadows as deep water constituted about 1.5% of the total deep-water recognition area. They also found that in the Everglades region of Florida, different depths of shallow water could be inferred from the dominant plant species distribution, which could be readily classified using multispectral data. Sutcliffe (1974) also related species types to water depth ranges in the Southern Sudd swamp region of the White Nile, and similar relationships are to be found in salt- and freshwater wetland in the UK (Goodier, 1970).

Whilst multispectral scanner data has been used for most of the above water-depth measurements, analysis of multispectral photography should provide similar relationships; however, very strict control of film exposure and processing would be required, followed by densitometric analysis of the imagery. Multispectral scanner data is therefore more reliable and is easier and cheaper to process.

The characteristics of surface waves, such as their wavelength and periodicity (which may be recorded on aerial imagery), can also be used to estimate water depth, some of these methods being described by Polcyn and Sattinger (1969). Waves advancing through unrestricted deep water have a velocity which is related to their wave period and wavelength. As the waves approach water of depth less than about half a wavelength, their velocity and subsequently their wavelength decreases considerably. By measuring their wavelength in deep water (L) and also in shallow water (L_0), this often being possible from a single photograph, the wavelength ratio L/L_0 can be found, which is functionally related to d/L_0, so that water depth (d) can be determined. If it is not possible to monitor the wave trains as they pass from deep to shallow water, it is still possible to calculate water depth over shallow water only, provided that successive, short-interval photographs can be taken. Using this method, the velocity of the waves can be measured in relation to some fixed reference point which must be present within each photograph. Given the velocity and wavelength in shallow water, the mean water depth can be estimated with an accuracy largely dependent on the regularity of the wave patterns, since once $d/L_0 \leqslant \frac{1}{2}$, the wave velocity becomes proportional to $\sqrt{d}$. Such methods of depth estimation are suitable for many shorelines of large lakes and coastal waters of fairly uniform slope, but not for small water bodies or physically complex shorelines. Their main advantage over the multispectral techniques is that no specialized equipment is really necessary and data analysis is straightforward. Optical Fourier processing of the wave pattern images has however been used to highlight slight wave diffractions caused by underwater shoals, and to speed depth calculations over large areas. A method has been used which measures such refractive effects on the wave trains caused by changing water depth, but its applications are really restricted to straight beaches having parallel contours; otherwise very complex calculations are necessary. The likely presence of underwater shoals can also be roughly located by visual analysis if Fourier transform methods are not available.

11.4   Water quality and turbidity

11.4.1 *Introduction*

Many of the remote sensing methods used to achieve water penetration and to estimate water depth must take account of water-quality effects, and so it is often a small step to redesign such methods to observe variations in water quality when the water depth and bottom characteristics are known. Many remote water-quality sensing techniques work more successfully in deep water where bottom effects are negligible, and therefore in shallow lakes and rivers more control observations are generally required. As the effects of suspended organic and inorganic material and those of dissolved minerals are somewhat similar from a remote sensing point of view, they will all be dealt with in this section. Most suspended materials and some dissolved materials generally cause a change in emitted light intensity from a water body or a change in its colour due to their presence. Using simple photographic recording techniques, differences in water colour or brightness can frequently be recognized either as variations in image density in the case of black-and-white film, or, more usefully, as changes in colour, hue, saturation and brightness with colour film. Although differences in water colour can be detected and mapped with unfiltered black-and-white panchromatic film, the use of colour film represents the first step towards identification of the organic, inorganic or chemical cause of the colour change, as shown in Plate 21. Thus, effluent outfalls from certain types of industry may be recognizable, for example the bright red coloration of waste from a tomato canning factory (Reeves *et al.*, 1975), dense white from the waste materials used in papermaking (Klooster and Scherz, 1973), and black from coal washings (Lo, 1976). Similarly, if the colour of a suspended sediment can be detected, it may be possible to determine whether it derives from a particular source of erosion (Currey, 1977). As long as only qualitative information is required from aerial photographs, uncontrolled photography with minimal ground verification may satisfy the requirements.

11.4.2 *Materials in suspension*

Once measures of suspended sediment concentrations or dissolved chemical concentrations are required, many more factors must be taken into con-

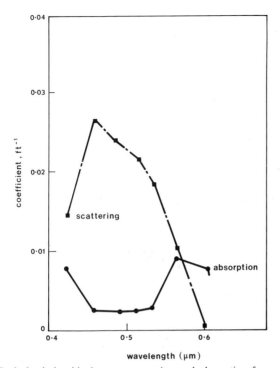

Figure 11.7   Typical relationship between scattering and absorption for near-shore waters. (After Brown *et al.*, 1971.)

sideration, such as the intensity and angle of sun illumination, atmospheric and water surface conditions, water depth and bottom reflectance, film exposure and processing variations and of course ground control aspects. Good descriptions exist of the basic physical and optical properties of natural water bodies bearing dissolved and suspended materials, e.g. the ESRO Contractor Report on Spectral Properties of Materials (Fitzgerald, 1974) (and also Reeves (1968) and Reeves *et al.* (1975)). The following figures have been included however to illustrate some of the basic relationship which take place in idealized uniform water bodies. Figure 11.7 shows the relative importance of scattering and absorption as mechanisms of attenuation and how they are dependent upon wavelength within the visible region of the spectrum. Table 11.1 shows the attenuation/wavelength relationship as found in typical surface waters, whilst Figure 11.8 shows the alteration in the reflectance spectra of a deep body of water when increasing concentrations of particulate matter of constant colour are added.

Turbidity is a measure of light attenuation through a body of water and is commonly measured in Jackson units which are based on one candle-power of light. As the shape, size and composition of suspended particles can all affect the scattering of light, it is not possible to relate turbidity directly to weight per

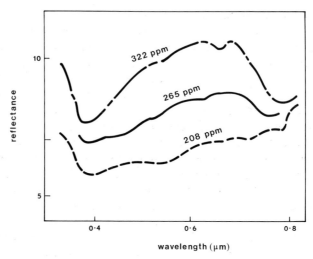

Figure 11.8   Change in reflectance of a water body as a function of suspended sediment concentration. (After Scherz, 1971.)

unit volume of material in suspension for different sites. The relationship must first be determined by on-site measurement of water transmission and by analysis of suspended sediment samples which should be taken simultaneously with the remote sensing overflights.

Probably the most that can be achieved with the use of broad-band photographic film is to relate image or colour density with the integrated measured concentration of suspended or dissolved solids in a body of water. If a simple relationship can be shown to exist between these two variables, then contouring of the water's concentration over a given depth may be possible. A drastic reduction in the number of water samples required can thus be expected when compared to conventional water quality mapping methods which rely solely on point water sampling. Such as exercise was carried out by Lillesand *et al.* (1975) who used false colour infrared film to monitor the waste outfall plume from a paper mill into the Lower Falls River, Wisconsin. The results of their work showed that

> For typical non-thermal discharges, photo-image density measurements can be used quantitatively to predict water quality throughout the mixing zone if (1) a systematic relationship is determined between water sample reflectance and some measure of water quality (suspended solids, turbidity, etc); (2) the relationship between film exposure and scene reflectance is accounted for; and (3) the relationship between film density and film exposure is adequately approximated. If these three criteria are met, the measured image densities can be used to find film exposure levels, film exposure levels can be used to find scene reflectance levels and scene reflectance levels can be used to predict water quality parameter values.

Similar work was carried out by Psuty and Allen (1975) on digitized 35 mm photographs of a coastal sewage outfall plume. They carried out trend surface analysis of the data and found a high correlation between the image density effects caused by the presence of sewage and of *in-situ* dissolved oxygen concentrations. Blanchard and Leamer (1973) made spectral reflectance measurements of water from various sources containing suspended sediment and found that peak sediment reflectance generally occurred around 0.57 μm.

In order to gain some measure of effluent concentrations at different depths within a water body rather than simply surface or depth integrated estimates, however, it is necessary to return once again to multi-spectral sensing techniques. Because different wavelengths of light are absorbed by water bodies to varying degrees depending on their state, certain wavelengths are capable of greater depth of penetration into the water than others (see Figures 11.4 and 11.5), and therefore the resulting radiation corresponding to each waveband will result from different column depths of water. Coker *et al.* (1973) looked at the response of Landsat RBV imagery to a turbidity plume caused by dredging in Tampa Bay, Florida. The three spectral bands used were green, red and near infrared. The near infrared radiation was almost totally absorbed by the surface water so that only particulate matter at the very surface caused a reflection of the radiation, which appeared as a small, light-toned area on the image. The light area on the red band was much larger than in the infrared, whilst the area of the plume recorded in the green band was subsequently larger than the red. Also in each band the centre of the area was observed to be lighter than the outer edges which gradually faded to dark tones. These confirmed that turbidity concentration of the light-coloured sediment was highest in the centre of the plume and that the outer areas either contained less particulate matter in suspension or else the particles were at a greater settling depth. Thus, although a definite measure of sediment concentration with depth was not possible, considerable information on the three-dimensional dynamics of the plume was obtained and its outward spread coupled with its increase in depth could be readily inferred. Figure 11.9 illustrates the results obtained using this technique. If however point water samples were also taken within the three dimensions of the sediment plume, a complete water quality and turbidity model could be reconstructed (see Wertz *et al.*, 1976). Although we have been dealing here with variations in suspended sediment, dissolved solids including tracer dyes are observed to behave in a somewhat similar fashion (but with less light scattering effects) and can similarly be observed as changes in recorded image signal strength.

In order to obtain truly three-dimensional remotely sensed information on water quality variations using multispectral techniques, complex spectro-radiometric calculations are necessary which are generally best applied by computer processing methods. The Grumman Aerospace report (1973) describes how subsurface turbidity profiles were achieved using a 'digital photometric mapper' which is basically a very stable single channel vidicon which may be operated through narrow band-pass filters. The analog output from this instrument and from a non-scanning photometer operating along

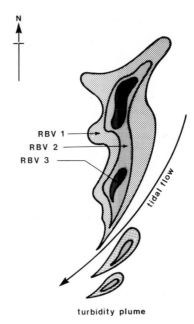

turbidity plume

Figure 11.9   Extent of turbidity plume as recorded on bands 1, 2 and 3 Landsat 1 RBV. (After Coker *et al.*, 1973.)

the centre line of the scanned field was converted to a digital form and was stored directly on to computer-compatible tape (CCT). Using this equipment configuration, it was possible to construct a model of water depth which accounted for the effects of water attenuation of different wavelengths along with the effects of bottom reflectance, water reflectance, sky reflectance, polarization etc. on a given water body. By taking measurements in different spectral bands such as the green and red, different measured signal attenuation could be used to calculate water depth as previously described in section 11.3.2. It was observed that an increase in turbidity may often result in a decrease in reflectance in the blue part of the spectrum, but in an increase in the red part due to different forms of light scattering. In order to evaluate the degree of particulate contamination, a measurable effect in either direction must be present. Successful estimations of water turbidity at given depths were carried out by measuring the resulting reduction of polarization of light in the red region, but different modelling approaches were found necessary for different physical situations. Although the polarimetric approach was found to be the best single method, it was concluded that a combination of polarimetric, multispectral and laser techniques coupled with *in-situ* water sampling and measurements of incoming solar radiation would be the best combination. Computer-compatible sensor outputs would be necessary for the complex calculations involved.

1.4.3 *Materials in solution*

The delineation of dissolved solids may often be straightforward if they exhibit different colour against their background water mass. Airborne spectrometers and especially tunable laser spectrometers (Figure 11.10) have been used very successfully for identifying solute types, and considerable literature is available on the types of sensors and analytical techniques used. For some examples see Figure 11.10, Goldberg and Weiner (1971), Querry *et al.*, (1971) and Weldon (1973).

Laser-Raman spectroscopy is well suited for remote sensing as the spectrometer detects the effect on the dissolved molecules of its own laser illumination source, thereby reducing the effect of changing solar illumination. This results in a more sensitive and more reproducible system in comparison with conventional spectrometers. When a monochromatic beam of light is shone into an aqueous solution, the molecules constituting that solution have a scattering effect on the incoming light and the resulting small changes in wavelength (Raman shifts) provide precise identification of the chemical composition of the solution. A good introduction to the Raman spectroscopy technique is given by Davis *et al.* (1973). As low concentrations of materials in solution may often be difficult to detect above the relatively high background water signal, it is highly desirable to have a continuously tunable light source so that the wavelength causing greatest resonance with the desired molecules can be selected (Klainer *et al.*, 1974). This is known as Resonance Raman Spectroscopy. Additionally by pulsing the light beam (generally a laser) a measure of time of travel can be used to calculate the object distance which enables three-dimensional measurements of solute concentration to be made. This measurement is available only in point form or along a line of

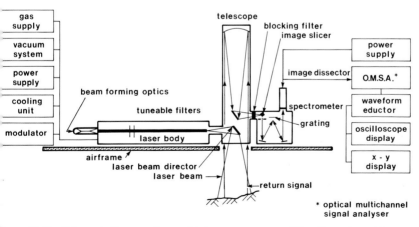

Figure 11.10   Schematic diagram of a tunable laser spectrometer. (After Fantasia and Ingrao, 1974.)

travel, as scanning systems of this type have not yet been developed. Whilst the increasingly complex instrumentation chosen for water-quality monitoring obviously results in increased costs, these may be somewhat offset by the ability to provide accurate data with less intense ground verification; a factor which may be of great importance in poorly accessible regions.

11.5   Water temperature

11.5.1   *Surface effects*

In comparison with many of the hydrological variables discussed in this chapter, water-temperature measurement using remote sensing techniques can be regarded as relatively straightforward. What must be stressed at the outset, however, is that only the surface temperature of a water body is normally sensed and that this can be used only as an indicator of possible subsurface water state. In order to extrapolate the surface temperature to greater depths, accurate models of water circulation or of water temperature profiles must be established. To enable calculations such as evaporation rates from open water bodies to be made, temperature measurements within the top few millimetres of water may be adequate, but if surface temperature is to be used as an indicator of (say) current behaviour, additional information, possibly in the form of *in-situ* sampling, would be required. Another important phenomenon which must be recognized when using remotely sensed water temperature data is the boundary layer effect. As a result of heat exchange between the atmosphere and the water surface the top few millimetres of water normally differ in temperature from the underlying water by as much as $1-2°C$, except in turbulent conditions. Such boundary layer effects can generally be allowed for when relating remotely sensed data to *in-situ* water temperature measurements, but where high accuracies are required, great difficulty has been found in taking contact temperature measurements in such a thin surface 'skin' of water (Fitzgerald, 1974). Additional errors may result from unrepresentative surface variations caused by density effects where the less saline or warmer water tends to ride over the more dense layers.

   The most common and as yet the most successful sensor used for remote surface temperature sensing is the infrared radiometer which may be used either for taking temperature readings at a point or for producing temperature profiles along a line. In linescanner form it is capable of measuring changes in surface temperature over an area, this often being recorded as variations in tone of a photographic image. By correlating image density with measured surface temperature at several points within an image, intermediate image densities can be assigned an assumed temperature (Hoffer and Bartolucci, 1972). However, most infrared radiometers nowadays are fitted with an internal reference source of known temperature and emissivity which enables absolute temperature measurements to be made. Nevertheless, the received signal from the ground varies with look angle and is likely to be distorted by atmospheric effects and these must be quantified before absolute surface temperatures can be given, especially when sensing from satellites.

11.5.2 Correction of atmospheric effects

Accurate allowance for atmospheric effects can be made simply by relating the sensed signal to a known surface temperature on the ground. This may be a reasonable approach for very small areas, but it is a rather unsatisfactory calibration technique for large areas, as local atmospheric variations cannot be allowed for without the provision of extensive ground control. Because of this attenuation by the atmosphere, infrared sensors are generally filtered or have detectors made sensitive to radiation in one of the atmospheric 'window' wavelength regions, discussed in Chapter 1, the most common being the 8.0–13.5 μm region. In this wavelength region, the emissivity of a water surface is about 98% provided that the angle of incidence of the sensor is almost normal to the surface (Stingelin and Avis, 1973). This means that even in sunlight, only a very small proportion of the infrared signal detected by the sensor is reflected radiation, and therefore the measured signal is directly related to the actual surface temperature of the water. Although nighttime sensing is thus possible, strong absorption still results from the presence of cloud and atmospheric haze (Farrow, 1975) thus precluding an all-weather capability.

By measuring the proportions of water vapour, carbon dioxide, ozone, particulates and air temperature of an atmospheric column, models can be constructed to estimate the likely absorption emission and scattering of the infrared signal so that corrections can be made to the apparent ground temperature. For detailed explanations of atmospheric effects on infrared wavelengths, reports such as those of the ESRO CR series are ideal (Farrow, 1975). Because the effects of atmospheric attenuation are more pronounced as the path length increases, more complex calculations may be needed for satellite-borne sensing. However, for platforms operating at a height of only a few hundred metres in clear conditions, atmospheric effects may lie within the range of acceptable temperature measurement error, in which case no allowances would be necessary. Normally errors caused by the atmosphere increase almost linearly up to about 1000 m and then increase less quickly above this height due to the thinning air. The main cause of error is the difference in temperature between the atmosphere and the target, and the humidity distribution within the intervening block of atmosphere. In clear but hazy weather conditions these effects could result in a combined error of around 1°C at 300 m sensor altitude, whilst the presence of thin cloud could increase this error by 3 or 4°C or even more (Atwell et al., 1971). Atmospheric effects can often be lessened by narrowing the spectral range of sensitivity of the instrument to coincide with regions of low atmospheric absorption, for example from 8–14 μm to 9–11 μm. However, a lower signal level would then result and hence a compromise between the two requirements may sometimes be necessary.

As monitoring of atmospheric constituents by direct sampling is very difficult, an alternative approach is to have sensors operating in at least two different wavelengths. As surface radiance is attenuated and path radiance from the atmosphere is added with increasing altitude, such a multispectral approach becomes more desirable as sensor altitudes increase. Absorption by gases is strongly wavelength-dependent, so comparison between ground signals using two wavelengths which are differentially absorbed, enables correction for the effect of the absorbing material to be made. Anding et al. (1971) recommended the use of three narrow infrared channels centred at 4.9, 9.1 and 11.0 μm. Under cloud-free conditions, the ratio of signals recorded in these channels allows very accurate measurements of varying molecular absorption such as water vapour, carbon dioxide, ozone, etc., and partial correction for the presence of clouds was found possible, along with some correction for atmospheric scattering effects. An alternative but less accurate atmospheric correction technique is to observe a given target at two or more path angles. If, for example, a target is viewed vertically and also at a 60° oblique angle, then the atmospheric path length is doubled and comparison of the two recorded signals enables correction for the transmission loss to be made. Strong layering in the atmosphere would cause error using this correction method, and account must also be taken of changes in surface characteristics such as reflectance, emittance and roughness with changing look angle.

11.5.3 Thermal infrared sensing

Infrared radiometry has been extensively and successfully used for mapping the surface temperature of many different water types and in general, scanning or imaging radiometers have proved to be most popular. From relatively low-altitude aircraft equipped with scanning infrared radiometers, stream and river surface temperatures have been mapped, often with the aim of detecting groundwater or pollution inputs (Souto-Maior, 1973), and their mixing characteristics with the main water body. Borgese et al. (1973) describe the mapping of river temperatures at 1°C intervals in order to trace the outfall from a paper mill and power station using an 8–14 micron scanner, whilst Atwell et al. (1971) using the same spectral range, claim surface temperature measurements in river experiments to be correct to ± 0.3 °C from an altitude of 900 m. The remotely sensed data was verified by measurements of water temperature using thermistor thermometers which were accurate to ± 0.1°C. Souto-Maior (1973) used 8–14 μm thermal scanner data taken from 500–600 m altitude for very small-scale studies of water flow in the vicinity of a refuse tip by detecting seeps, springs and the location of groundwater into small natural drainage channels. Shoreline springs were detected in lakewater

(Lee, 1969) by the use of a Bendix infrared scanner operating in both the 3–5.5 μm and 8–14 μm regions, and spring flows of < 0.1 litres s^{-1} were readily observed as they mixed with the warmer lake water. It was found that sensor altitude variations below 900 m did not have any noticeable effect on the resulting data, indicating that atmospheric attenuation up to 900 m was small. Similarly Boettcher *et al.* (1976) successfully located groundwater inflows into several large rivers in Montana and Idaho.

Temperature sensing over the sea has been successfully used for detecting and tracking sewage and power station outfall waste (Kingston, 1970; Scarpace *et al.*, 1975), for monitoring river outfall plumes (Brereton and Downing, 1975) and for mapping nearshore currents (Huh, 1976). McAlister (1969) found that sudden surface temperature discontinuities such as convection cells, wind streaks, breaking waves, etc., were particularly easy to record. Water-temperature sensing from satellites is of greatest application over large lakes and oceans where surface resolutions often of several kilometres may be advantageous in acting as a form of data reduction for obtaining mean water temperatures. Platt and Troup (1973) compared satellite and aircraft infrared data of the same area. The satellite was Nimbus 4 with a 10.5–12.5 μm THIR radiometer providing 8 km resolution from a height of 1112 km. The aircraft flying at 3 km was equipped with a similar scanner having a ground resolution of 20 m. After correction for atmospheric effects, the mean temperature of a test site was recorded as 21.4 °C from Nimbus and 21.7 °C from the aircraft—a good indication of the state of the technology in this field of remote sensing. NOAA 2–4 imagery has also been widely used for surface temperature mapping using the 10.5–12.5 μm VHRR sensors, and on clear days temperature mapping of the Great Lakes has been possible to stated accuracies of 2 °C (Strong *et al.*, 1974, and see also Albuisson *et al.*, 1976).

For coarse resolution, satellites such as Nimbus, NOAA and Explorer can have some limited hydrological use. For more local requirements, aircraft infrared scanner surveys can be quite costly as relatively few operational systems are as yet generally available. However, the overall size of infrared scanners need not be great and their operation from light aircraft is feasible provided that navigational accuracy and platform stability can be maintained to prevent large distortions. For basic thermal sensing of small areas, relatively low cost and lightweight imaging equipment is already available, such as the Aga 680 Thermovision system which allows video recording of a cathode ray image. Even so, purchase costs are of the order of £25 000, but these could well be reduced with the future use of non-cooled vidicon sensors (Sommerard, 1977).

11.5.4 Microwave sensing

In order to overcome the weather dependence of infrared sensors, water surface temperature can be measured using passive microwave techniques even though the amount of microwave energy emitted by a water body is very small. The temperature measured by microwave sensors is very dependent on the emissivity of the water surface, which in turn is dependent on its wave state and surface roughness (Axelsson and Edvardsson, 1973). Ryan (1969) describes the testing of a 1.55 cm (19.4 GHz) electrically scanning passive microwave radiometer which from an altitude of 10 000 m had a resolution cell size of approximately 500×500 m. Using a computer-controlled colour quantization process, 32 shades of colour could be assigned to a scene to delineate variations in surface temperature more easily. Images of ground and water surfaces could be obtained under all-weather, day or night conditions, flooded river areas being readily visible through dense cloud cover. By altering the brightness temperature range of the sensor, clouds (which have a high emissivity) could be observed and estimates of their density and water content could be made. Surface water temperature discrimination of about $\pm 2°C$ was possible.

11.6   Soil moisture

11.6.1   *Introduction*

An adequate knowledge of the distribution of moisture in soil and of its variations in time and space is fundamental to the understanding of the hydrological cycle. Quantitative knowledge of the soil moisture regime is needed in order to construct water balance models for water resources purposes, for vegetation studies and crop management and for surface and sub-surface flow predictions, whilst qualitative indications of soil wetness may also help in the prediction of catastrophic events such as landslides or flash floods. Conventional ways of measuring soil moisture by physical means include gravimetric soil sampling, neutron scattering methods, soil lysimetry, tensiometry and measurement of soil electrical resistance. These methods provide the most accurate measures of soil moisture content, but only at a given point or series of points. This is a definite disadvantage, as soil moisture values can be highly variable spatially, therefore only fairly crude estimates of total soil moisture content can be made even when numerous point samples are taken. It is unlikely that the remotely sensed measurement of soil moisture at a point can ever be as accurate as a ground-based measurement, but remote sensing does have the potential of providing mean values of surface soil moisture over large areas, which is simply not possible using conventional methods. The main disadvantage of remotely sensing soil moisture is that only the surface or near surface soil layers contribute to the sensed signal and these often give little indication of sub-surface soil moisture state. However, by combining the information provided by both the ground sampled and the remotely sensed measurements, a much better understanding of soil moisture variability and of soil moisture processes should be possible.

11.6.2 *Visible and near infrared sensing*

In the USA, attempts at remote sensing of soil moisture have normally been highly quantitative and strongly based on soil physics and radiation theory. As these theories are too complex to be dealt with in a broad study such as this, only descriptions of the positive findings will be given. Similarly, results of controlled laboratory tests will not be given here in detail as few have produced results which can be directly applied to field conditions. In the USSR a more qualitative approach has often been favoured in which certain topographic and vegetational combinations have been recognized as indicators of soil moisture state. Nefedov and Popova (1972) relied on their extensive knowledge of the preferences of plant species in terms of soil type, acidity, available water, etc., to determine likely moisture and groundwater conditions from aerial photographs. A simple example of this is the marked change in plant species or plant vigour which often occurs where groundwater approaches the soil surface.

In the USA, test site correlations were run between the available soil moisture (< 15 bars) in irrigated and non-irrigated fields of grain sorghum, and the image density of filtered black-and-white and also false colour infrared film of the fields (Werner *et al.*, 1971). The results indicated that for the whole of the crop growing cycle, the red band (after correction for seasonal radiative changes) of spectral range $0.59–0.70\ \mu$m, provided best correlation with soil moisture and after mid-July when the canopy was well developed, almost all correlations were significantly different from zero at the 99.99% confidence level where the number of observations was 195, with some correlations being above 0.9. Werner found that near infrared bands were good for indicating plant stress due to excesses or lack of soil moisture, but under normal growing conditions very erratic correlations were observed.

Given the present state of the art it is likely that vegetation-derived measures of soil moisture will be more useful than many direct electromagnetic techniques, as an indication of moisture in the top 10–30 cm of soil may result. The major disadvantage of all direct radiative measures of soil moisture based on wavelengths of less than tens of centimetres is that only moisture in the thin surface layer is sensed (assuming there are no vegetational effects) (see Figure 11.11). This is probably only of use for estimates of bare soil evaporation rates as the important underlying soil may have an entirely different and unpredictable moisture content. Hoffer and Johannsen (1969) noted that a dry surface crust could form on a soil surface within only a few hours after rainfall, whilst the underlying soil was still wet. A definite relationship would therefore have to be established between moisture levels in these two zones through extensive ground measurements before useful spatial information could be extracted. Also, much of the work carried out so far has established soil moisture radiation relationships with bare homogeneous soil surfaces and has taken little account of vegetation and other random surface

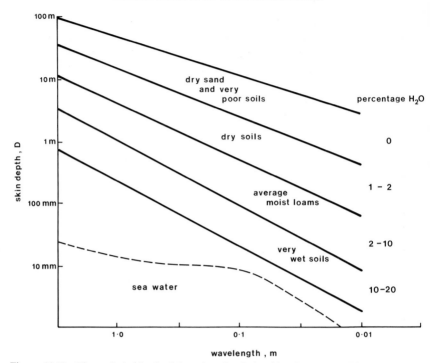

Figure 11.11   Theoretical skin depth/wavelength relationships for soils of different moisture content. (After Deane, 1973.)

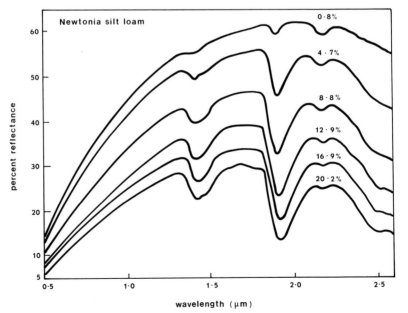

Figure 11.12   Variation of surface soil reflectance with changing soil moisture. (After Bowers and Hanks, 1965.)

effects which are generally found in 'real' conditions (Blanchard *et al.*, 1974). However it is generally agreed that reflectance from a bare homogeneous soil is reduced as soil moisture content is increased (Hoffer and Johanssen, 1969); and because of this effect it is possible to map areas where rain has recently fallen on dry ground (Figures 11.12, 11.13). This has been possible in arid areas using satellite data but it must be realized that the surface reflectance of soil is also dependent on such things as its emissivity, surface roughness, the

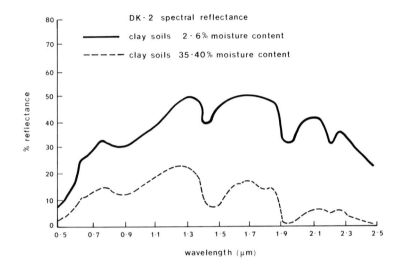

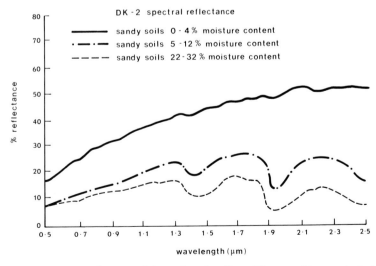

Figure 11.13   Spectral reflectance of clay and sandy soils at different moisture contents. (After LARS, 1970.)

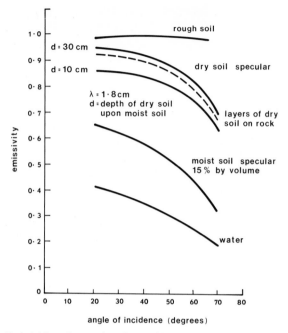

Figure 11.14   Emissivities of natural surfaces with changing viewing angle. (After Pascalar, 1969.)

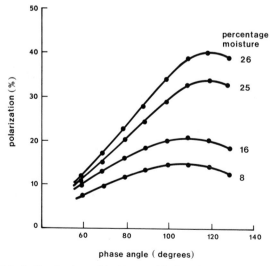

Figure 11.15   Polarization in plane of incidence with changing soil moisture (After Stockhoff and Frost, 1971.)

prevailing intensity and angle of incoming radiation and the sensor viewing angle (Figure 11.14). The polarization of light in visible wavelengths has been shown to increase with increasing surface soil moisture content (Plessey report, 1976 and Figure 11.15), but this too is dependent on the above-mentioned variables. Both of these techniques however should be adequate for the delineation of waterlogged areas.

The effects of surface wetting also vary greatly according to soil type. Dry, sandy soils have a very flat spectral reflectance curve, but with slight wetting (more than 4% moisture content by weight) strong water absorption bands form at approximately 1.45 and 1.95 μm (see Figure 11.13). Clay soils, however, always show the water absorption bands, making any transition from dry to wet less obvious than with sandy soils (Hoffer and Johanssen, 1969). For light clay loams, the greatest change in reflectance is generally between 2–12% of field capacity, for clays it is between 5–25% and for humic gley soils it is between 7–30%, whilst the greatest magnitude in reflectance change has been found in dark soils having a high humic content (Merritt et al., 1973). The results of a study to assess the capability of the Nimbus-3 near infrared radiometer (0.7–1.3 μm) to monitor changes in soil moisture and resulting vegetational effects in a low level non-forested area of the Mississippi (Merritt et al., 1973) showed that mean surface reflectances could be related to mean seasonal soil moisture change. The greatest problem encountered was the patchiness and variability of precipitation events over the area which in turn resulted in great local variability in surface reflectance and created statistical sampling and ground verification problems. It is to be expected that this type of precipitation problem would be encountered in the UK and therefore greater chances of success are likely in areas of more uniform rainfall.

11.6.3 Thermal sensing

Measurements of ground surface temperature are theoretically capable of providing soil moisture information, but as with reflected ground radiation, problems are encountered with calibration and once again only surface information is directly available. Since water has a higher specific heat and therefore a higher thermal capacity than soil, the wetter the soil becomes, the higher will be its thermal capacity and conductivity (Gillespie and Kahle, 1977). A measure of a soil's thermal inertia (conductivity × thermal capacity)$^{1/2}$ is most easily obtained by taking daily maximum and minimum soil temperature measurements, where, under similar conditions, high diurnal temperature variations should result from dry soils and low diurnal variations from wet soils with a predictable relationship between the two extremes. Figure 11.16 shows the effect of a gradually drying soil on diurnal temperature variation, and Plate 22 illustrates an example of thermal linescan imagery from which thermal inertia could be deduced. However, in addition to the marked effect of air temperature variations, the ground surface temperature is

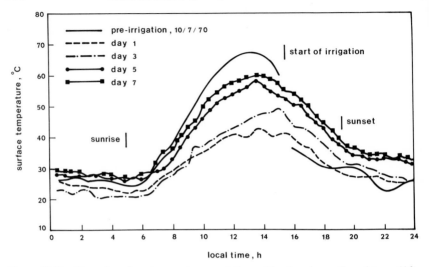

Figure 11.16   Diurnal surface temperature variation with changing soil moisture. (After Schmugge, 1976.)

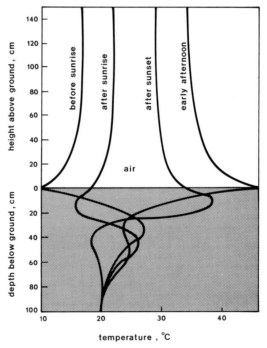

Figure 11.17   Diurnal temperature variations at the soil/atmosphere interface. (After Gates, 1970.)

also dependent on such things as wind velocity, surface roughness and associated evaporative cooling, its positional exposure, slope and aspect and most importantly, the nature of any vegetational cover. Because of these additional variables, it is likely that only gross or long term changes in soil moisture can be recognized with any degree of confidence using thermal techniques, especially when sensing from high altitudes where atmospheric effects cannot be readily accounted for. The effect of surface emissivity variations on thermal inertia measurements can be reduced, provided that diurnal measurements can be repeated at known points and provided that no change in moisture state occurs between measurements (Blanchard et al., 1974). Atmospheric effects can be largely overcome by sensing in completely cloud and haze-free conditions although this becomes an unworkable solution in regions such as the UK where consecutive days and nights with clear conditions can only be expected a few times each year. It is claimed that such temperature measurements give indications of soil moisture state down to a depth of 7–10 cm as a result of heat conduction. Theoretical physical models have been constructed in an attempt to account for the process of soil/atmosphere heat exchange (Rosema, 1976; Soer, 1976; see also Figure 11.17). Plants behave in a similar way to soil in that their diurnal temperature range falls with increasing water content and so some indication of gross changes in soil moisture may be possible. For aerial remote sensing, homogeneous areas of a single land-use type should be chosen in order to reduce the effects of species variation as much as possible.

11.6.4 Microwave sensing

Microwave measurements of soil moisture have two outstanding advantages over the other methods described so far: (i) little atmospheric attenuation is experienced, enabling measurements to be taken day or night in all weathers, and (ii) they have the potential to integrate sub-surface moisture values.

11.6.4.1 *Passive microwave systems.* These measure the natural radiation from a body, which is dependent on the body's emissivity and its temperature. The natural microwave emission from a soil target is very dependent on its surface roughness and on its bulk electrical properties. A change in soil moisture causes a change in a soil's dielectric constant (see Figure 11.18) which is generally less than 5 for dry soil and about 80 for pure water. This results in an emissivity change from about 0.9 for dry soil to about 0.6 for wet soil (see Figure 11.14). Thus a change in water content of a soil target would be recorded as an apparent change in its temperature. The depth at which the bulk of the energy originates is determined by the sensor wavelength and the water content profile of the soil and may vary from several metres in dry sand when sensing at long wavelengths, to only a few centimetres in wet soil, as previously illustrated by Figure 11.11. For example, the 21 cm wavelength

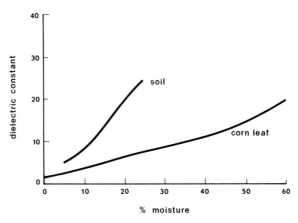

Figure 11.18   Dielectric constant of soil and corn leaf as a function of moisture content. (After Mathews, 1975.)

S.194 passive radiometer which operated on Skylab has been quoted as measuring radiation primarily from the top 2.5 cm when the soil was 'wet' and from the top 15 cm when 'dry'. Eagleman *et al.* (1975) produced an extensive publication on the results of Skylab experiments which gives a full and clear account of the theories behind passive and active microwave sensing of soil moisture, especially from satellite altitudes. The results of their tests indicate that the S.194 radiometer was very sensitive to soil moisture content even under varying vegetation, atmospheric and soil conditions. The mean correlation of five passes over a test site was -0.96 which corresponded to a stated soil moisture measurement accuracy of $\pm 5\%$. In order to compare emission data more easily from soils of different types, their soil moisture content is best expressed as a percentage of their field capacity. Low-altitude tests by Schmugge (1976) concluded that a 21 cm wavelength passive radiometer was responding generally to the top 2 cm of soil, whereas a 1.55 cm radiometer responded only to surface moisture. Also, the longer wavelength radiometer still responded linearly to soil moisture when there was a vegetation cover 15–20 cm high, whereas the 1.55 cm radiometer gave results which were independent of soil moisture and only responded to variations in vegetation emission. Longer wavelengths are also less affected by variations in surface roughness, although they will still react to variation of the same order of magnitude as their wavelengths. It was also found that by measuring both horizontally and vertically polarized signals from a soil surface, additional information on soil moisture variations could often be inferred and that the observed brightness temperature of the surface was highly dependent upon sensor viewing angle (see Figure 11.19). Passive microwave radiometry is somewhat restricted by the large physical dimensions of antennas which are required to achieve satisfactory resolutions, especially if imaging of the target is required.

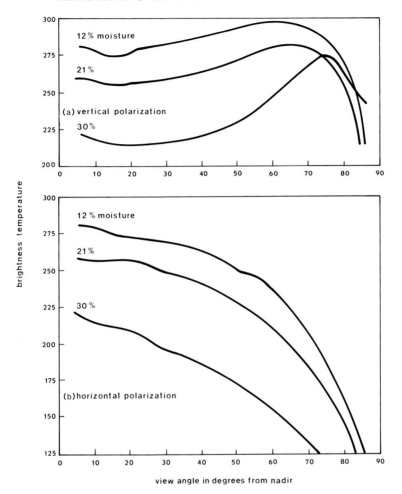

Figure 11.19   Brightness temperature of playa sediments as recorded by passive microwave radiometry (13.5 GHz). (After Kennedy *et al.*, 1967.)

11.6.4.2 *Active microwave systems.* These are not as restricted, primarily because electrically scanning synthetic apertures can be used. With active microwave systems (radar), the backscattering of an emitted signal from a soil surface is dependent on the surface roughness of the soil and its moisture-related dielectric properties (given that wavelength, polarization and angle of incidence are constant). Depending on the wavelength chosen and the mean surface roughness, optimum look angles can be calculated for measuring soil moisture content, but generally the best relationships occur as nadir is approached, and therefore the apparent surface roughness effect is reduced, 5°–10° off nadir being normal (Mathews, 1975). High spatial resolutions along the flight path are not a prerequisite for soil moisture estimation, and with synthetic aperture radars, range resolution does not deteriorate with distance from target. Satellite-based systems are therefore quite feasible assuming that sufficient power can be generated, and their all-weather capability makes them especially desirable. The radar sensor on the Seasat satellite achieved ground resolutions of 25 m, but the data is unlikely now to be adequately evaluated for soil moisture estimation.

The collection of information on soil moisture profiles is in principle possible using a single wavelength radar. However, any sub-surface signal will be weak in comparison to the surface return so that the pulse duration must be made very short and the range resolution must be extremely precise in order to decode the signal into the form of a soil profile (Barrett et al., 1977). An alternative and probably a more desirable method would be to utilize a multi-frequency or continuous frequency system. Waite et al. (1973) describe a continuous-frequency radar system which operates in the 4–26.5 GHz range, at various incident angles and with a horizontal and vertical polarization facility. As approximately one-half of the incident microwave energy is reflected from the soil surface, the remainder of the signal will be derived from different 'skin' depths according to the instrument frequency. By comparing these weaker signals, an estimate of soil moisture content throughout a shallow soil profile is possible. Moreover, by comparing the main surface brightness temperature signal for each wavelength, an estimate of surface roughness can be made. This was found to be very necessary because roughness changes can cause more brightness temperature variation than changes in soil moisture, and it was found that even at very long wavelengths the effect of surface roughness could not be ignored. (See Mathews, 1975, for detailed surface roughness experimental data.)

Although the multifrequency approach appears to be the ultimate answer, suitable equipment is not yet readily available in the UK. As an alternative approach, it should be possible to correlate radar signatures of the same type when at different moisture states. If a library of signatures is collected for different surface types it may be possible to obtain best fits by comparing known data with new data (Barrett et al., 1977). The main problem once again is the highly variable effect of different vegetation cover types at different stages of development. Possibly a multifrequency approach will eventually be able to deal with such vegetation problems, but for the next few years at least, remote sensing measurements of soil moisture will be largely restricted to bare soil or short vegetation such as pasture. In any event, considerable amounts of additional ground information will be required for both microwave and any other remote method of soil moisture estimation. Whilst many remote sensing techniques can be applied most easily to arid situations, the use of microwaves for soil moisture sensing may not always be the best method for deserts. Good penetration of dry sands by microwaves has some potential for the identification of near-surface aquifers (Wermund, 1971). However they are of little use in measuring differences in soil moisture below about 10% as no direct relationship exists with dielectric constant which in deserts may be also influenced by variations in soil salinity. (Poe, 1971)

11.6.5 Radio waves

Radio-wave theory of soil moisture measurement is similar to that of microwave theory in that soil dielectric constant varies with soil moisture value and it is this which affects the radio wave signals. As yet, it appears that only ground-based experiments have been carried out using radio waves (Chadwick, 1973). By passing radio waves (170 MHz) between two ground-based antennae, the measured strength of the received signal can be related to soil moisture values (see Figure 11.20). Vertically polarized waves are not affected greatly by the ground, whereas horizontally polarized waves are short-circuited and induce a current flow through the earth which is dependent on its conductivity and hence on the soil moisture value of the ground lying between the antennae. Optimum antenna separation distance depends on the radio frequency used, but it must be large enough to eliminate direct induction effects from the transmitter, whilst at the same time retaining good field strengths over the prevailing soil types. Generally antenna separations of greater than eight wavelengths are used, whilst the height of the antennae above the ground is also found to be of importance. Numerous ground tests indicated that mean soil moisture could be measured between the antennae even when trees lay in the main path. Green vertical vegetation such as cereals attenuated the vertically polarized signal and caused spurious results, this being the major drawback of the technique, which could only be overcome by calibration allowances made for each stage of vegetation growth. Where no dense vertical vegetation is present, calibration is necessary only at

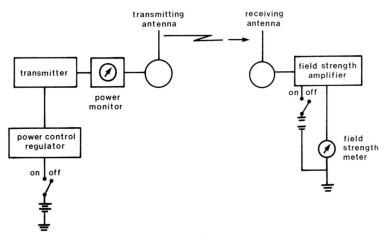

Figure 11.20 Instrument configuration for radio wave soil moisture measurement. (After Chadwick, 1973.)

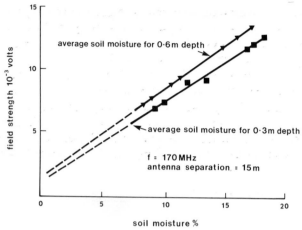

Figure 11.21   Relationship of radio field strength to mean soil moisture between antennae. (After Chadwick, 1973.)

soil field capacity and at wilting point, the signal relationship being linear between these states. While the technique has great potential as a means of providing mean ground soil-moisture verification values for calibrating aerially sensed data, the physical problems involved make its use from moving aerial platforms unlikely. Any aerial methods would have to rely on data from a reflected ground signal, this being transmitted and received by the same antenna, as in active microwave systems. The advantage of this type of sensing at radio wavelengths is that soil moisture information from a deeper column of soil may be available (see Figure 11.21) and this possibility warrants further investigation of the technique.

11.6.6   Natural gamma radiation

This method of soil-moisture estimation relies on the highly constant rate of natural gamma photons which is radiated from the Earth's surface at any given point. 75% of the gamma rays from the ground come from the top 10 cm of the soil and almost nothing is detected from below 40 cm due to the strong absorbance of the surface soil water. The limitations of this technique are therefore once again that only near-surface soil-moisture values can be estimated. As the level of radiation from this thin layer of surface soil is very weak, attenuation by atmospheric gases and water particles is so strong that sensors must be flown no higher than 100–200 m. In order to be able to calculate soil moisture values, an area or flight path must be first overflown at a known soil moisture state, in order to obtain a reference signature from which to work. Subsequent gamma measurements over the same area will be subject to greater or lesser amounts of attenuation as a result of variations in the amount of moisture in the top 10 cm or so of soil. As the half-life of gamma radiation is several thousand years, no change in source values will occur, but it is necessary to measure the atmospheric pressure and temperature at the time of overflights in order to calculate the density of the attenuating air column and also the pressure of atmospheric water (Plessey Report, 1976).

The natural gamma technique has been used for some years in the USA for calculating snow water equivalent, and during these programmes tests conducted to estimate soil water content were encouraging and repeatable (Weisnet, 1972). Practical problems such as flying repeatedly at low altitudes over a given flight path became obvious, whilst the low-altitude restriction meant only small areas could be covered at a time. Helicopters were well suited to this type of survey and in areas of high relief they would be invaluable.

11.7 Groundwater resources

11.7.1 Introduction

In contrast to the monitoring of surface water by remote sensing, little literature exists on groundwater applications, presumably as a result of the difficulties encountered. As the presence of deep groundwater cannot be detected directly using present remote sensing techniques (and that of shallow groundwater only in exceptional circumstances), indirect inferential methods must generally be adopted. Most of these methods rely either on the recognition of surface water or moisture anomalies and their related vegetational effects as indicators of possible groundwater presence (Nefedov and Popova, 1972) or on the interpretation of geologic and topographic information and surface hydrology (Boettcher et al. 1976). Thus, remotely-sensed data may be used to enhance conventional hydrogeological prospecting, to speed up the process of field surveying and perhaps to increase the probability of success in drilling water wells. It cannot yet independently locate an underground body of water or determine whether a promising rock type actually contains water, nor is it possible in known aquifers to determine the full extent of the water body, its depth below ground or the quality of the water it contains. This is understandable since to achieve such success would require the ability to penetrate the atmosphere, any vegetation cover, the soil (ignoring any moisture it might contain) and whatever rock overlies the underground water (Debney, 1978).

Where remote sensing can offer the greatest direct aid is in situations where groundwater emerges from an aquifer to the surface either in the form of locally increased soil moisture, or as springs (Souto-Maior, 1973). Spring water is generally of a different temperature to that of its surroundings and can thus be readily detected using thermal infrared linescanners (see Chapter 10). These must normally be operated from aircraft flying at relatively low altitudes to obtain the required spatial resolution for detecting small springs. Thermal remote sensing is now widely used to identify previously unknown sources of groundwater discharge into large water bodies such as rivers, lakes and coastal waters, and even in well prospected regions this additional data can be of considerable value (Davies, 1978). The timing of data acquisition is important in that maximum thermal contrast between the ground water and its surroundings is required, whilst the minimum volume of discharging groundwater which can be detected depends very much on this thermal contrast and its degree of dilution in the larger water body. Thermal sensing provides a prospecting tool for locating minor aquifers, particularly in alluvial and floodplain areas, and facilitates a better understanding of the inter-relationships between ground and surface water. For example, in fractured aquifer systems, wells can be sited to intercept groundwater inland from spring discharges to the sea, or alternatively, zones of groundwater discharge to rivers can be protected from extraction where river baseflow conditions require conservation (Debney, 1978).

Where shallow groundwater locally increases soil moisture content, a number of remote sensing techniques may be applied, but their success depends very much on the local prevailing conditions such as the type of vegetation cover and background soil moisture levels. In areas possessing little vegetation cover, a lowering of soil reflectance in the visible wavelengths combined with an increase in the degree of light polarization can be expected as soil moisture increases. Daytime soil surface temperature will fall as a result of evaporative cooling, and diurnal temperature variations will be reduced as a result of the soils' higher heat capacity and thermal inertia. The dielectric constant of the soil will increase, which in turn will result in an increase in brightness at microwave wavelengths. As ground conditions move away from the ideal, the operation of these techniques becomes more complex to a degree which cannot be dealt with in this summary. In practice, however, increased soil moisture in developing countries is often associated with an increase in vegetation density and vigour which can be readily detected in the near-infrared spectral region (Wermund, 1971). A great deal of information relating to the extent and type of aquifer can often by extracted from vegetation data alone and this, coupled with the interpretation of geological structures and surface hydrology as detailed by aircraft and satellite remote sensing, forms the basis of the majority of groundwater resources studies at the moment. One particular example of this approach to groundwater detection is illustrated by Plate 23. Because of the high level of soil moisture and vegetation cover in temperate climates, even long wavelength sensing techniques offer little hope of directly detecting groundwater deeper than a few centimetres below the soil surface. In very arid regions where surface lithology is dry and little vegetation is present, some possibilities do however exist, so these will be briefly covered for completeness.

11.7.2 Microwave sensing

The effect of soil state on passive and active microwave signals was discussed in sections 11.6.4.1 and 11.6.4.2 where it was concluded that the soil penetration ability of microwaves was mainly dependent on the water content of the soil. Figure 11.11 shows the theoretical penetration capabilities of microwaves of different wavelengths into typical soil types and it can be seen that at metre wavelengths, penetration depths of 50 m or more could theoretically be achieved. This assumes that a homogeneous sandy soil is present to such a depth, but in practice the presence of rock layers or traces of water lying in cracks and fissures would prevent further microwave penetration. More detailed explanations of microwave theory can be found in Axelsson and Edvardsson (1973) and also in Matthews (1975).

Recent data collected by the Space Shuttle SIR-A L-band radar confirms the theory that under extremely dry desert conditions, penetration of surface soils is possible to such an extent that details of ancient drainage networks and tectonic fractures are revealed (Covault, 1982). The depth of soil penetration rapidly reduces with any increase in soil moisture, but even penetration of 1 m or so in areas surrounding the major deserts could provide additional information of value to groundwater resources studies.

11.7.3 Electrical induction and radiowave methods

In the exploration for mineral deposits, sensors which are sensitive to radioactivity (such as Geiger counters and scintillometers) have been widely used, along with force-field sensors such as magnetometers and gravimeters. It is quite possible that the presence of very large underground masses of water may produce effects which can be detected using this type of equipment, but this possibility will not be further explored here. One mineral exploration technique which does appear worthy of further explanation is known by the somewhat confusing term as 'electromagnetic' sensing. This method relies either on ground induction of electrical currents or radio interference effects similar to those described in section 11.6.5 for the ground-based measurement of soil moisture.

With the induction method, a strong alternating current of frequency generally between 100 Hz and 4000 Hz is generated in a primary coil carried on board an aircraft. The a.c. magnetic field generated by this current induces eddy currents in the ground which in turn generate a secondary magnetic field which can be detected by a secondary coil carried either in the aircraft, on the end of a drogue line behind the aircraft, or even in a second aircraft. The power and form of the e.m.f. generated in the pick-up coil provides information on the conductivity of the ground below. Generally only ground discontinuities in a horizontal plane can be detected, so that extensive homogeneous aquifers may not be recognizable, whereas rock fissure storage or vertical permeability changes may allow an aquifer to be recognised (Fitzgerald et al., 1976). For this type of operation, flying heights are usually kept below about 100 m and because low air speeds are also preferable, helicopters are often used.

Radiowave methods detect variations in radio signals (from distant ground-based transmitters) caused by large changes in conductance of the ground, such as may be caused by large ore deposits or large vertically variable masses of waterbearing rocks. The detectors required for this are quite small and are generally carried at low altitudes in either helicopters or light aircraft. Neither of the above techniques has been extensively tested for applications towards groundwater prospecting, but a potential exists where high conductivity anomalies can be expected between the water bearing and surrounding rocks (Fitzgerald, *et al.* 1976). In carbonate terrains especially, the association of groundwater storage in deep fractures has enabled exploration through radar detection of surface lineaments (Waite and McDonald, 1972).

11.7.4 *Thermal inertia measurement*

Large masses of near surface groundwater may act as 'heat sinks' due to their high thermal inertia, which may result in surface temperatures different to those of the surrounding land. Cartwright (1968) claimed to have detected aquifers as much as 15 m below ground level due to the surface temperature variations of up to 2°C above the groundwater area. Since land under the influence of a groundwater mass would be expected to have a low diurnal temperature variation (Pohn, 1976), the thermal inertia effect should be most apparent when using data of this type. Such data has been obtained using infrared sensors on board several satellite systems, including the Explorer A satellite. Effects of this type may be detectable in very arid regions, but in temperate regions variations in surface soil moisture, vegetation, air temperature, soil and geology would almost certainly overrule the use of such an exploration technique.

11.7.5 *Summary*

For temperate regions, therefore, the most profitable methods of ground-water detection and delineation rely on interpretative methods of surface indicator features such as geological outcrops and fracture lineaments, surface lithology, soil moisture and vegetation and occasionally groundwater discharge. Remote sensing methods can efficiently provide the necessary synoptic information in ways described throughout this chapter.

References

(i) *Water extent*

Anderson, R. R. and Wobber, F. J. (1972) 'Wetlands mapping in New Jersey', presented at the Annual Convention of the *American Society of Photogrammetry*, Washington D.C., pp. 353–358.

ARGOS (1977) *Report of Second Informative and Introductory Meeting with the Users of ARGOS* Centre National de la Recherche Scientifique, Paris.

Baker, V. R. (1973) *Stream Network Analysis from Orbital and Suborbital Imagery*. Colorado River Basin, Texas, quarterly progress report, Univ. Texas, 6 pp.

Blyth, K. and Nash, G. P. (1980) Aerial infrared photography for flood plain investigations. *J. Inst. Water Engineers and Scientists*, 34(5) 425–434.

Blyth, K. and Rodda, J. C. (1973) A stream length study. *Water Resources Research* 9(5) 1454–1461.

Institute of Hydrology (1976) *Water Resources Survey of Northern Oman* Vol. III, Appendix B, 'Surface water flow'. Final Report, Sir Alexander Gibb & Partners and Institute of Hydrology, England, 45 pp.

Brown, R. E. and Holz, R. K. (1976) Land-use classification utilizing infrared scanning imagery. *Photogrammetric Engineering and Remote Sensing* 42(10) 1303–1314.

Carter, V. and Smith, D. G. (1974) Utilization of remotely-sensed data in the management of inland wetlands. *U.S. Geological Survey* E73-11161, 15 pp.

Cooper, S., Beck, P., Harowitz, J. and Toran, D. (1975) *The Use of ERTS Imagery in Reservoir Management and Operation*. Final Report of Corps of Engineers, Waltham, Massachusetts, 118 pp.

Deutsch, M. *et al.* (1973) Mapping of the 1973 Mississippi River floods from the Earth Resources Technology Satellite (ERTS) *Remote Sensing and Water Resources Management*, Proc. No 17, Amer. Water Res. Assoc.

Entres, S. L. (1974) 'Fundamentals of remote sensing of the Earth', in *Proc. 1st Technical Session of the Remote Sensing Society* (eds. Collins, W. G. and Van Genderen, J. L.), Remote Sensing Society, London, pp. 1–47.

Goddard, J. E. (1973) *An Evaluation of Urban Flood Plains*. Amer. Soc. Civ. Eng. Urban Water Research Programme Technical Memorandum No 19, ASCE, New York, 40 pp.

Goodier, R. (ed.) (1970) The application of aerial photography to the work of the Nature Conservancy. *Proc. Nature Conservancy*, Edinburgh, 183 pp.

Hallberg, G. R. and Hoyer, B. E. (1973) 'Application of ERTS-1 imagery to flood inundation mapping', in *Symposium on significant results obtained from ERTS-1*, Vol 1: Technical presentations, Paper W5.

Hoffer, R. M. *et al.* (1972) *Land utilisation and water resource inventories over extended test sites*. LARS information note 012772, Purdue University, Indiana.

Klemas, V., Bartlett, D. and Rogers, R. (1975) Coastal zone classification from satellite imagery. *Photogrammetric Engineering and Remote Sensing* 41(4) 499–514.

Matthews, R. E. (ed.) (1975) 'Water resources, coastal wetlands', Part B, *Active Microwave Workshop Report*, NASA, Lyndon B. Johnson Space Center, Scientific and Technical Information Office publn., Washington D.C. pp 79–84.

McCoy, R. M. (1961) Drainage network analysis with K-band radar imagery. *The Geographical Review* 51(4) 493–512.

McEwen, R. B., Kosco, W. J., Carter, V. (1976) Coastal wetland mapping. *Photogrammetric Engineering and Remote Sensing* 42(2) 221–232.

Meier, M. F. (Chairman) (1976) 'Informal planning meeting on the satellite applications in hydrology', in final report, Geneva Meeting, World Meteorological Organisation. 42 pp.

NASA (1977) *Detection and mapping (dam) package*. NASA News Release 76–4, Johnson Space Centre, Houston.

Sutcliffe, J. V. (1974) A hydrological study of the southern Sudd region of the Upper Nile. *Hydrological Sciences Bulletin* XIX, 26, 237–255.

(ii) *Water penetration and depth measurement*

Anderson, D. M. *et al.* (1973) 'Sediment distribution and coastal processes in Cook Inlet, Alaska', in *Symposium on significant results obtained from the Earth Resources Technology Satellite-1*, Paper M9, Goddard Space Flight Centre.

Blyth, K. (1981) *Remote Sensing in Hydrology*. Report No. 74, Institute of Hydrology, Wallingford, 170 pp.

Brown, W. L., Polycn, F. C. and Stewart, S. R. (1971) 'A method for calculating water depth, attenuation coefficients and bottom reflectance characteristics', in *Proc. 7th Int. Symp. on Remote Sensing of the Environment*, Ann Arbor, Michigan, pp. 663–682.

Clark, D. K. *et al.* (1974) 'Computer derived coastal water classifications via spectral signatures', in *Proc. 9th Int. Symp. on Remote Sensing of Environment*, Vol. II, Session 10, Ann Arbor, Michigan.

Fitzgerald, E. (1974) *'Multispectral scanning systems and their potential application to Earth resources surveys. Spectral properties of materials'*. ESRO Contract Report No. 232, 231 pp.

Geary, E. L. (1967) Coastal hydrography. *Photogrammetric Engineering* 34(2) 44–50.

Goodier, R. (ed.) (1970) 'The application of aerial photography to the work of the Nature Conservancy', in *Proc. Nature Conservancy*, Edinburgh, 183 pp.

Grumman Aerospace Corporation (1973) *Photometric and polarimetric mapping of water turbidity and water depth*. Final report for NASA, CR-134030, Grumman Aerospace Corp., Bethpage, New York, 134 pp.

Hickman, G. D. and Hogg, J. E. (1969) 'Application of an airborne pulsed laser for near shore bathymetric measurements', in *Symp. on Remote Sensing of the Environment*, Vol. 1, Ann Arbor, Michigan.

Jerlov, N. G. (1951) 'Optical studies of ocean waters', *Reports of the Swedish Deep-Sea Expedition*, Vol. 3, No. 1, pp. 3–57.

Keller, M. (1975) Photogrammetric circulatory surveys (PHOCIS) *Photogrammetric Engineering and Remote Sensing*, 41(9) 1123–1130.

Kolipinski, M. C. and Higer, A. L. (1969) 'Inventory of hydrobiological features using automatically processed multispectral data', in *Symp. on Remote Sensing of the Environment*, Ann Arbor, Michigan, pp. 79–95.

Lockwood, H. E. *et al.* (1974) Water depth penetration film test. *Photogrammetric Engineering*, 40(12) 1303–1314.

Naval Office (1972) *Test report on PLADS (pulsed light airborne depth sounder)*. Naval Oceanographic Office Technical Note 6620-102-72.

Polcyn, F. C. and Lyzenga, D. R. (1973) 'Calculation of water depth from ERTS-MSS data', in *Symposium on significant results obtained from ERTS-1*, Paper M20, Goddard Space Flight Center.

Polcyn, F. C. and Sattinger, I. J. (1969) 'Water depth determinations using remote sensing techniques', in *Symp. on Remote Sensing of the Environment*, Ann Arbor, Michigan, pp. 1017–1028.

Reeves, R. G. (ed.) (1968) *Introduction to Electromagnetic Remote Sensing*. Amer. Geol. Inst. Short Course Lecture notes, Houston, 167 pp.

Specht, M. R., Needler, D. and Fritz, M. L. (1973) New colour film for water-photography penetration. *Photogrammetric Engineering* 39(4) 359–369.

Sutcliffe, J. V. (1974) A hydrological study of the Southern Sudd region of the Upper Nile. *Hydrological Sciences Bulletin* XIX (26) 237–255.

Vary, W. E. (1969a) 'A new non-blue sensitive aerial colour film', presented at *Colour Aerial Photography Symposium*, New York.

Vary, W. E. (1969b) 'Remote sensing by aerial colour photography for water depth penetration and ocean bottom detail', in *Symp. on Remote Sensing of the Environment*, Ann Arbor, Michigan, pp. 1045–1059.

Wenderoth, S., Yost, E., Kalia, R. and Anderson, R. (1975) *Multispectral Photography for Earth Resources*. Remote Sensing Information Center, Greenvale, New York, 257 pp.

Williams, R. S. Jnr. (1973) 'Coastal and submarine features on MSS imagery of south-eastern Massachusetts: comparison with conventional maps', in *Symposium on Significant results obtained from the ERTS-1*, Paper M18, Goddard Space Flight Center.

Yentsch, C. S. (1960) 'The influence of phytoplankton on the colour of seawater', in *Deep Sea Research*, Vol. 1.

Yost, E. and Wenderoth, S. (1968) 'Coastal water penetration using multispectral photographic techniques', in *Symp. on Remote Sensing of the Environment*, Ann Arbor, Michigan, pp. 571–586.

Yost, E. and Wenderoth, S. (1972) 'Coastal and estuarine applications of multispectral photography', in *4th Annual Earth Resources Program Review*, Section 110, 17 pp.

(iii) *Water quality and turbidity*

Blanchard, B. J. and Leamer, R. W. (1973) 'Spectral reflectance of water containing suspended sediment', in *Remote Sensing and Water Resources Management*, Amer. Water Res. Assoc., Urbana, Illinois, pp. 339–348.

Brown, W. L., Polcyn, F. C. and Stewart, S. R. (1971) 'A method for calculating water depth, attenuation coefficients and bottom reflectance characteristics', in *Proc. 7th Int. Symp. on Remote Sensing of Environment* Vol. 1, Univ. Michigan, Ann Arbor, pp. 663–681.

Coker, A. E., Higer, A. and Goodwin, C. R. (1973) 'Detection of turbidity dynamics in Tampa Bay, Florida, using multispectral imagery from ERTS-1', in *Symp. on Significant Results*

Obtained from ERTS-1, Paper W20, Maryland.

Currey, D. T. (1977) 'Identifying flood water movement', in *Remote Sensing of Environment* 6(1) 51–60.

Davis, A., Bristow, M. and Koningstein, J. (1973) 'Raman spectroscopy as a water quality indicator', in *Remote Sensing and Water Resources Management*, Amer. Water Res. Assoc., Urbana, Illinois, pp. 239–246.

Fantasia, J. F. and Ingrao, H. C. (1974) 'Development of an experimental airborne laser remote sensing system for the detection and classification of oil spills', in *Proc. 9th Int. Symp. on Remote Sensing of Environment*, Vol. 3, p. 1721.

Fitzgerald, E. (1974) *Multispectral scanning systems and their potential application to Earth Resources Surveys. Spectral Properties of Materials*. ESRO Contractor Report No. 232, 231 pp.

Goldberg, M. C. and Weiner, E. R. (1971) *Applications of spectroscopy to remote determination of water quality*. 4th Annual Earth Resources Program Review, Section 81, 14 pp.

Grumman Corporation (1973) *Photometric and polarometric mapping of water turbidity and water depth*. Final report for NASA, CR-134030, Grumman Aerospace Corp., Bethpage, New York, 134 pp.

Klainer, S. M. Arden, W. and Hirschfield, T. (1974) 'The remote Raman spectrometer as a viable instrument for remote sensing of the environment', in *9th Int. Symp. on Remote Sensing of Environment*, Vol. III, Ann Arbor, Michigan, pp. 1865–1876.

Klooster, A. and Scherz, J. P. (1973) 'Water quality determination by photographic analysis', in *Proc. 2nd Annual Conf. on Remote Sensing of Earth Resources*, Univ. Tennessee Space Institute, 14 pp.

Lillesand, T. M., Scarpace, F. L. and Clapp, J. P. (1975) 'Water quality in mixing zones', *Photogrammetric Engineering and Remote Sensing* 41(7) 380–395.

Lo, C. P. (1976) Photographic analysis of water quality changes. *Photogrammetric Engineering and Remote Sensing*, 42(3) 309–315.

Psuty, N. P. and Allen, J. R. (1975) Trend surface analysis of ocean outfall plumes. *Photogrammetric Engineering and Remote Sensing* 41(6) 721–730.

Querry, M. R. *et al.* (1971) 'Specular reflectance of aqueous solutions', in *Symp. on Remote Sensing of the Environment*, Ann Arbor, Michigan, pp. 1053–1069.

Reeves, R. G. (ed.) (1968) *Introduction to electromagnetic remote sensing, with emphasis on applications in geology and hydrology*. American Geological Institute, Washington D.C., pp. 1–16 to 1–20.

Reeves, R. G., Anson, A. and Landen, D. (eds.) (1975) *Manual of Remote Sensing*, Vol. II—*Interpretation and Applications* American Society of Photogrammetry, Virginia, p. 1520.

Scherz, J. P. (1971) 'Remote sensing considerations for water quality monitoring', in *Proc. 7th Int. Symp. on Remote Sensing of the Environment*, Vol. 2, Ann Arbor, Michigan, pp. 1071–1087.

Weldon, J. W. (1973) *Measurement of Water Colour in Coastal Waters*. Johnson Space Center Report No 083, St. Louis, 47 pp.

Wertz, D. L. *et al.* (1976) Correlation between multispectral photography and near surface turbidities. *Photogrammetric Engineering and Remote Sensing*, 42(5) 695–701.

(iv) *Water temperature*

Albuisson, M., Monget, J. M. and Poisson, M. (1976) 'Investigation of coastal and marine environments using NOAA digital data', in *Proc. 3rd Annual Conference*, Remote Sensing Society, Reading.

Anding, D. *et al.* (1971) *Atmospheric Effects on Infrared Multispectral Sensing of Sea Surface Temperature from Space*. NASA Contract Report CR-1858.

Atwell, B. H., MacDonald, R. B. and Bartolucci, L. A. (1971) Thermal mapping of streams from airborne radiometric scanning. *Water Resources Bulletin* 7(2) 228–242.

Axelsson, S. and Edvardsson, O. (1973) *Passive Microwave Radiometry and its Potential Applications to Earth Resources Surveys*. ESRO Contractor Report No 71, 96 pp.

Boettcher, A. J. *et al.* (1976) Use of thermal infrared imagery in ground water investigations, N. W. Montana. *Journal of Research of U.S.G.S.* 4(6) 727–732.

Brereton, N. R. and Downing R. A. (1975) Some applications of thermal infrared linescan in water resource studies. *Water Services* 79(949) 91–98.

Borgese, D., Dinelli, G. and Hodder, D. T. (1973) 'Use of thermal infrared scanning in evaluating predictive models for power plant thermal plume mixing in Italian coastal waters', in *Remote Sensing and Water Resources Management*, Amer. Water Res. Assoc., pp. 270–284.

Farrow, J. B. (1975) *The influence of the atmosphere on remote sensing measurements— ultraviolet, visible and infrared regions*. European Space Agency Contractor Report CR-354, 170 pp.

Fitzgerald, E. (1974) *Multispectral Scanning Systems and their Potential Application to Earth Resources Surveys. Spectral Properties of Materials*. ESRO Contract Report No. 232.

Hoffer, R. M. and Bartolucci, L. A. (1972) Calibration techniques for remote sensing measurements of water temperatures. *Proc. Indiana Academy of Science* (1971) 81, 150–153.

Huh, O. K. (1976) 'Detection of oceanic thermal fronts off Korea with Defense Meteorological Satellites', in *Remote Sensing of Environment* 5(3) 191–215.

Kingston, E. S. (1970) *An Infrared Aerial Survey Equipment Operating in the 3.0 to 5.5 Micrometer Band*. Systems and Weapons Division, EMI Electronics, Ltd., Feltham, UK, 11 pp.

Lee, K. (1969) *Infrared exploration for shoreline springs at Mono Lake, California, test site*. Colorado School of Mines, Golden, Colorado, under USGS contract 14-08-0001-11217, 35 pp.

McAlister, E. D. (1969) 'Sea-surface temperature and heat flow', in *NASA Annual Earth Resources Aircraft Programme Status Reserve*, Vol 2.

Platt, C. M. R. and Troup, A. J. (1973) A direct comparison of satellite and aircraft infrared ($10\,\mu m$–$12\,\mu m$) remote measurements of surface temperature. *Remote Sensing of Environment*, 2, 243–247.

Ryan, A. (1969) in *Electromagnetic Sensor Correlation Study* (eds. Kennedy, J. M. and Janza, F. J.). Environmental Science Services Administration Weather Bureau, final report, No. 29, pp. 167–175.

Scarpace, F. L. *et al.* (1975) Scanning thermal plumes. *Photogrammetric Engineering and Remote Sensing* 41(10) 1223–1232.

Sommerard, R. (1977) Homing in on hot spots. *New Civil Engineer*, June 1977.

Souto-Maior, J. (1973) 'Applications of thermal remote sensing to detailed ground water studies', in *Remote Sensing and Water Resources Management*, Amer. Water Res. Assoc., pp. 284–299.

Stingelin, R. W. and Avis, G. B. (1973) 'Digital processing techniques in thermal plume analysis', in *Remote Sensing and Water Resources Management*, Amer. Water Res. Assoc., pp. 299–311.

Strong, A. E. *et al.* (1974) 'Extensive summer upwelling on Lake Michigan during 1973 observed by NOAA-2 and ERTS-1 satellites', in *Proc. 9th Int. Symp. on Remote Sensing of Environment*, Session 8, Ann Arbor, Michigan, pp. 923–933.

(v) *Soil moisture*

Barrett, E. C. *et al.* (eds.) (1977) *Remote Sensing of the Terrestrial Environment* (Colston Papers No. 28), Butterworth & Co., London, 309 pp.

Blanchard, M. B., Greeley, R. and Geottelman, R. (1974) *Use of Visible, Near Infrared and Thermal Infrared Remote Sensing to Study Soil Moisture*. NASA Ames Research Centre report, 10 pp.

Bowers, S. A. and Hanks, R. J. (1965) Reflection of radiant energy from soils. *Soils Science* 100(2) 130–138.

Chadwick, D. G. (1973) *Integrated Measurement of Soil Moisture by Use of Radio Waves*. Prepared for Office of Water Resources Research by Utah Water Research Laboratory, Publication PRWG 103–1, 87 pp.

Deane, R. A. (1973) *Side Looking Radar Systems and their Potential Application to Earth Resource Surveys, Basic Physics and Technology*. European Space Research Organisation Contractor Report No. 136, 116 pp.

Eagleman, J. R., Pogge, E. C. and Moore, R. K. (1975) *Detection of Soil Moisture and Snow Characteristics from Skylab*. Final Report, Kansas University Center for Research, 313 pp.

Gates, D. M. (1970) 'Physical and physiological properties of plants', in *Remote Sensing*, produced by the Committee on Remote Sensing for Agricultural Purposes. National Academy of Sciences, Washington D.C., pp. 224–252.

Gillespie, A. R. and Kahle, A. B. (1977) Construction and interpretation of a digital thermal inertia image. *Photogrammetric Engineering and Remote Sensing* 43(8) 983–1007.

Hoffer, R. M. and Johannsen, C. J. (1969) 'Ecological potentials in spectral signature analysis', in *Remote Sensing in Ecology*, University of Georgia.

Kennedy, J. M. *et al.* (1967) *Passive microwave measurements of snow and soil—a study of the theory and measurements of the microwave emission properties of natural materials.* Tech. Report No. 3, Geography Branch, Earth Sciences Div., Office of Naval Research.

LARS (1970) *Remote Multispectral Sensing in Agriculture.* Laboratory for Agricultural Remote Sensing (LARS) Annual Report, Vol. 4, Research Bulletin 873, Purdue University, Indiana, 112 pp.

Matthews, R. E. (ed.) (1975) *Active Microwave Workshop Report,* Scientific and Technical Information Office, NASA, Washington, D.C.

Merritt, E. S. *et al.* (1973) *Soil moisture estimation applications of NIMBUS-3 HRIR-D (0.7–1.3 µm) observations.* Final report of Earth Satellite Corporation, Washington D.C.

Nefedov, N. E. and Popova, P. A. (1972) *Deciphering of Groundwater from Aerial Photographs.* Eng. tr. from Russian, Amerind Publ. Co., New York.

Pascalar, H. G. (1969) 'Microwave radiometric instrumentation for remote sensing applications', in *14th Technical Symposium,* Aerojet-General Corporation, Society of Photo-optical Instrument Engineering.

Plessey Co. (1976) *Report on Feasibility Study of Techniques for Remote Sensing of Snow and Soil Moisture.* Compiled by Plessey Radar Research Centre, Havant, UK, under Department of the Environment Contract Number DRG 480/64/17/76/RO2OU.

Poe, G. (1971) *Remote Sensing of the Near-surface Moisture Profile of Specular Soils with Multi-Frequency Microwave Radiometry.* Aerojet-General Corporation, El Monte, California, 10 pp.

Rosema, A. (1976) *A Mathematical Model for Simulation of the Thermal Behaviour of Bare Soils, Based on Heat and Moisture Transfer.* NIWARS publication No 11, Delft.

Schmugge, T J. (1976) *Remote Sensing of Soil Moisture.* NASA/Goddard Space Flight Center, Maryland, Report No. X-913-76-118, 21 pp.

Soer, G. J. R. (1976) 'Estimation of regional evapotranspiration and soil moisture conditions using remotely sensed crop surface temperatures. *Remote Sensing of Environment* 9, 27–45.

Stockhoff, E. H. and Frost, R. T. (1971) 'Polarisation of light scattered from moist soils', in *Proc. 7th Int. Symp. on Remote Sensing of Environment,* Vol. 1, Univ. Michigan, Ann Arbor, pp. 345–364.

Waite, W P., Cook, K. R. and Bryan, B. B. (1973) *Broad Spectrum Microwave Systems for Remotely Measuring Soil Moisture Content.* Arkansas Water Resources Centre, Fayetteville, Pubn. No. 18, 166 pp.

Wermund, E. G. (1971) Remote sensors for hydrogeologic prospecting in arid terrains. *IEEE Transactions On Geoscience Electronics,* GE-9(3) 120–130.

Werner, H. D., Schmes, F. A., Horton, M. L. and Waltz, F. A. (1971) *Application of Remote Sensing Techniques to Monitoring Soil Moisture.* Remote Sensing Institute, South Dakota State Univ. Interim Technical Report, 13 pp.

Wiesnet, D. R. (1972) *Comparison of Remote Sensors for Soil Moisture and Other Hydrologic Studies.* National Oceanic and Atmospheric Administration, Washington.

(vi) *Groundwater*

Axelsson, S. and Edvardsson, D. (1973) *Passive Microwave Radiometry and its Potential Applications to Earth Resources Surveys.* ESRO Contract Report No. 71, 96 pp.

Boettcher, A. J. *et al.* (1976) Use of thermal infrared imagery in ground water investigations, N. W. Montana. *J. Res. USGS* 4(6) 727–732.

Cartwright, K. (1968) *Temperature Prospecting for Shallow Glacial and Alluvial Aquifers in Illinois.* Illinois State Geol. Survey, Circular 433.

Covault, C. (1982) Images from space reshape NASA plans. *Aviation Week and Space Technology.*

Davies, M. C. (1973) A thermal infrared linescan survey along the Sussex Coast. *Water and Water Engineering,* No. 77.

Debney, A. G. P. (1978) Remote sensing detects groundwater in England. *Water and Sewage Works* 32–34.

Fitzgerald, E. *et al.* (1976) *Report on feasibility study of techniques for remote sensing of snow and soil moisture. Annex I, Detection of deep aquifers.* Dept. of the Environment, Contract Number DGR/480/64/17/RO2OU.

Mathews, R. E. (ed.) (1975) *Water Resources, coastal wetlands.* Active Microwave Workshop Report, Part B, NASA Lyndon B. Johnson Space Center, Scientific and Technical

Information Office, Washington, D.C.

Nefedov, N. E. and Popova, P. A. (1972) *Deciphering of Groundwater from Aerial Photographs.* Eng. trs. from Russian, Amerind Publ. Co., New York.

Pohn, H. A. (1976) A comparison of LANDSAT images and NIMBUS for thermal-inertia mapping of Oman. *J. Res. USGS*, 4(6).

Souto-Maior, J. (1973) 'Applications of thermal remote sensing to detailed groundwater studies', in *Remote Sensing and Water Resources Management*, Amer. Water Res. Assoc., pp. 284–299.

Waite, W. P. and Macdonald, H. C. (1972) Fracture analysis with imaging radars. *EOS Trans. Amer. Geophys. Union*, 53.

Wermund, E. G. (1971) Remote sensors for hydrogeological prospecting in arid terrains. *IEEE Transactions on Geoscience Electronics* GE9(3) 120–130.

Appendix A: Availability of remote sensing data

i) Aerial photography and other airborne imagery

Enquiries for existing vertical imagery of the UK should be accompanied by a tracing from the 1:50 000 Ordnance Survey map showing clearly the area of interest and the lines of the National Grid which should be numbered. The sheet number of the Ordnance Survey map should also be shown on the tracing. It is also helpful to show major roads or railway lines that pass near or through the area of interest. The preferred date, contact scale, and type (e.g. vertical or oblique, black-and-white, colour or infrared linescan) of imagery should be stated, together with the type of cover required (e.g. full stereoscopic cover (60% overlap) or minimum overlap (20%)) if the enquiry concerns aerial photography. If a study of site history is being made the relevant dates should be stated. In some cases all available cover may be required.

Enquiries for existing vertical aerial photographs of overseas areas may be made with reference to an appropriate base map in a manner similar to that described above.

Oblique photographs may be catalogued by place or building featured in the photograph. For example, the oblique photographs of Stag Hill shown in Figures 8.3 and 8.4 may be catalogued under Guildford Cathedral.

The checklist below gives a guide to the major sources of air photography in the UK.

a) *Official sources*

England (from 1st February 1984)

Royal Commission on Historical Monuments, 23 Savile Row
London W1 Tel: 01-734 6010.

This collection comprises RAF photography of England together with pre-1969 Ordnance Survey photography. Photographs may only be viewed at the above address. For cover searches and ordering copies of photographs applications should be made to:

Ministry of Defence F6t2 (Air), St. Georges Road,
Harrogate, N. Yorkshire.

Wales

Air Photographs Officer
Central Register of Air Photography of Wales
Welsh Office
Room G-003, Crown Office
Cathays Park
Cardiff CD1 3NQ
Tel: 0222 823815.

Scotland

The Air Photographs Officer
Air Photographs Unit
Scottish Development Department
Room 1/21, New St Andrews House St James Centre
Edinburgh EH1 3SZ
Tel: 031 556 8400 ext. 4766.

The Scottish Air Photographs Unit also holds oblique coverage for urban areas and villages and has cover of 2575 km of the Scottish coast in the form of true colour obliques and true colour vertical (scale 1:10 000) photographs.

Northern Ireland

Central Register of Aerial Photography of Northern Ireland
Department of the Environment (Northern Ireland)
Ordnance Survey of Northern Ireland
83 Ladas Drive
Belfast BT6 9FJ
Northern Ireland

Ordnance Survey

Air Photo Cover Group
Ordnance Survey
Romsey Road
Maybush Southampton SO9 4DH
Tel: 0703 775555 ext. 584.

O.S. holds cover from 1970 onwards only. Ordnance Survey leaflet (Nov. 1981) gives information about the services provided.

County and Local Authorities

Many county councils have their regions covered by air photography every four or five years, usually in black-and-white panchromatic at a scale of 1:10 000. The County Planning Departments may be able to give details of available cover and how to obtain copies of prints. In many cases copies of the photographs taken for local authorities are held in the libraries of the commercial survey companies that took the photographs, but permission in writing may be required from the local authority concerned before the photographs can be examined, or copies purchased.

(b) Universities

Mr D R Wilson
Curator in Aerial Photography

University of Cambridge Committee for Aerial Photography
The Mond Building
Free School Lane
Cambridge CB2 3RF
Tel: 0223 358381 ext. 347.

The committee has a large and growing collection of oblique aerial photographs of towns, villages and archaeological features, together with an increasing quantity of vertical photography.

The Keeper of Aerial Photography
Department of Geography
University of Keele
Keele
Staffordshire ST5 5BG
Tel:: 0782 621111.

This is the official repository for surplus RAF cover of areas outside the UK. The collection has 5.5 million prints of RAF World War II photography of Europe and limited cover of Africa and Asia.

(c) *Commercial organizations*

Table A1 lists the services provided by the main commercial organizations involved in aerial photography in the UK. Companies specialising in vertical and oblique photography using model aircraft:

Iris Surveys Ltd
Small Mill
Pincot Lane
Pitchcombe
Stroud
Gloucestershire GL6 6LY
(Surveys carried out near to the Gloucestershire area.)

Sigma Visuals
Passengers Farm
Bailes Lane
Normandy
Guildford
Surrey GU3 2BA
Tel: Worplesdon 0483 235151.
(Surveys carried out in South-East England.)

(d) *Air photographs in other collections*

The Directory of British Photographic Collections (Wall, J., 1977, *Directory of British Photographic Collections*, Heinemann, London) lists 48 collections in which air photographs are a subsidiary subject; these include County Record Offices, central and local libraries, County Planning Offices, museums and universities.

(e) *Air photograph cover of overseas areas*

In most cases copies of photographs can be obtained only with the permission of the country concerned.

Table A1 Commercial sources of aerial photography and interpretation services

Commercial organization	Address	AERIAL Carry out/supply					Comments
		Photography	Thermal infra red	Side scan radar	Processing	Interpretation	
Aero Films Ltd	Gate Studios, Station Road, Borehamwood, Herts. WE6 IEJ. Tel: 01 207 0666	✓					An extensive collection of oblique and vertical photography. Obliques date from the foundation of the company in 1919
Airviews (Manchester) Ltd	Manchester Airport, Manchester M22 SPQ. Tel: 061 437 2502	✓					Mainly oblique air photographs, dating from 1947 and relating to the whole country
BKS Surveys Ltd	47 Ballycairn Rd, Coleraine, Co. Londonderry. Tel: Coleraine (0265) 52311	✓			✓		
Cartographical Services Ltd	Landford Manor, Salisbury, Wilts. Tel: Earldoms (0794 39) 321	✓			✓		
Clyde Surveys Ltd	Reform Rd, Maidenhead, Berks. Tel: Maidenhead (0628) 21371	✓	✓		✓	✓	Formerly Fairey Air Surveys Ltd
Fisher-Spence Associates	4 Ardross St, Inverness IV3 5NN. Tel: (0463) 242121	✓			✓	✓	Specializes in Stereo oblique photography for land surface evaluation
Geosurvey International	Geosurvey House, Orchard Lane, East Molesey, Surrey. Tel: 01 398 8371	✓			✓	✓	
Hunting Surveys Ltd, Hunting Geology and Geophysics Ltd	Elstree Way, Borehamwood, Herts. Tel: 01-953-6161	✓	✓	✓	✓	✓	Source of Airborne MSS data.

				Notes
Meridian Airmaps Ltd	Marlborough Road, Lancing, Sussex. Tel: Worthing (0903) 752992	✓		An extensive collection of black-and-white vertical photography with many large scale photographs
J. W. Norman	35 Brangwyn Avenue, Brighton, Sussex. Tel: Brighton (0273) 507833		✓	
Sealand Aerial Photography	10 East Gate Square, Chichester, Sussex. Tel: Chichester 781025	✓		
Soil Mechanics Ltd	Foundation House, Eastern Rd, Bracknell, Berks. Tel: Bracknell (0344) 24567		✓	
J. A. Story & Partners	92–94 Church Rd, Mitcham, Surrey. Tel: 01 640 1971	✓		
Survey & Development Services Ltd	Scottish Survey Centre, 1 Atholl Place, Edinburgh. Tel: 031 228 1446	✓		
Mr. A. Weltman	Smalls Mill, Pincot Lane, Pitchcombe, Stroud, Gloucester. Tel: Gloucester (0452) 812705	✓	✓	Small-scale surveys
West Air Photography	The Airport, Weston-Super-Mare, Avon. Tel: Weston-Super-Mare. (0936) 2133	✓	✓	Mainly oblique air photographs of the West and South West of England and South Wales

Royal Air Force Film Library
Ministry of Defence
Air Force Board Secretariat
Room 8239, Main Building
Whitehall
London SW1A 2HB
Tel: 01-218 7136.

Overseas Survey Directorate
Technical Information and Support Services
Ordnance Survey
Romsey Road
Southampton SO9 4DH
Tel: (0703) 775555.

Enquiries for aerial photography of all areas excluding Africa should be addressed to Area 1 Library, and enquiries relating to coverage of Africa to Area 2 Library.

(ii) Satellite data

The most general source of satellite data in the UK is the National Remote Sensing Centre and the methods illustrated here for selecting scenes and products from the product range are those used by the Centre. However, where one of the other organizations listed below has the data, the user will find that the ordering systems will be similar. Although the product range may be more restricted and the technical support more limited, the interpretation assistance may be more comprehensive.

The data most commonly used for earth resources and survey applications are produced by the MSS on the Landsat series of spacecraft. As described in Chapter 3, these spacecraft are held in precisely controlled orbits so that the satellite passes over the same area on the ground every 18 days (Landsat 1, 2, 3) or 16 days (Landsat 4, 5). Therefore, unlike aerial photographs which are collected fairly randomly, these satellite images are collected routinely, at the same resolution, at the same orientation, at the same time of day, and in the same spectral bands. For these reasons, locating an image containing the area of interest (cloud cover permitting), is relatively simple and applies world-wide.

The user must first specify the area of interest. Initially, this may be the name of a town in a country, a river estuary, or a mountain. Such descriptions, provided they enable the location of the area in a reasonable atlas, are quite acceptable. Specifying latitude and longitude for world-wide applications or National Grid co-ordinates for the UK, is a more precise method. Ultimately, however, the Landsat World Reference System (LWRS) of a path and row number is the most suitable, when the user is more familiar with the system.

Having approximately located the area of interest, a search can then be undertaken to find all the scenes that have been taken of the area over many years. Currently for the UK, the Centre holds on computer tape over 500 scenes, increasing by about 70 scenes per year. These images are either totally or mostly cloud-free. Since parts of the UK appear on 49 different scenes, there are on average more than 10 dates on which any one area has been observed over the last few years. Thus there are choices of season, year, atmospheric conditions, and so on.

Having specified suitable dates, the user may wish to examine the 'browse file' (i.e. a collection of proof prints of all the scenes) at the Centre or at the Scottish Development Department (which has a collection for Scotland only), to select the required scene. Alternatively, a photocopy of a scene can be sent to the user to check the exact location and the broad cloud cover.

Standard photographic products can be supplied in black-and-white or colour on paper sizes of 240 mm square up to over 1 m square. Positive and negative films in black-and-white or colour can be supplied on 240 mm square material. Scales can vary from the standard 1:1 000 000 in the 240 mm format to 1:250000 in the 1 m format. Part scenes can be reproduced at even larger scales on papers up to about 1 m square.

For users with their own computing and image processing facilities, tapes can be supplied in the format used by the ground station which received the data (and there are many such formats), or in the format which is used at the Centre, and which is the same for all images, no matter the type of spacecraft or the source of the data.

Image processing facilities can also be hired at the Centre. These enable the user to undertake specific enhancements or processes allowing him to extract much more precise or subtle information from the scenes. Photographic products of user enhanced images can be produced on an individual basis. If classifications have been produced, then, besides the photographic products, maps can be made with the plotters at the Centre.

For areas outside the UK, the Centre has more than 500 scenes on tape, covering about 17 million square kilometres. This archive is again rising by about 70 scenes a year. For a scene which is already in stock, the above ordering procedures apply. For other areas, browse information is available, and the full resolution data can be acquired from the EROS data centre in America, from Earthnet in Italy, or from any of the national organizations listed, which archive data. Contacts with these organizations can be direct, through the Centre, or through any of the companies listed.

Other data which are available at the Centre in varying quantities include RBV from Landsat 3, TM from Landsat 4 and 5, Seasat SAR, HCMM and Nimbus. Arrangements are being made for the collection of data from SPOT and ERS-1, at the Centre. Data from the meteorological spacecraft Meteosat, Goes and the NOAA series, are collected directly from the satellites, but very small 'rolling' archives are maintained unless a user requires a specific collection programme.

In the following list of sources (a, b, c), the facilities codes are:
A: Browse facilities.
B: Supply of images on computer tape.

C: Supply of photographic products.
D: Hire of image processing facilities.
E: Bulk processing of computer data.
F: Interpretation capability.

(a) *Official Sources in the UK*

National Remote Sensing Centre
Space Department
Royal Aircraft Establishment
Farnborough
Hants GU14 6TD.
Tel: 0252 24461, ext. 2291. Telex 858442.
(A, B, C, D, E)

The Air Photographs Officer
Air Photographs Unit
Scottish Development Department
Room 1/21 New St Andrews House
St James Centre
Edinburgh EH1 3SZ.
Tel: 031 556 8400, ext. 4766.
(A)

(b) *UK companies*

Clyde Surveys
Reform Road
Maidenhead
Berks.
(B, C, F)

Environmental Remote Sensing Applications Centre (ERSAC) Ltd
Peel House
Ladywell
Livingstone
West Lothian EH54 6AG.
(B, D, F)

Geosurvey International Ltd
Geosurvey House
Imber Court Estate
Orchard Lane
East Molesey
Surrey.
(B, F)

Hunting Surveys Ltd and Hunting Geology and Geophysics Ltd
Elstree Way
Borehamwood
Herts.
(B, C, D, F)

Nigel Press Associates Ltd
99 High Street

Edenbridge
Kent.
(B, C, D, F)

(c) *UK universities*

Department of Electrical Engineering
University of Dundee
Dundee DD1 4HN.
(B, C—meteorological data only).

Centre for Remote Sensing
Imperial College
Prince Consort Road
London SW7 2AZ.
(B, C (meteorological data only), F)

Department of Geography
University of Sheffield
Sheffield S10 2TN.
(D, F)

(d) *Overseas sources of data*

The following organizations all supply data and may have other facilities or services for hire.

EROS Data Center
Sioux Falls
South Dakota 57198
USA.

The Canada Centre for Remote Sensing (CCRS)
717 Belfast Road
Ottawa
Ontario KIA OY7
Canada.

Earthnet Programme Office
ESRIN 00044
Frascati
Italy.

Australian Landsat Station
14–16 Oatley Court
P.O. Box 28
Belconnen ACT 2616
Australia.

National Institute for Telecommunications Research (NITR)
Satellite Remote Sensing Centre
P.O. Box 3718
Johannesburg 2000
Republic of South Africa.

Comision Nacional de Investigaciones Especiales (CNIE)
Centro de Teleobservacion

Avda Dorrego 4010
Buenos Aires
Argentina.

Instituto de Pesquisas Espacias (INPE)
Departmento de Prodacao de Imagens
ATUS Banco de Imagens Terestres
Rodovia Presidente Dutra, Km. 210
Cachoeira Paulista CEP 12.630,
Sao Paulo
Brazil.

National Remote Sensing Agency
No 4 Sardar Patel Road
P.O. Box 1519
Secunderabad 500 003
Andhra Pradesh
India.

Remote Sensing Technology Center of Japan (RESTEC)
7-Floor Uni Roppongi Building
7-15-17 Roppongi
Minato-Ku
Tokyo
Japan 106.

Remote Sensing Division
National Research Council
Bangkok 9
Thailand.

Appendix B: Glossary

absorption band   Wavelength interval at which electromagnetic radiation is absorbed by the atmosphere or by other substances. For example, there is an atmospheric absorption band at 5 to 8 μm, caused by water vapour, that absorbs thermal IR radiation of those wavelengths.

active remote sensing   Remote sensing methods that provide their own source of electromagnetic radiation. Radar is one example.

additive primary colours   The colours blue, green and red. Filters of these colours transmit the primary colour of the filter and absorb the other two colours.

air base   Ground distance between principal points of successive overlapping aerial photographs.

analogue   A form of data display in which values are shown in graphic form such as curves.

antenna   The device that transmits and receives microwave and radio energy in SLAR systems.

aperture   The opening in a remote sensing system that admits electromagnetic radiation to the film or detector.

atmospheric windows   Wavelength intervals at which the atmosphere transmits most electromagnetic radiation.

azimuth   The geographic orientation of a line given as an angle measured clockwise from north.

azimuth direction   In SLAR images this refers to the direction of the aircraft ground track.

azimuth resolution   In SLAR images this is the spatial resolution in the azimuth direction. In real-aperture SLAR systems azimuth resolution is determined by the angular width of the transmitted beam.

backscatter   In SLAR usage, this refers to the portion of the microwave energy scattered by the terrain surface that is directed back towards the antenna.

base-height ratio   Air base divided by aircraft height. This ratio determines vertical exaggeration on stereo models.

beam width   In SLAR usage this is the angle subtended in the horizontal plane by the radar beam.

black body   A substance that radiates energy at the maximum possible rate per unit area at each wavelength for any given temperature. A black body also absorbs all the radiant energy incident upon it.

classification   The process of assigning individual pixels of multispectral image to categories, generally on the basis of spectral-reflectance characteristics.

colour additive viewer   Device in which black-and-white multispectral images are registered and projected through coloured filters to produce a colour composite image.

colour composite image   A colour image prepared by projecting individual black-and-white multispectral images in colour.

complementary colours   Two colours of light that produce white light when added together, such as red and cyan.

contact print   A reproduction made from a photographic negative placed in direct contact with photosensitive paper.

contrast ratio   The ratio between the reflectance of the brightest and darkest parts of the image. Commonly referred to as 'contrast'.

contrast stretching   Improving the contrast of images by digital processing. The original range of digital values is expanded to utilize the full contrast range of the recording film or display device.

cross polarized   Radar return pulse in which the polarization direction is normal to the polarization direction of the transmitted pulse. Images recorded with cross-polarized energy may be HV (horizontal transmit, vertical return) or VH (vertical transmit, horizontal return).

definition (photography).   The degree of sharpness or distinctness of small detail in the picture image, negative, or print.

density slicing   The process of converting the continuous grey tone of an image into a series of density intervals, or slices, each corresponding to a specific digital range.

depolarization   Change in polarization of a radar pulse as a result of multiple reflections from the terrain surface.

depression angle   In SLAR usage this is the angle between the horizontal plane passing through the antenna and the line connecting the antenna and the target.

detector   The component of a remote sensing system that converts electromagnetic radiation into a signal that is recorded.

diazo film   A transparent material on which image transparencies may be reproduced in specific colours.

dielectric constant   Electrical property of matter that influences radar returns.

digital image processing   Computer manipulation of the digital values which form the picture elements or pixels of an image.

digitization   The process of converting an image recorded originally on photographic material into numerical format.

distortion   On an image, this refers to changes in shape and position of objects with respect to their true shape and position.

Doppler principle   Describes the change in the observed frequency of electromagnetic or other waves caused by relative movement between the source of waves and the observer.

electromagnetic radiation   Energy which travels in a periodic, harmonic manner at the velocity of light.

emission   The process by which a body emits electromagnetic radiation, usually as a consequence of its kinetic temperature.

emissivity   The ratio of radiant flux from a body to that from a black body at the same kinetic temperature (symbol ε).

emulsion   A suspension of photosensitive silver halide grains in gelatin that constitutes the image-forming layer on photographic materials.

enhancement   The process of altering the apperance of an image so that the interpreter can extract more information. Enhancement may be done by digital or photographic methods.

far range   Refers to the portion of a SLAR image farthest from the aircraft flight path.

filter, digital   A mathematical procedure for removing unwanted values from numerical data.

filter, optical   A material that, by absorption or reflection, selectively modifies the radiation transmitted through an optical system.

flight path   The line on the ground directly beneath a remote-sensing aircraft or satellite.

fluorescence   The emission of light from a substance caused by exposure to radiation from an external source.

focal length   In cameras the distance measured along the optical axis from the optical centre of the lens to the plane at which the image of a very distant object is brought into focus.

format   The size of an image produced by a remote sensing system.

grain (photography):   (1) One of the discrete silver particles resulting from the development of an exposed light-sensitive material. (2) A lack of smoothness of the silver deposit, caused by clumps or groups of particles. Excessive graininess reduces quality, especially when magnified or enlarged.

grey scale   A calibrated sequence of grey tones ranging from black to white.

ground control   Accurate data on the horizontal and (or) vertical positions of identifiable ground points.

ground resolution cell   The area on the terrain that is covered by the instantaneous field of view of a detector. Size of the ground resolution cell is determined by the altitude of the remote-sensing system and the instantaneous field of view of the detector.

hue   The attribute of a colour that differentiates it from grey of the same brilliance and that allows it to be classed as blue, green, red or intermediate shades of these colours.

instantaneous field of view   The solid angle through which a detector is sensitive to radiation. In a scanning system this refers to the solid angle subtended by the detector when the scanning motion is stopped. Instantaneous field of view is commonly expressed in milliradians.

interactive processing The method of data processing in which the operator views preliminary results and can alter the instructions to the computer to achieve optimum results.

image The representation of a scene as recorded by a remote sensing system. Although image is a general term, it is commonly restricted to representations acquired by non-photographic methods.

latent image The invisible image produced by the photochemical effect of light on silver halide grains in the emulsion of film. Photographic development renders the latent image visible.

layover In SLAR images this is the geometric displacement of the top of objects toward the near range, relative to their base.

line-pair A pair of light and dark bars of equal sizes. The number of such line-pairs that can be distinguished per unit distance is used to express resolving power of imaging systems.

lineament A linear topographic or tonal feature on the terrain and on images and maps that may represent a zone of structural weakness.

look direction Direction in which pulses of microwave energy are transmitted by a SLAR system. Look direction is normal to the azimuth direction. Also called **range direction**.

modulate To vary the frequency, phase, or amplitude of electromagnetic waves.

mosaic An image or photograph made by piecing together individual images or photographs covering adjacent areas.

multispectral camera A system that simultaneously acquires photographs at different wavelengths of the same scene.

multispectral scanner A scanner system that simultaneously acquires images in various wavelength regions of the same scene.

nadir The point on the ground vertically beneath the centre of a remote sensing system.

near range Refers to the portion of a SLAR image closest to the aircraft flight path.

parallel polarized Radar return pulse in which the polarization is the same as the transmitted pulse. Images recorded with parallel-polarized energy may be HH (horizontal transmit, horizontal return) or VV (vertical transmit, vertical return).

pass In digital filters this refers to the spatial frequency of data transmitted by the filter. High-pass filters transmit high-frequency data; low-pass filters transmit low-frequency data.

passive remote sensing Remote sensing of energy naturally reflected radiated from the terrain.

pitch Rotation of an aircraft about the horizontal axis normal to its longitudinal axis that causes a nose-up or nose-down attitude.

picture element (pixel) In a digitized image this is the area on the ground represented by each digital value. Because the analog signal from the detector of a scanner may be sampled at any desired interval, the picture element may be smaller than the ground resolution cell of the detector.

polarization The direction of vibration of the electrical field vector of electromagnetic radiation. In SLAR systems polarization is either horizontal or vertical.

primary colours The three colours, either additive or subtractive, that may be combined to produce the full range of colours.

pulse A short burst of electromagnetic radiation transmitted by a radar antenna.

pulse length Duration of a burst of energy transmitted by a radar antenna, measured in microseconds.

radar shadow A dark area of no return on a radar image.

radiant flux The electromagnetic energy radiated from a source.

radiant power peak The wavelength at which the maximum electromagnetic energy is radiated at a particular temperature.

radiant temperature Concentration of the radiant flux from a material. Radiant temperature is the product of the kinetic temperature multiplied by the emissivity to the one-fourth power.

radiation The propagation of energy in the form of electromagnetic waves.

radiometer A non-imaging device for quantitatively measuring radiant energy, especially thermal radiation.

random-line dropout A defect in scanner images caused by the loss of data from individual scan lines in a non-systematic fashion.

range direction For radar images this is the direction in which energy is transmitted from the antenna and is normal to the azimuth direction. Also called **look direction**.

range resolution For radar images this is the spatial resolution in the range direction and is determined by the length of the transmitted pulse of microwave energy.

raster lines   The individual lines swept by an electron beam across the face of a CRT that constitute the image display.

real time   Time in which reporting on events or recording of events is simultaneous with the events. For example, the real time of a satellite is the time in which it simultaneously reports its environment as it encounters it: the real time of a computer is the time during which it is accepting data and performing operations on it.

rectification   The process of projecting a tilted or oblique photograph onto a horizontal reference plane.

reseau   A system of lines or crossmarks of standard size, used in a camera or imaging system to produce a corresponding network on photographs or images.

reflectance   The ratio of the radiant energy reflected by a body to that incident upon it.

reflectance, spectral   Reflectance measured at a specific wavelength interval.

registration   The process of superimposing two or more images or photographs so that equivalent geographic points coincide. Registration may be done digitally or photographically.

relief displacement   The geometric distortion on vertical aerial photographs. The tops of objects are located on the photograph radially outward from the base.

resolution   The ability to distinguish closely spaced objects on an image or photograph.

reversal film   A photographic film in which the negative image is converted to a positive image during the developing process.

roll   Rotation of an aircraft about the longitudinal axis to cause a wing-up or wing-down attitude.

scattering   Multiple reflection of electromagnetic waves by gases or particles in the atmosphere.

scatterometer   A non-imaging radar device that records backscatter of terrain as a function of incidence angle.

scene   The area on the ground that is covered by an image or photograph.

sensor   A device that receives electromagnetic radiation and converts it into a signal that can be recorded and displayed as numerical data or as an image.

signature   A characteristic, or combination of characteristics, by which a material or an object may be identified on an image or photograph.

slant range   For radar images this term represents the distance measured along a line between the antenna and the target.

slant-range image   For radar images this term represents an image in which objects are located at positions corresponding to their slant-range distances from the aircraft flight path. On slant-range images the scale in the range direction is compressed in the near-range region.

spectral sensitivity   The response, or sensitivity, of a film or detector to radiation in different spectral regions.

smoothing   The averaging of densities in adjacent areas to produce more gradual transitions.

stereo model   A three-dimensional mental impression produced by viewing the left and right images of an overlapping pair with the left and right eye, respectively.

stereopair   Two overlapping images or photographs that may be viewed stereoscopically.

stereoscope   A binocular optical device for viewing overlapping images or diagrams to obtain the mental impression of a three-dimensional model.

subtractive primary colours   Yellow, cyan, and magenta. When used as filters for white light these colours remove blue, red, and green, respectively.

sun synchronous   An earth satellite orbit in which the orbit plane is near polar and the altitude such that the satellite passes over all places on earth having the same latitude twice daily at the same local sun time.

target   An object on the terrain of specific interest in a remote sensing investigation.

telemeter   To transmit data by radio or microwave links.

thermal inertia   A measure of the response of a material to temperature changes.

thermal model   A mathematical expression that relates thermal and other physical properties of a material to its temperature. Models may be used to predict temperature for given properties and conditions. Thermal properties may be estimated on the basis of observed variations in temperature.

transparency   A positive or negative image on a transparent photographic material. The ability of a material to transmit light.

training Informing the computer system which sites to analyse for spectral properties or signatures of specific land cover classes.

travel time In radar systems this term refers to the time interval between transmission of a pulse of microwave energy and its return from the terrain.

vertical exaggeration In a stereo model this is the extent to which the vertical scale is larger than the horizontal scale.

yaw Rotation of an aircraft about its vertical axis which causes the longitudinal axis to deviate from the flight line.

zenith The point in the celestial sphere that is exactly overhead.

Appendix C: Abbreviations

AC	alternating current
AERE	Atomic Energy Research Establishment
AMI	active microwave instrumentation
A to D	analogue to digital
BERS	bottom echo recording system
CAV	colour additive viewer
CCD	charge coupled device
CCRS	Canadian Centre for Remote Sensing
CCT	computer compatible tape
CNES	Centre National d'Études Spatiales
CRIS	Centre for Rectification of Images from Space
CRT	cathode ray tube
DFVLR	German Aerospace Research Establishment
DN	digital number
DOS	Directorate of Overseas Surveys
DTM	digital terrain model
EDC	EROS Data Center
EDIES	EDC digital image
EM	electromagnetic
ERIM	Environmental Research Institute of Michigan
EROS	Earth Resources Technology Satellite
ERS-1	ESA Resource Satellite—1
ESA	European Space Agency
ESRO	European Space Research Organization
ETC	earth terrain camera
GCP	ground control point
GeHg	mercury doped germanium

GPS	global positioning satellite
GSFC	Goddard Space Flight Center
HCMM	heat capacity mapping mission
HgCdTe	mercury cadmium telluride
HRV	high resolution visible
IFOV	instantaneous field of view
IGN	Institut Géographique National
IMC	image motion compensation
InSb	indium antimonide
IR	infrared
ISPRS	International Society of Photogrammetry and Remote Sensing
ITC	International Training Centre for the Earth Sciences
JPL	Jet Propulsion Laboratory
JRC	Joint Research Council
LARS	Laboratory for Agricultural Remote Sensing
LEPS	lidar echo processing system
LFC	large format camera
LOS	land observation satellite
LSB	least significant bit
LUT	look up table
MBB	Messerschmitt Bölkow Blohm
MOMS	modular optoelectronic multispectral scanner
MSB	most significant bit
MSS	multispectral scanner
NA	normal angle
NAS	National Academy of Sciences
NASA	National Aeronautics and Space Administration
NERC	Natural Environment Research Council
NOAA	National Oceanic and Atmospheric Administration
NPOC	National Point of Contact
OMI	Ottico Meccanica Italiana
OMSA	optical multichannel signal analyser
PC	principal components
PHOCIS	photogrammetric circulatory surveys
PLADS	pulsed light airborne depth sounder

PNC   programmed neuro-cybernetics

PTRC   planning transportation research and computation

RAE   Royal Aircraft Establishment

RBV   return beam vidicon

RPA   remotely piloted aircraft

SAR   synthetic aperture radar

SIR-A   Shuttle Imaging Radar—A

SLAR   Side-looking airborne radar

SLR   side-looking radar

SPAS   shuttle pallet satellite

SPINE   Space Informatics Network Experiment

SPOT   Le Système Probatoire d'Observation de la Terre

SWA   super wide angle

TDRS   tracking and data relay satellite

THIR   temperature humidity infrared radiometer

TIMS   thermal infrared multispectral scanner

TIPS   thematic mapper image processing system

TM   thematic mapper

TRRL   Transport and Road Research Laboratory

UV   ultraviolet

USJOG   United States Joint Operation Graphics

USGS   United States Geological Survey

VHRR   very high resolution radiometer

WA   wide angle

WRS   world reference system (for Landsat)

ZTS   zoom transfer scope

Index